Discovering
Algebra
An Investigative Approach

Solutions Manual

DISCOVERING

MATHEMATICS

Key Curriculum Press
Innovators in Mathematics Education

Teacher's Materials Project Editor: Elizabeth DeCarli

Consulting Editor: Kendra Lockman

Project Administrator: Aaron Madrigal

Writer: Abby Tanenbaum

Accuracy Checker: Dudley Brooks

Project Manager: Rose M. Rummel-Eury, Interactive Composition Corporation

Copyeditor: Victoria P. Thulman

Editorial Production Supervisor: Christine Osborne

Production Supervisor: Ann Rothenbuhler

Production Director: McKinley Williams

Text Designer: Jenny Somerville

Composition, Technical Art, Prepress: Interactive Composition Corporation

Cover Designers: Jill Kongabel, Marilyn Perry, Jensen Barnes

Printer: Alonzo Printing

Textbook Product Manager: James Ryan

Executive Editor: Casey FitzSimons

Publisher: Steven Rasmussen

Cover Photo Credits: Background image: Pat O'Hara/DRK Photo. Boat image: Marc Epstein/DRK Photo. All other images: Ken Karp Photography.

Key Curriculum Press
1150 65th Street
Emeryville, CA 94608
(510) 595-7000
editorial@keypress.com
www.keypress.com

Printed in the United States of America
10 9 8 7 6 5 4 3 2   11 10 09 08 07 06   ISBN-13: 978-1-55953-764-3
ISBN-10: 1-55953-764-7

Contents

Chapter 3

Chapter 4

Chapter 5

Chapter 6

Chapter 7

Chapter 8

Introduction

The *Solutions Manual* for *Discovering Algebra: An Investigative Approach* contains solutions to the exercises at the end of each lesson and to the Improving Your Reasoning Skills, Improving Your Visual Thinking Skills, Improving Your Geometry Skills, and Take Another Look features. You can find solutions for the Investigations from the student text in the *Teacher's Edition*.

The solutions in this *Solutions Manual* are more complete than those offered as annotations in the *Teacher's Edition* or in the selected answers in the back of the student book. Although complete solutions for the problems are provided here, keep in mind that often there is more than one method students might use to solve a particular problem. Also, the answers will vary for some problems, depending on assumptions that students make. For problems that could have many different answers, a sample solution is given.

Refer to these solutions when your students have difficulty solving a problem and need some assistance in determining a possible approach toward solving it. You might also want to provide a copy of certain solutions for students who have been absent for an extended period of time.

LESSON 0.1

EXERCISES

1. a. $\frac{1}{16} + \frac{1}{16}$ or $2 \times \frac{1}{16}$; total area $= \frac{2}{16}$ or $\frac{1}{8}$

b. $\frac{1}{64} + \frac{1}{64} + \frac{1}{64}$ or $3 \times \frac{1}{64}$; total area $= \frac{3}{64}$

c. $\frac{1}{25} + \frac{1}{25} + \frac{1}{25} + \frac{1}{25} + \frac{1}{25} + \frac{1}{25} + \frac{1}{25} + \frac{1}{25} +$

$\frac{1}{25} + \frac{1}{25} + \frac{1}{25} + \frac{1}{25} + \frac{1}{25} + \frac{1}{25} + \frac{1}{25}$ or

$15 \times \frac{1}{25}$; total area $= \frac{15}{25}$ or $\frac{3}{5}$

d. $\frac{1}{625} + \frac{1}{625} + \frac{1}{625} + \frac{1}{625} + \frac{1}{625} + \frac{1}{625} + \frac{1}{625}$

or $7 \times \frac{1}{625}$; total area $= \frac{7}{625}$

2. a. $\frac{1}{4} + \frac{1}{16} = \frac{4}{16} + \frac{1}{16} = \frac{5}{16}$

b. $\frac{2}{16} + \frac{3}{64} = \frac{8}{64} + \frac{3}{64} = \frac{11}{64}$

c. $9 \times \frac{1}{81} = \frac{9}{81} = \frac{1}{9}$

d. $\frac{1}{9} + \frac{2}{81} = \frac{9}{81} + \frac{2}{81} = \frac{11}{81}$

3. a.

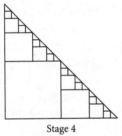

Stage 4

b. The area of the square is half the area of the Stage 0 triangle. So, the area of the square is 32.

c. At Stage 1, the area of each small triangle is 16. The area of each smallest square at Stage 2 is half this area, or 8. So, the total area of the squares at Stage 2 is $8 + 8 + 32$, which equals 48.

d. At Stage 2, the area of each smallest triangle is 4. The area of each smallest square at Stage 3 is half this area, or 2. So, the total area of the squares at Stage 3 is $2 + 2 + 2 + 2 + 8 + 8 + 32$, which equals 56.

4. a. $\frac{1}{3} + \frac{2}{9} = \frac{3}{9} + \frac{2}{9} = \frac{5}{9}$

b. $\frac{3}{4} + \frac{1}{2} + \frac{1}{3} = \frac{9}{12} + \frac{6}{12} + \frac{4}{12} = \frac{19}{12}$

c. $\frac{2}{5} \times \frac{3}{7} = \frac{6}{35}$

d. $2 - \frac{4}{9} = \frac{18}{9} - \frac{4}{9} = \frac{14}{9} = 1\frac{5}{9}$

5. Several answers are possible for each problem. Samples are shown.

a.   **b.**

c.   **d.**

6. Answers will vary. Students should mention that the figure is created by a recursive process and that smaller parts are similar to the whole figure.

7. a. Answers will vary. Possible description: Divide each side of the square into thirds and connect those points with lines parallel to the sides. A square is formed in the middle. Trace around the square and then erase the other lines. To get the next stage, do the same thing in all eight squares formed around the middle square.

b.

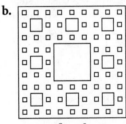

Stage 3

c. The hole at Stage 1 has an area of $\frac{1}{9}$. At Stage 2, each of the 8 new holes has an area of $\frac{1}{9} \times \frac{1}{9}$, or $\frac{1}{81}$, so the combined area of the holes at Stage 2 is $\frac{1}{9} + \left(8 \times \frac{1}{81}\right) = \frac{9}{81} + \frac{8}{81} = \frac{17}{81}$. At Stage 3, each of the 64 new holes has an area of $\frac{1}{9} \times \frac{1}{81}$, or $\frac{1}{729}$, so the combined area of the holes at Stage 3 is $\frac{17}{81} + \left(64 \times \frac{1}{729}\right) = \frac{153}{729} + \frac{64}{729} = \frac{217}{729}$.

d. At each stage, the area of the carpet is 1 minus the combined area of the holes. The area of the carpet at Stage 1 is $1 - \frac{1}{9} = \frac{8}{9}$. The area of the carpet at Stage 2 is $1 - \frac{17}{81} = \frac{64}{81}$. The area of the carpet at Stage 3 is $1 - \frac{217}{729} = \frac{512}{729}$.

8. a. The large triangle is divided into four equal-size smaller triangles. Because the area of the large triangle is 8, the area of each smaller triangle is $8 \div 4 = 2$.

b. $\frac{1}{4}$; $8 \times \frac{1}{4} = 2$

c. There is no difference. Dividing by 4 is the same as multiplying by its reciprocal, $\frac{1}{4}$.

d. Together, the three shaded triangles make up $\frac{3}{4}$ of the total area. Because the total area is 8, the area of the shaded triangles is $8 \times \frac{3}{4}$, or 6.

9. a. Each smallest triangle makes up $\frac{1}{16}$ of the total area. Because nine smallest triangles are shaded, $\frac{9}{16}$ of the area is shaded.

b. Answers will vary. Here are two possibilities: Because the large triangle has area 12 and $\frac{9}{16}$ of the triangle is shaded, the total shaded area is $12 \times \frac{9}{16}$. Or, because the large triangle could be divided into 16 equal-size smallest triangles, each with area $\frac{12}{16}$, or $\frac{3}{4}$, and because 9 smallest triangles are shaded, the total area shaded is $9 \times \frac{3}{4}$. Both these expressions are equal to $\frac{27}{4}$, or $6\frac{3}{4}$.

10. a. $\frac{1}{9}$

b. Each small triangle is $\frac{1}{9}$ of a medium triangle, so its area is $\frac{1}{81}$ of the original triangle.

c. The total shaded area is $\left(\frac{4}{9} \times 24\right) + \left(\frac{3}{81} \times 24\right) = \frac{96}{9} + \frac{72}{81} = \frac{96}{9} + \frac{8}{9} = \frac{104}{9} = 11\frac{5}{9}$. Another way to calculate this is $24 \times \left(\frac{4}{9} + \frac{3}{81}\right) = 24 \times \left(\frac{36}{81} + \frac{3}{81}\right) = 24 \times \left(\frac{39}{81}\right) = \frac{936}{81} = \frac{104}{9}$.

11. Answers will vary, but should be equivalent to those shown.

a. The Stage 0 triangle has area 32. At each stage, the area of the smallest triangle is $\frac{1}{4}$ the area of the smallest triangle at the previous stage. So, at Stage 2, the area is $\frac{1}{4}$ of $\frac{1}{4}$ of 32.

$\frac{1}{4} \times \frac{1}{4} \times 32 = \frac{32}{16} = 2$

b. The area of one smallest Stage 3 triangle is $\frac{1}{4}$ of $\frac{1}{4}$ of $\frac{1}{4}$ of 32. So, the area of three smallest Stage 3 triangles is $\frac{3}{4}$ of $\frac{1}{4}$ of $\frac{1}{4}$ of 32.

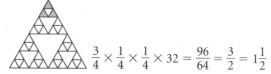

$\frac{3}{4} \times \frac{1}{4} \times \frac{1}{4} \times 32 = \frac{96}{64} = \frac{3}{2} = 1\frac{1}{2}$

c. $\frac{1}{4}$ of $\frac{1}{4}$ of $\frac{1}{4}$ of 32 is the area of one Stage 3 triangle. Because $\frac{1}{2}$ is twice as much as $\frac{1}{4}$, $\frac{1}{2}$ of $\frac{1}{2}$ of $\frac{1}{4}$ of 32 is four times the area of one Stage 3 triangle, so it is equal to the area of four Stage 3 triangles.

$\frac{1}{2} \times \frac{1}{2} \times \frac{1}{4} \times 32 = \frac{32}{16} = 2$

12. $\frac{1}{4} + \frac{1}{16} + \frac{1}{32} = \frac{8}{32} + \frac{2}{32} + \frac{1}{32} = \frac{11}{32}$

13. $1 - \frac{11}{32} = \frac{32}{32} - \frac{11}{32} = \frac{21}{32}$

EXERCISES

1. a. 5^4 **b.** 7^5 **c.** 3^7 **d.** 2^3

2. a. $3 \times 3 \times 3 \times 3$; $3 \cdot 3 \cdot 3 \cdot 3$; $3(3)(3)(3)$

b. $5 \times 5 \times 5 \times 5 \times 5 \times 5$; $5 \cdot 5 \cdot 5 \cdot 5 \cdot 5 \cdot 5$; $5(5)(5)(5)(5)(5)$

c. $\frac{1}{2} \times \frac{1}{2} \times \frac{1}{2}$, $\frac{1}{2} \cdot \frac{1}{2} \cdot \frac{1}{2}$, $\frac{1}{2}\left(\frac{1}{2}\right)\left(\frac{1}{2}\right)$

3. a. 3^3 **b.** 2^5

c. 5^4 or 25^2 **d.** 7^3

4. a. $\frac{2}{3} \cdot 12 = \frac{24}{3} = 8$

b. $\frac{1}{3} + \frac{3}{5} = \frac{5}{15} + \frac{9}{15} = \frac{14}{15}$

c. $\frac{3}{4} - \frac{1}{8} = \frac{6}{8} - \frac{1}{8} = \frac{5}{8}$

d. $5 - \frac{2}{7} = \frac{35}{7} - \frac{2}{7} = \frac{33}{7}$, or $4\frac{5}{7}$

e. $\frac{1}{4} \cdot \frac{1}{4} \cdot 8 = \frac{8}{16} = \frac{1}{2}$

f. $\frac{3}{64} + \frac{3}{16} + \frac{3}{4} = \frac{3}{64} + \frac{12}{64} + \frac{48}{64} = \frac{63}{64}$

5. a. At Stage 2, two new branches are added to each of the two Stage 1 branches, so there are a total of 2^2 or four new branches. At Stage 3, two branches are added to the end of each of the Stage 2 branches, so there are a total of $2 \cdot 2^2$, or 2^3, or eight new branches.

b. Stage 0 has one branch. To find the number of new branches at each stage, you multiply the number at the previous stage by 2. By Stage 5, you will have done this five times. So, the total number of new branches at Stage 5 is 2^5.

6. a. At Stage 2, five new branches are added to each of the five new Stage 1 branches, so there are a total of 5^2, or 25 new branches.

b. There are five new branches at Stage 3 for every new branch at Stage 2, for a total of $5 \cdot 5^2$, or 5^3, or 125 branches.

c. Stage 0 has one branch. To find the number of new branches at each stage, you multiply the number at the previous stage by 5. By Stage 5, you will have done this five times. So, the total number of new branches at Stage 5 is 5^5.

7. a. Each stage has 8 times as many square holes as the previous stage, so Stage 3 has $8 \cdot 8$, or 64 new square holes.

b. Stage 4 would have $8 \cdot 64$, or 512 new square holes.

c. 8^2; 8^3

d. At Stage 7, there would be 8^6, or 262,144 new holes.

e. The exponent is always one less than the stage number.

f. According to the pattern, the Stage 1 figure should have 8^0 holes. $8^0 = 1$, so the pattern does work.

8. a. Stage 1 is made up of five segments (three along the long vertical segment, plus the two branches). At Stage 2, two new branches are added to each of these segments, for a total of $2 \cdot 5$, or 10 branches.

b. Stage 2 is made up of 25 segments. At Stage 3, two new branches are added to each of these segments, for a total of $2 \cdot 25$, or 50 branches.

c. At Stage 3, there are $2 \cdot 5^2$ new branches; at Stage 4, there are $2 \cdot 5^3$ new branches; and at Stage 5, there are $2 \cdot 5^4$ new branches.

d. At each stage, each segment from the previous stage is replaced by five new smaller segments. At each stage, two branches are added to each segment from the *previous* stage.

9. a, b.

Stage number	Area of one shaded triangle	Total area of the shaded triangles
0	1	1
1	$\frac{1}{4} \cdot 1 = \frac{1}{4}$	$\frac{3}{4}$
2	$\frac{1}{4} \cdot \frac{1}{4} = \frac{1}{16}$	$9 \cdot \frac{1}{16}$, or $\frac{3}{4} \cdot \frac{3}{4} = \frac{9}{16}$
3	$\frac{1}{4} \cdot \frac{1}{16} = \frac{1}{64}$	$27 \cdot \frac{1}{64}$, or $\frac{3}{4} \cdot \frac{9}{16} = \frac{27}{64}$

c. Answers will vary. The area of one shaded triangle at each stage is $\frac{1}{4}$ the area of one shaded triangle at the previous stage. The total area of the shaded triangles at each stage is $\frac{3}{4}$ the shaded area at the previous stage.

10. $2 \cdot 2 \cdot 2 \cdot 2 \cdot 2 \cdot 2 \cdot 2 \cdot 2 = 2^8 = \$256.00$

11. Answers will vary. One possibility: The restaurant had $\frac{3}{4}$ of a pie left. Five people wanted pie. After cutting the pie into fifths, how much did each person get? $\frac{3}{20}$.

12. a. $\frac{1}{4} + \frac{1}{16} + \frac{1}{64} = \frac{16}{64} + \frac{4}{64} + \frac{1}{64} = \frac{21}{64}$

b. $\frac{1}{4} + \frac{2}{16} + \frac{5}{64} = \frac{16}{64} + \frac{8}{16} + \frac{5}{64} = \frac{29}{64}$

LESSON 0.3

EXERCISES

1. a. $\frac{125}{8}$; 15.63 **b.** $\frac{25}{9}$; 2.78

c. $\frac{2401}{81}$; 29.64 **d.** $\frac{729}{64}$; 11.39

2. $\frac{5^2}{3^2} - \frac{5}{3} = \frac{25}{9} - \frac{5}{3} = \frac{25}{9} - \frac{15}{9} = \frac{10}{9}$; or, using the rounded decimal values, $2.78 - 1.67 = 1.11$.

3. $\left(\frac{5}{3}\right)^4 \approx 7.72$. $\left(\frac{5}{3}\right)^5 \approx 12.86$. The Stage 5 figure is the first figure with a total length of more than 10.

4. a. $\frac{1}{5} + \frac{3}{4} = \frac{4}{20} + \frac{15}{20} = \frac{19}{20}$

b. $3^2 + 2^4 = 9 + 16 = 25$

c. $\frac{2}{3} \cdot \left(\frac{6}{5}\right)^2 = \frac{2}{3} \cdot \frac{36}{25} = \frac{72}{75} = \frac{24}{25}$

d. $4^3 - \frac{2}{5} = 64 - \frac{2}{5} = 63\frac{3}{5}$, or $\frac{318}{5}$

5. a.

Stage number	Total length		
	Multiplication form	Exponent form	Decimal form
2	$5 \cdot 5 \cdot \frac{1}{4} \cdot \frac{1}{4} = \frac{25}{16}$	$5^2 \cdot \left(\frac{1}{4}\right)^2$	1.56
3	$5 \cdot 5 \cdot 5 \cdot \frac{1}{4} \cdot \frac{1}{4} \cdot \frac{1}{4}$ $= \frac{125}{64}$	$5^3 \cdot \left(\frac{1}{4}\right)^3$ $= \left(\frac{5}{4}\right)^3$	1.95

b. $\left(\frac{5}{4}\right)^4 \approx 2.44$; $\left(\frac{5}{4}\right)^5 \approx 3.05$. So, the figure at Stage 5 is the first to be longer than 3. $\left(\frac{5}{4}\right)^{10} \approx 9.31$; $\left(\frac{5}{4}\right)^{11} \approx$ 11.64. So, the figure at Stage 11 is the first to be longer than 10.

6. a. Note that each stage has six times as many segments as the previous stage, and each segment is $\frac{1}{4}$ the length of the segments in the previous stage. (*See table at bottom of page.*)

b. Because $\left(\frac{3}{2}\right)^5 = \frac{243}{32}$, Stage 5 has length $\frac{243}{32}$.

c. $\left(\frac{6}{4}\right)^{11} \approx 86.50$; $\left(\frac{6}{4}\right)^{12} \approx 129.75$. So, the figure at Stage 11 has a length closest to 100.

Lesson 0.3, Exercise 6. a.

Stage number	Total length		
	Multiplication form	Exponent form	Decimal form
2	$6 \cdot 6 \cdot \frac{1}{4} \cdot \frac{1}{4} = \frac{36}{16} = \frac{9}{4}$	$6^2 \cdot \left(\frac{1}{4}\right)^2 = \left(\frac{6}{4}\right)^2 = \left(\frac{3}{2}\right)^2$	2.25
3	$6 \cdot 6 \cdot 6 \cdot \frac{1}{4} \cdot \frac{1}{4} \cdot \frac{1}{4} = \frac{216}{64} = \frac{27}{8}$	$6^3 \cdot \left(\frac{1}{4}\right)^3 = \left(\frac{6}{4}\right)^3 = \left(\frac{3}{2}\right)^3$	3.38

7. a. Note that each stage has seven times as many segments as the previous stage, and each segment is $\frac{1}{3}$ the length of the segments in the previous stage. (*See table at bottom of page.*)

b. Because $\left(\frac{7}{3}\right)^5 = \frac{16,807}{243}$, Stage 5 has length $\frac{16,807}{243}$.

c. No. Stage 6 has a length of slightly more than 161, and Stage 7 has a length of over 376. There is no stage between these two stages.

8. a.

Stage number	Total length		
	Multiplication form	Exponent form	Decimal form
2	$8 \cdot 8 \cdot \frac{1}{3} \cdot \frac{1}{3} = \frac{64}{9}$	$8^2 \cdot \left(\frac{1}{3}\right)^2$ $= \left(\frac{8}{3}\right)^2$	7.11
3	$8 \cdot 8 \cdot 8 \cdot \frac{1}{3} \cdot \frac{1}{3} \cdot \frac{1}{3}$ $= \frac{512}{27}$	$8^3 \cdot \left(\frac{1}{3}\right)^3$ $= \left(\frac{8}{3}\right)^3$	18.96

b. Estimates will vary. The actual value is $\left(\frac{8}{3}\right)^4$, or about 50.

c. Answers may vary. On many calculators, Stage 23 is the last to be shown without resorting to scientific notation.

9. 2.8

10. $\frac{8}{3} - \frac{12}{9} = \frac{8}{3} - \frac{4}{3} = \frac{4}{3} = 1\frac{1}{3}$

11. a. 4

b. 16

c. The 16 segments drawn at Stage 3 divide the figure into 64 pieces. In Stage 4, a segment would be drawn across each of these pieces, so 64 new segments would be drawn.

d. $4^1, 4^2, 4^3$

e. In general, the exponent is one less than the stage number. This holds true for Stage 1 because $4^0 = 1$, and 1 new segment is added at Stage 1.

LESSON 0.4

EXERCISES

1. a. $-4 + 7 = 3$

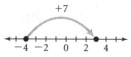

b. $5 + -8 = -3$

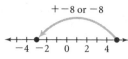

c. $-2 - 5 = -7$

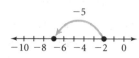

d. $-6 - (-3) = -3$

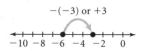

2. a. $-2 \cdot 5 = -10$

b. $6 \cdot -4 = -24$

c. $-3 \cdot -4 = 12$

d. $-12 \div 3 = -4$

e. $36 \div -6 = -6$

f. $-50 \div -5 = 10$

3. a. $5 \cdot -4 - 2 \cdot -6 = -20 - (-12) =$ $-20 + 12 = -8$

b. $3 + -4 \cdot 7 = 3 + -28 = -25$

c. $-2 - 5 \cdot (6 + -3) = -2 - 5 \cdot 3 =$ $-2 - 15 = -17$

d. $(-3 - 5) \cdot -2 + 9 \cdot -3 =$ $-8 \cdot -2 + -27 = 16 + -27 = -11$

4. a. $8 + -6 = 2$

Starting at 0, go 8 units to the right and then 6 units to the left. This is illustrated by diagram i.

Lesson 0.3, Exercise 7.a.

Stage number	Total length		
	Multiplication form	Exponent form	Decimal form
2	$7 \cdot 7 \cdot \frac{1}{3} \cdot \frac{1}{3} = \frac{49}{9}$	$7^2 \cdot \left(\frac{1}{3}\right)^2 = \left(\frac{7}{3}\right)^2$	5.44
3	$7 \cdot 7 \cdot 7 \cdot \frac{1}{3} \cdot \frac{1}{3} \cdot \frac{1}{3} = \frac{343}{27}$	$7^3 \cdot \left(\frac{1}{3}\right)^3 = \left(\frac{7}{3}\right)^3$	12.7
4	$7 \cdot 7 \cdot 7 \cdot 7 \cdot \frac{1}{3} \cdot \frac{1}{3} \cdot \frac{1}{3} \cdot \frac{1}{3} = \frac{2401}{81}$	$7^4 \cdot \left(\frac{1}{3}\right)^4 = \left(\frac{7}{3}\right)^4$	29.64

b. $-8 + -6 = -14$

Starting at 0, go 8 units to the left and then 6 more units to the left. This is illustrated by diagram iv.

c. $8 - (-6) = 14$

Starting at 0, go 8 units to the right and then 6 more units to the right. This is illustrated by diagram ii.

d. $-8 - 6 = -14$

Starting at 0, go 8 units to the left and then 6 more units to the left. This is illustrated by diagram iii.

e. $-8 - (-6) = -2$

Starting at 0, go 8 units to the left and 6 units to the right. This is illustrated by diagram v.

5. Answers will vary. Students may talk of "numbers without their signs" instead of "absolute values." Possible answers:

a. Add the absolute values. Make the result negative.

b. Subtract the number with the smaller absolute value from the number with the larger absolute value. Give the result the sign of the number with the larger absolute value.

c. Add the opposite of the negative number to the positive number.

d. Subtracting a negative number is the same as adding a positive number, so the problem actually involves adding a negative number and a positive number. See the answer to 5b.

e. Multiply the absolute values. Make the result negative.

f. Multiply the absolute values. The result is positive.

g. Divide the absolute values. Make the result negative.

h. Divide the absolute values. The result is positive.

6. a. In the first recursion, he made a mistake when finding $-0.2 \cdot 2$. He should have gotten -0.4, not 0.4. In the second recursion, he used the wrong value (-3.6 instead of -4.4) because of his previous error. His arithmetic was also incorrect because $-0.2 \cdot -3.6 = 0.72$, not -0.72.

b. $-0.2 \cdot (2) - 4 = -0.4 - 4 = -4.4$
$-0.2 \cdot (-4.4) - 4 = 0.88 - 4 = -3.12$
$-0.2 \cdot (-3.12) - 4 = 0.624 - 4 = -3.376$
$-0.2 \cdot (-3.376) - 4 = 0.6752 - 4 = -3.3248$

c. $-0.2 \cdot (-1) - 4 = 0.2 - 4 = -3.8$
$-0.2 \cdot (-3.8) - 4 = 0.76 - 4 = -3.24$
$-0.2 \cdot (-3.24) - 4 = 0.648 - 4 = -3.352$

d. Yes. The calculations in 6b and c seem to be approaching a value close to -3.3.

7. a. (*See table at bottom of page.*)

b. Answers may vary, but probably will be about -2.222.

c. Entering -2.222222222222 as a starting value in the calculator returns the same value as an answer.

8. a.

Starting value	2	-1	10
First recursion	-3	3	-19
Second recursion	7	-5	39
Third recursion	-13	11	-77

b. The values get farther and farther apart with each recursion. The expression does not reach an attractor value.

c. Using the starting value $\frac{1}{3}$ gives $\frac{1}{3}$ as the result: $-2 \cdot \left(\frac{1}{3}\right) + 1 = \frac{1}{3}$. The value $\frac{1}{3}$ is a fixed point for this expression.

9. a. i. 12   **ii.** -16 **iii.** -8

b. The attractor value is twice the constant term (if you rewrite the expression as addition). For example, in the expression $0.5 \cdot \square + 3$, the constant term is 3, and the attractor value is $2 \cdot 3$, or 6. In the expression $0.5 \cdot \square - 4$, the constant term is -4, and the attractor value is $2 \cdot -4$, or -8. In general, for an expression in the form *coefficient* $\cdot \square + $ *constant term*, the attractor value is $\frac{constant\ term}{1 - coefficient}$.

c. Many answers are possible. One choice is $0.5 \cdot \square + 3$.

10. a. i. 7.5   **ii.** -10 **iii.** 6.25

b. The attractor value is 1.25 times the constant (if you rewrite the expression as addition). For example, in the expression $0.2 \cdot \square - 8$, the constant term is -8 and the attractor value is $1.25 \cdot -8$, or -10. In general, for an expression in the form *coefficient* $\cdot \square + $ *constant term*, the attractor value is $\frac{constant\ term}{1 - coefficient}$.

c. Many answers are possible. One choice is $0.2 \cdot \square + 1.8$.

Lesson 0.4, Exercise 7.a.

Starting value	2	-1	10
First recursion	$0.1 \cdot (2) - 2 = -1.8$	$0.1 \cdot (-1) - 2 = -2.1$	$0.1 \cdot (10) - 2 = -1$
Second recursion	$0.1 \cdot (-1.8) - 2 = -2.18$	$0.1 \cdot (-2.1) - 2 = -2.21$	$0.1 \cdot (-1) - 2 = -2.1$
Third recursion	$0.1 \cdot (-2.18) - 2 = -2.218$	$0.1 \cdot (-2.21) - 2 = -2.221$	$0.1 \cdot (-2.1) - 2 = -2.21$

11. All involve repeating a process. Each time, the result of one repetition becomes the starting value or figure for the next repetition.

12. a. $-3(-5) + 6 = 15 + 6 = 21$, so the missing value is 21.

    b. $0.2(-14) - (-3) = -2.8 + 3 = 0.2$, so the missing value is 0.2.

    c. $13 + \frac{2}{3}(-9) = 13 + -6 = 7$, so the missing value is 13.

    d. $\frac{3}{0.5} - 6 = 6 - 6 = 0$, so the missing value is 3.

13. $4 - 12 \div 4 \cdot \frac{1}{2} - 5^2$

$$= 4 - 12 \div 4 \cdot \frac{1}{2} - 25 \qquad \text{Evaluate the exponents first.}$$
$$= 4 - 3 \cdot \frac{1}{2} - 25 \qquad \text{Divide.}$$
$$= 4 - \frac{3}{2} - 25 \qquad \text{Multiply.}$$
$$= \frac{8}{2} - \frac{3}{2} - \frac{50}{2} \qquad \text{Rewrite with a common denominator.}$$
$$= -\frac{45}{2} = -22\frac{1}{2} \qquad \text{Subtract.}$$

14. $(-3 \cdot -4) - (-4 \cdot 2) = 12 - (-8) = 12 + 8 = 20$

15. $\frac{3}{8} - \frac{1}{2} + \left(\frac{3}{4}\right)^2 = \frac{3}{8} - \frac{1}{2} + \frac{9}{16} = \frac{6}{16} - \frac{8}{16} + \frac{9}{16} = \frac{7}{16}$

IMPROVING YOUR REASONING SKILLS

The polygon with "an infinite number of sides" is the circle, and the area between the inscribed polygon and the circle approaches 0 as the number of sides increases. Although the process shown for generating regular polygons isn't recursive (no stage builds on the previous one), it could be made so, by repeatedly doubling the number of sides. Some students may believe that the resulting circle is a fractal because it's the result of an infinite sequence of recursive operations, others that it's not a fractal because it's not self-similar.

LESSON 0.5

EXERCISES

1. a. 8.0 cm   **b.** 4.3 cm   **c.** 7.2 cm

2. a. The segment should be 2.8 cm long.

    b. The segment should be 5.7 cm long.

    c. The segment should be 5.08 cm long, or about 5.1 cm.

3. a–c. Answers will vary but should look proportional to this.

    d. Points D and B are closest together. This relationship does not change with the length of the original segment.

4. a. $-2 + 5 - (-7) = 3 - (-7) = 3 + 7 = 10$

    b. $(-3)^2 - (-2)^3 = 9 - (-8) = 9 + 8 = 17$

    c. $\frac{3}{5} + \frac{-2}{3} = \frac{9}{15} + \frac{-10}{15} = \frac{-1}{15}$

    d. $-0.2 \cdot 20 + 15 = -4 + 15 = 11$

    e. $4 - 6(-2) = 4 - (-12) = 4 + 12 = 16$

    f. $7 - 4(2 - 5) = 7 - 4(-3) = 7 + 12 = 19$

    g. $-2\frac{1}{3} - 4\frac{1}{6} = -2\frac{2}{6} - 4\frac{1}{6} = -6\frac{3}{6} = -6\frac{1}{2}$

5. The resulting figure should resemble a right-angle Sierpiński triangle.

6. a–b. Answers will vary.

    c.

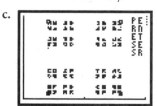

    d. The resulting figure slightly resembles the Sierpiński carpet from Exercise 7 of Lesson 0.1.

    e. Answers will vary. Because there are six numbers on a die and only four corners, you could ignore rolls of 5 or 6 and move toward the corner 1, 2, 3, or 4 depending on the roll of the die.

7. a. This game fills the entire square.

    b. This game creates a small Sierpiński triangle at each corner of the triangle.

    c. This game creates four small Sierpiński carpets, one at each corner of the square.

    d. This game creates a pattern like the Sierpiński triangle. It is difficult to see this figure clearly on the calculator screen, but if you let the program run for a very long time, you'll begin to see the pattern below.

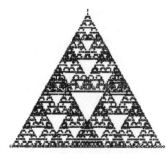

8. Answers will vary. One possibility is to use a die and ignore rolls of 6 and then use the others to indicate the five corners. Another possibility is to use five playing cards and choose one to indicate the move. The answer should describe a process by which all corners are equally likely to be chosen.

9. The point should divide the segment into an 8 cm and a 4 cm segment.

10. a. i. 2   **ii.** 4   **iii.** −6

b. Answers will vary. The attractor value is $\frac{2}{3}$ of the constant.

c. Answers will vary. One possibility: $-0.5 \cdot \boxed{} - 15$.

11. Each stage has 6 times as many segments as the previous stage, and each segment is $\frac{1}{4}$ as long as the segments in the previous stage. (*See table at bottom of page.*)

CHAPTER 0 Review

EXERCISES

1. a. iii   **b.** v   **c.** ii

d. iv   **e.** i

2. a. $2 \times (24 + 12) = 2 \times 36 = 72$

b. $2 + 24 \times 12 = 2 + 288 = 290$

c. $2 - 24 + 12 = -22 + 12 = -10$

d. $(2 + 24) \times 12 = 26 \times 12 = 312$

e. $(2 + 24) \div 12 = 26 \div 12 = \frac{13}{6} = 2.1\overline{6}$

f. $2 - (24 + 12) = 2 - 36 = -34$

3. a. $\frac{1}{3} \times \frac{1}{3} \times \frac{1}{3}$ **b.** $\frac{2}{3} \times \frac{2}{3} \times \frac{2}{3} \times \frac{2}{3}$

c. 1.2×1.2

d. $16 \times 16 \times 16 \times 16 \times 16$

e. $2 \times 2 \times 2 \times 2 \times 2 \times 2 \times 2$

4. a. $\frac{1}{16} + \frac{1}{16} + \frac{1}{16} = \frac{3}{16}$

b. $\frac{1}{9} + \frac{1}{9} + \frac{1}{81} + \frac{1}{81} = \frac{20}{81}$

c. $\frac{1}{4} + \frac{1}{16} + \frac{1}{64} + \frac{1}{64} = \frac{22}{64}$, or $\frac{11}{32}$

5. a.

Stage 3

At each stage, add a branch at the midpoint of each branch from the previous stage. The length of the new branch should be half the length of the previous branch, and it should be rotated 45° counterclockwise from the midpoint of previous branch.

b.

Stage 3

Replace the "right" half of each segment from the previous stage with a "bottomless" equilateral triangle.

c.

Stage 3

Cross each segment from the previous stage at its midpoint with a centered perpendicular segment of the same length.

d.

Stage 3

Each unshaded square is divided horizontally and vertically to create four congruent squares; the bottom right square is shaded.

Lesson 0.5, Exercise 11.

Stage number	Total length		
	Multiplication form	Exponent form	Decimal form
0	1	1^0	1
1	$6 \cdot \frac{1}{4}$	$6^1 \cdot \left(\frac{1}{4}\right)^1 = \left(\frac{6}{4}\right)^1 = \left(\frac{3}{2}\right)^1$	1.5
2	$6 \cdot 6 \cdot \frac{1}{4} \cdot \frac{1}{4}$	$6^2 \cdot \left(\frac{1}{4}\right)^2 = \left(\frac{6}{4}\right)^2 = \left(\frac{3}{2}\right)^2$	2.25
3	$6 \cdot 6 \cdot 6 \cdot \frac{1}{4} \cdot \frac{1}{4} \cdot \frac{1}{4}$	$6^3 \cdot \left(\frac{1}{4}\right)^3 = \left(\frac{6}{4}\right)^3 = \left(\frac{3}{2}\right)^3$	3.38
4	$6 \cdot 6 \cdot 6 \cdot 6 \cdot \frac{1}{4} \cdot \frac{1}{4} \cdot \frac{1}{4} \cdot \frac{1}{4}$	$6^4 \cdot \left(\frac{1}{4}\right)^4 = \left(\frac{6}{4}\right)^4 = \left(\frac{3}{2}\right)^4$	5.06

6. a. Each stage has seven times as many segments as the previous stage, and each segment is $\frac{1}{5}$ the length of segments in the previous stage.

Stage number	Total length		Decimal form
	Multiplication form	Exponent form	
0	1	1^0	1
1	$7 \cdot \frac{1}{5}$	$7^1 \cdot \left(\frac{1}{5}\right)^1 = \left(\frac{7}{5}\right)^1$	1.4
2	$7 \cdot 7 \cdot \frac{1}{5} \cdot \frac{1}{5}$	$7^2 \cdot \left(\frac{1}{5}\right)^2 = \left(\frac{7}{5}\right)^2$	1.96

b. $\left(\frac{7}{5}\right)^{20} \approx 836.68$

7. No matter what value you start with, the result approaches 5, so the attractor is 5.

TAKE ANOTHER LOOK

The behavior of numbers raised to a power depends on the kinds of numbers involved.

Number in box	Exponent of 3 (or any odd integer greater than 1)	Exponent of 4 (or any even integer greater than 0)
Positive number greater than 1	Bigger	Bigger
Negative number less than -1	Smaller (negative yet farther from 0)	Bigger (becomes positive)
0 or 1	Stays the same	Stays the same
-1	Stays the same	Bigger (becomes 1)
Positive fraction between 0 and 1	Smaller (positive yet closer to 0)	Smaller (positive yet closer to 0)
Negative fraction between 0 and -1	Bigger (negative yet closer to 0)	Bigger (becomes positive)

The statement "If the denominator of a fraction increases, the value of the fraction decreases" is true for positive fractions written with both numerator and denominator positive. For negative fractions—written with only the numerator negative—increasing the denominator makes the magnitude of the fraction decrease, thereby moving it closer to zero. Because the fraction moves to the right along the number line, it becomes greater.

For $\frac{\bigcirc}{\square^3}$ to be smaller than $\square^3$, the numerator would have to be less than $\square^6$ if the number in the box is positive. For $\frac{\bigcirc}{\square^3}$ to be greater than $\square^3$, the numerator would need to be greater than $\square^6$ if the number in the box is positive. For $\frac{\bigcirc}{\square^4}$, the numerator would be compared to $\square^8$.

CHAPTER 1

LESSON 1.1

EXERCISES

1. Max: 93 bpm; min: 64 bpm; range: $93 - 64 = 29$ bpm.

2. The categories in this problem are the elements (note that the chemical abbreviations are used in the graph below). Percentages are shown on the vertical axis. The height of each bar represents the percentage for that element.

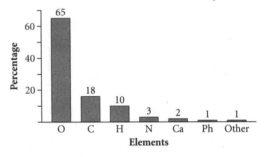

Elements in the Human Body

3. a. Jupiter (There are 38 named satellites.)

b. Mercury and Venus have no satellites.

c. $38 - 8 = 30$ more satellites.

d. $30 \div 2 = 15$ times as many satellites.

4. a. Draw a number line to represent the times. Your number line will need to include values from at least 1 (the minimum time) to 15 (the maximum time). Make a column of dots over each time to represent the number of students who take that much time to get to school. For example, because two people spend 3 minutes traveling to school, there are two dots over the number 3.

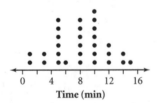

Travel Time to School

b. To find the total number of students, add the numbers of students in the table, or count the dots. There are 30 students in the class.

c. To find the combined time, multiply each time by the number of students who take that long to get to school. Then, add the results: $2 \cdot 1 + 2 \cdot 3 + 6 \cdot 5 + 1 \cdot 6 + 6 \cdot 8 + 7 \cdot 10 + 3 \cdot 12 + 2 \cdot 14 + 1 \cdot 15 = 241$. So, the combined time is 241 min, or 4 h and 1 min.

d. To find the average, divide the combined time by the number of students. The average is $\frac{241}{30} \approx 8$ min.

5. a. 80 bpm (the number with the tallest column of dots)

b. 93 − 64 = 29 bpm

c. Answers will vary. She probably counted her pulse rate for one full minute.

d. Any whole number could occur, not just multiples of four.

e. A full minute, sometimes longer, to ensure accuracy.

6. a. Graph iii is the best match. The values in graphs ii and iv are too large. Graph i has some values of 0, which cannot be correct because at least one person (the student) must live in each student's home.

b. Graph ii is the best match. The values in graphs i and iii are too small. The values in graph iv seem too large. The shortest person represented in that graph is 5 ft 8 in., the tallest person is 6 ft 5 in., and more than half the students are over 6 ft tall!

c. Graph iv is the best match. The values in the other graphs are too low.

d. Graph i is the best match. The values in the other graphs are too large.

7. Knowing there are 3 students in the R&B category, you can see that there are 2 in Country, 5 in Rap, and 7 in Pop/Rock. That leaves 3 in Classical to reach the known total of 20 students.

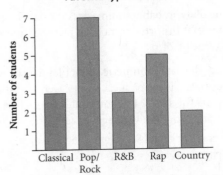

Favorite Types of Music

8. A bar graph because the information falls into categories, is not numeric data, and cannot be scaled on a number line.

9. a. Answers will vary. Possible answer: Jonesville's Varsity Basketball Team.

b. Answers will vary. Possible answer: Jonesville's Kindergarten Class and their Teacher.

c. Answers will vary. Possible answer: Jonesville's Algebra Class.

d. Answers will vary. Possible answers: Group A: Everyone in the school is very tall. Group B: Most people in the school are very short. Group C: Jonesville School is a high school only.

e. Graphs will vary.

10. a. 10^4 **b.** $2^3 \cdot 5^6$ **c.** $\dfrac{3^6}{8^3}$

11. a. $7 + (3 \cdot 2) - 4 = 7 + 6 - 4 = 9$

b. $8 + 2 - 4 \cdot 12 \div 16 = 8 + 2 - 48 \div 16 = 8 + 2 - 3 = 7$

c. $1 - 2 \cdot 3 + 4 \div 5 = 1 - 6 + 0.8 = -5 + 0.8 = -4.2$

d. $1 - (2 \cdot 3 + 4) \div 5 = 1 - (6 + 4) \div 5 = 1 - 10 \div 5 = 1 - 2 = -1$

e. $1^2 \cdot 3 + (4 \div 5) = 1^2 \cdot 3 + 0.8 = 1 \cdot 3 + 0.8 = 3 + 0.8 = 3.8$

12. a. Double 225 until you go past 4050. Double 1 the same number of times.

Doubles of 225	450	900	1800	3600	7200
Doubles of 1	2	4	8	16	32

Find doubles of 225 that add to 4050: 450 + 3600 = 4050. Then, add the corresponding doubles of 1: 2 + 16 = 18. So, 4050 ÷ 225 = 18.

b. Double 6 until you get past 57.

Doubles of 6	6	12	24	48	96
Doubles of 1	1	2	4	8	16

Look for doubles of 6 that add to 57. There is no combination that works. The closest you can get is 6 + 48 = 54. You need 3 more to get to 57. Because 3 is half of 6, find half of 1 as well. Add these values to the table:

3	6	12	24	48	96
1/2	1	2	4	8	16

Because 3 + 6 + 48 = 57, you can find the quotient by adding the corresponding "doubles" of 1: 0.5 + 1 + 8 = 9.5. So, 57 ÷ 6 = 9.5.

13. $\dfrac{1}{16} + \dfrac{1}{16} + \dfrac{1}{4} = \dfrac{3}{8}$

IMPROVING YOUR REASONING SKILLS

Perhaps JoAnn's graph illustrates low temperatures better, because negative values fall under the axis, but her graph makes it hard to compare the low temperatures. However, the side-by-side feature of Janet's graph allows easy comparison between high and low temperatures.

LESSON 1.2

EXERCISES

1. a. To find the mean, add the values and divide by the number of values. The sum is 54, and there are 9 values. So, the mean is 54 ÷ 9 = 6. To find the median, list the values in order: 1, 3, 5, 5, 6, 7, 8, 9, 10. The median is the middle value, which is 6. The mode is 5, the value that occurs most often.

b. The mean is 51 ÷ 10 or 5.1. Order the list to find the median: 1, 2, 3, 3, 4, 6, 7, 8, 8, 9. The median is the average of the middle two numbers (4 and 6), or 5. The modes are 3 and 8.

c. The mean is 82 ÷ 8 = 10.25. Order the list to find the median: 2, 5, 6, 7, 11, 12, 18, 21. The median is 9. There is no mode.

d. Mean: 17.5; median: 20; mode: 20

2. a. Read the data values from the graph. The number of dots above a number indicates the number of times that number occurs in the data set. So, the values are 1, 1, 1, 2, 2, 2, 3, 4, 5, 6, 6, 6, 8, 9, 9. The mean of this data is $\frac{65}{15} \approx 4.3$. The median is 4. There is no mode because there are too many most common values.

b. Mean: $\frac{53}{15} \approx 3.5$; median: 2; modes: 1 and 2

3. a. To find the number of students, just count the dots. Twenty student responses are shown.

b. Range = maximum − minimum = 8 − 0 = 8

c. 1 (the number with the tallest column of dots)

4. a. Mean: $\frac{161 + 205 + 215 + 310 + 420}{5} = \frac{1311}{5} =$ 262.2 ft; median: 215 ft

b. Mean: $\frac{155 + 195 + 206 + 300 + 400}{5} = 251.2$ ft; median: 206 ft

5. The average cost $= \frac{\text{total bill}}{\text{number of items}}$, so you can find the total bill by multiplying the average cost by the number of items. This gives you 16 · 1.14 = 18.24, making the total bill $18.24.

6. a. Mean: 97.485 m; median: 60 m

b. The median is the most appropriate measure of center. The mean is affected by the extreme value of 525.

7. The first three members averaged 53 seconds each, so together they took 53(3), or 159 seconds. The total time for the whole team must be 50(5), or 250 seconds. The two remaining members must have a total of 250 − 159, or 91 seconds. So, the last two people must average 91 ÷ 2, or 45.5 seconds each.

8. The mean, 83.8, is lower than all but one of his scores. The median, 88, is more representative.

9. Answers will vary. If the speaker is talking about the entire state, this cannot occur. All scores cannot be greater than the middle score. In fact, exactly half of the scores will be above, and half will be below, the median.

10. a. The mean weight $= \frac{\text{total weight}}{\text{number of fish}}$; you can find the total weight by multiplying the mean weight by the number of fish. So, the total weight is 1527.4 · 10 or 15,274 lb.

b. Five of the fish caught weigh 1449 lb or less, and five weigh 1449 lb or more.

c. Maximum = minimum + range = 991 + 1673 = 2664. So, the maximum weight is 2664 lb.

11. Answers will vary. Sample answers are provided.

a. When the five data values are listed in order, the third value must be 12. Because the mean of the five values is 19, the total value must be 19 · 5 or 95. So, the remaining values must add to 95 − 12 or 83, and there must be two values less than 12 and two values greater than 12. One possibility is {8, 10, 12, 32, 33} years.

b. When the six values are listed in order, the mean of the two middle values is 4, and the value 5 must occur most often. One possibility is {2, 3, 3, 5, 5, 5} people.

c. {7, 14, 20, 21, 24, 27, 27} points

12. a. (*See graph at bottom of page.*)

b. Mean: 32.65; median: 30; mode: 28

c. The median probably summarizes the data best. The mean is distorted somewhat by the extremely high value of 74.

13. a. Because the data is numeric, a dot plot may be most appropriate. However, if each value were translated into years (divide by 12), you could make a bar graph or pictograph with ages as categories.

b. Answers may vary. (*See graph at bottom of next page.*)

14. a. 12 cm   **b.** 8 cm   **c.** 2.4 cm

LESSON 1.3

EXERCISES

1. a. The minimum is 5 and the maximum is 50. The median is the middle value, 23. The first quartile (Q1) is 10, the middle value in the first half of the data. The third quartile (Q3) is 37, the middle

Lesson 1.2, Exercise 12. a.

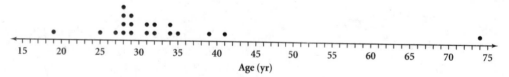

Highest-Paid Athletes

Age (yr)

value in the second half. So, the five-number summary is 5, 10, 23, 37, 50.

   5 5 8 10 14 16 22 23 32 32 37 37 44 45 50

b. The minimum is 10 and the maximum is 50. Because there are an even number of values, the median is the number halfway between the two middle values, 30 and 33. So, the median is 31.5. The first quartile (Q1) is 22, the middle value in the first half of the data. The third quartile (Q3) is 37, the middle value in the second half of the data. The five-number summary is 10, 22, 31.5, 37, 50.

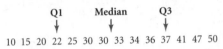

   10 15 20 22 25 30 30 33 34 36 37 41 47 50

c. 14, 22.5, 26, 41, 47. The values are listed in order below with the location of the median and quartiles indicated.

Q1	Median	Q3
↓	↓	↓

   14 16 20 25 26 26 26 33 37 40 42 44 47

d. 5, 10, 19, 34.5, 47. The values are listed in order below with the location of the median and quartiles indicated.

Q1	Median	Q3
↓	↓	↓

   5 5 9 11 16 17 21 32 34 35 43 47

2. a. i. There are 20 data values. Listed in order, they are 0, 0, 0, 1, 1, 1, 1, 1, 1, 1, 2, 2, 2, 3, 3, 3, 3, 4, 5, 7. The median is the value halfway between the tenth and eleventh values, which are 1 and 2. The first quartile is the median of the 10 values in the first half of the data. So, it is the number halfway between the fifth and sixth values, which are 1 and 1. The third quartile is the median of the 10 values in the second half of the data, so it is the number halfway between the fifteenth and sixteenth values, which are 3 and 3.

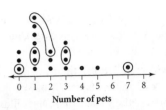

Number of pets

ii. (*See graph at bottom of page.*)

b. i. 0, 1, 1.5, 3, 7   **ii.** 64, 75, 80, 86, 93

3. The five-number summary is 1, 4, 6, 7, 9. To create a box plot, make dots over the minimum and maximum values. Draw vertical segments over the median and quartiles. Draw a box with ends at the first and third quartiles. Draw horizontal segments that extend from each end of the box to the minimum and maximum values.

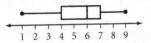

4. Choices a and d are both possible. Both have the five-number summary shown in the box plot. Choice b has the correct minimum, median, third quartile, and maximum, but the wrong first quartile. Choice c has the correct minimum, first quartile, median, and maximum, but the wrong third quartile.

5. a. Answers will vary. Quartiles are the boundaries dividing a data set into four groups, or quarters, with approximately the same number of values.

b. The range

c. The interquartile range, or IQR

d. Outliers are at or near the minimum and maximum values, which are the endpoints of the whiskers.

6. a. Answers will vary. The prediction should be less than the mean.

b. Because the mean of the four scores is 25.5, the total must be 4 · 25.5, or 102. The sum of the three scores Stu knows is 79, so the third score must be 103 − 79, or 23 points.

Lesson 1.2, Exercise 13. b.

Student Ages

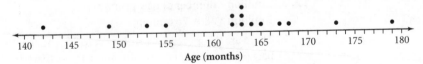

Age (months)

Lesson 1.3, Exercise 2. a. ii.

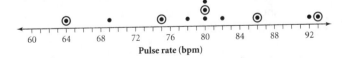

Pulse rate (bpm)

c. The four scores are 23, 23, 27, and 29. The five-number summary for this data set is 23, 23, 25, 28, 29.

d. Answers will vary. Because there are only four values, a five-number summary may be inappropriate—the values themselves illustrate the spread of the data.

7. a. 173, 292, 360, 915, 1383

b. The mean for the 1997–98 Bulls is about 675 points, and the mean for the 2003–04 Bulls is about 564 points; the medians are 416 points and 360 points, respectively. The means are both much higher than the medians because both teams have a few players that score very high. However, the 1997–98 mean is much higher than the 2003–04 mean because Michael Jordan scored so many total points.

c. The median probably best represents the total-points-scored data for the 1997–98 Bulls. Students can justify choosing either the mean or the median for the 2003–04 Bulls. As a team owner, you might think the mean better reflects your team's talents.

d. The box for the 2003–04 Bulls is longer, indicating that more of the team members are grouped toward the center. The minimum number of points scored by a player is about the same, but the maximum is much higher for the 1997–98 Bulls.

e. Without Jordan, the range of the data is much smaller and the box is a little shorter than the complete data for the 1997–98 Bulls. The box plot for 1997–98 without Jordan is more like the one for the 2003–04 Bulls than that for the complete 1997–98 Bulls team.

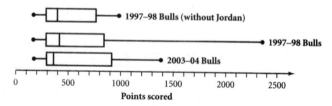

8. a. Answers will vary. For men, the mean salary is approximately $639.56, and the five-number summary is 342, 495, 629, 718.5, 1001; for women, the mean salary is approximately $466.69, and the five-number summary is 288, 353, 445, 563.5, 708.

Median Weekly Earnings, 2000

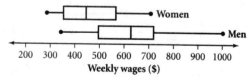

b. Women received less pay than men for the same type of work.

c. The box plots highlight the discrepancy in pay and spread of the data. However, dollar amount comparisons within a single profession are possible only in the table.

d. Answers will vary. The table shows that women are not paid as much as men, so people interested in gender equity are asking for equal pay for equal work.

9. a. 35 ft

b. No. We cannot read the sixth value from the graph. We can see that the median—which is between the fifth and sixth value—is 17.5, and that the third quartile—which is the eighth value—is 25. So, we do know that the length of the king cobra is greater than or equal to 17.5 ft and less than or equal to 25 ft.

c. 65 mi/h

d. The ten longest snakes vary in length from about 8 ft to 35 ft. About half of these snakes range in length from about 11 ft to 25 ft. Running speeds of the ten fastest mammals range from 42 mi/h to 65 mi/h. About half of the speeds are between 43 mi/h and 50 mi/h. The cheetah runs much faster than about three-fourths of the other fastest mammals.

e. No, because the units of these data sets are different.

f. The median is halfway between the fifth and sixth values. Because these values are the same, the median must be equal to these values. From the graph, we can see that the median is about 47. So, the fifth and sixth fastest mammals can run about 47 mi/h.

10. a. $1.5(841 - 288) = 829.5$

b. $288 - 829.5 = -541.5$

c. $841 + 829.5 = 1670.5$

d. An outlier would have to score fewer than -541.5 points or more than 1670.5 points. Michael Jordan is an outlier.

11. When the ages are listed in order, the third value is 14. The total of all ages must be $5 \cdot 22$ or 110 years. One possibility is {4, 10, 14, 39, 43}.

12. a. 2 million · number of paw prints = 2 million · 38 = 76 million

b. There are 7.5 more paw prints next to "Cat." Each paw print represents 2 million animals. So, there are 7.5 · 2 million, or 15 million more cats than dogs.

c. There are 21 million small mammals, and there would be one paw print for every 2 million. So, there would be 21 million ÷ 2 million, or 10.5 paw prints.

Discovering Algebra Solutions Manual
©2007 Key Curriculum Press

EXERCISES

1. a. To find the number of people surveyed, add the heights of the bars. For the matinee, the sum is 3 + 4 + 4 + 6 + 4 + 5 + 2 + 1, or 29. For the evening performance, the sum is 2 + 6 + 8 + 7 + 6 + 1, or 30.

b. Matinee **c.** None

d. Any 15-year-olds surveyed would be in the age 10–20 bin. You can't determine exactly how many (if any) of those four respondents were exactly 15 years old. You can say for certain only that the number is less than or equal to 4.

2. a. Possible graphs:

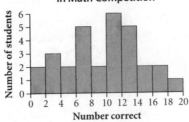

Number of Problems Correct in Math Competition

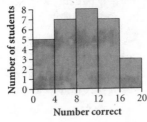

Number of Problems Correct in Math Competition

b. Answers will vary. Student scores tended to be in the middle of the range.

c. 1, 6, 10, 12, 18

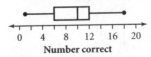

Number of Problems Correct in Math Competition

d. 7 and 12

3. a. To find the number of countries represented, add the bin heights: 2 + 2 + 5 + 8 + 3 + 4 + 7 + 10 + 18 + 16 + 1 = 76.

b. Approximately one fourth of the countries had a life expectancy between approximately 69 and 74 yr.

c. 24

d. There are no bins to the right of 85 in the histogram. Also, the maximum point in the box plot is located at approximately 83 yr.

4.

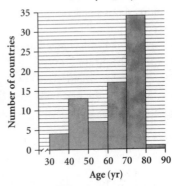

Life Expectancy

5. a. Minimum: 6.0 cm; maximum: 8.5 cm; range: 2.5 cm.

b. Put the ones digits in the stem. Use the tenths digits as the leaves.

Ring Finger Length

```
6 | 0  5  5
7 | 0  0  0  5
8 | 5
```

Key
```
6 | 0  means 6.0 cm
```

6. a. 24 · 10,000, or 240,000 cars

b. Two models sold between 80,000 and 119,999 cars, inclusive.

c. [0, 480000, 40000, 0, 9, 1]

d.

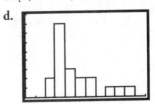

e. An approximate five-number summary is 115000, 131000, 157000, 241000, 434000. The actual five-number summary is 115428, 130650, 157278.5, 240712, 434145.

f.

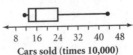

2002 Sales

7. Answers will vary.

a. With a bin width of 1, the bin heights should be about the same (because each number has the same chance of being rolled) with about 16 or 17 in each of six bins.

b. There will probably be a few short bins at the ends for students who estimated poorly and then taller bins near the middle for students whose estimates were closer to the actual measurements.

c. The horizontal axis should show the range of ages for students in the school. The heights of the bins should be about the same. There may be a few students who are younger or older than most of the rest of the students, so there could be shorter bins on the ends.

d. The combined height of the first two bins (2–3 and 3–4) should be a little less than 25. The combined height of the next four bins (4–5, 5–6, 6–7, 7–8) should be a little more than 25. The last two bins (8–9 and 9–10) should each have a height of 25.

8. a. The minimum is 1, the maximum is 9, and the median and both quartiles are 7. The data set must be $\{1, 7, 7, 7, 7, 7, 7, 9\}$.

b. Answers will vary. Each value must be greater than or equal to 5 and less than 6. One possible data set is $\{5, 5, 5, 5, 5, 5, 5, 5\}$.

c. Because there is one value in each bin, there is one value greater than or equal to 1 but less than 2, one value greater than or equal to 2 but less than 3, and so on. One possible data set is $\{1, 2, 3, 4, 5, 6, 7, 8\}$.

d. The minimum and Q1 are both 2, and the maximum and Q3 are both 4. The median is equal to either 2 or 4. There are two possible data sets: $\{2, 2, 2, 2, 2, 4, 4, 4\}$ or $\{2, 2, 2, 4, 4, 4, 4, 4\}$.

9. a. Answers will vary. You could give the top two students As, and the next seven (down to 15 points) Bs. Those students with 9 to 15 points would get Cs, and the bottom three students would get Ds. This scheme allows those students who score in the center to get a C.

b. Using the grading scheme described above, the student gets an A.

c. Answers will vary.

10. a. Look at the lowest stem value, 15, and read the lowest leaf, 0. This value represents the lowest price, $1.50.

b. Chips priced $1.75 and $1.79

c. Stem values from 15 through 19 represent the chips priced at $1.99 or less. So, to find the number of bags priced less than $2, count the leaves on those stems. There are 14 bags priced less than $2.

d. Look for the leaf that occurs the most times on a single stem. The leaf 9 occurs five times on the 19 stem, so the most common price is $1.99.

e. $2.59 - $1.50 = $1.09

11. a. Hospital A's histogram is mounded toward the left. Hospital B's histogram is mounded toward the right. Hospital C's histogram has all bins of equal height. Hospital D's histogram is mounded in the middle.

b. Hospital A had more shorter waiting times and fewer longer waiting times. Patients at Hospital B had fewer shorter waiting times and more longer times. There were an equal number of patients in each time range at Hospital C. At Hospital D, the largest number of patients had waiting times of 20–25 minutes; as the waiting time gets farther from that central value, there are fewer and fewer patients.

c. Answers will vary. No patients at Hospital B had to wait longer than 30 minutes, while approximately 40% of patients at Hospital A had to wait longer than 30 minutes. However, few patients at Hospital B waited less than 10 minutes, while almost 20% of patients at Hospital A waited less than 10 minutes.

d. Answers will vary. Students might prefer Hospital B because all patients were seen in less than 30 minutes. At Hospital A, many patients were seen in less than 20 minutes, but some patients had to wait a very long time.

12. a. Ida weighed the apples from the market, which are more uniform in weight, and Mac weighed the backyard apples, which vary more widely.

b. Mac's apples had a greater variety of weights. They were less uniform than Ida's apples.

c. Both of the histograms are shaped like mounds, higher in the middle and decreasing to the sides. For both kinds of apples, more apples have weights close to the mean weight, and fewer apples have weights farther from the mean.

13. (See graph at bottom of page.)

14. Answers will vary. The **bold** values are fixed. One possibility is $\{\mathbf{64}, 70, 74, 80, \mathbf{82}, \mathbf{82}, \mathbf{82}, \mathbf{82}, \mathbf{95}\}$.

Lesson 1.4, Exercise 13.

Student Ages

Age (months)

Discovering Algebra Solutions Manual
©2007 Key Curriculum Press

LESSON 1.5

Activity day: There are no answers for this lesson.

LESSON 1.6

EXERCISES

1.

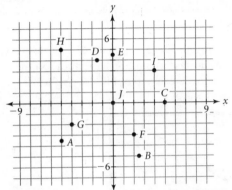

2. a. Positive *x*-axis   **b.** Quadrant II

    c. Quadrant I   **d.** Quadrant III

    e. The origin   **f.** Negative *y*-axis

3. All work is done on the calculator.

4. Answers may vary slightly.

    a. On the curve, find the point with *time* value 2. The *distance* value for the point is about 2. The walker was about 2 m from the sensor.

    b. The lowest point on the curve has the smallest distance value. This point has a *time* coordinate of about 5. So the walker is closest to the sensor after about 5 s.

    c. About 2.7 m

    d. Look for "flat" portions of the curve, where the distance value does not change for a period of time. The walker stopped for about one second between 4.5 and 5.5 s and paused at the beginning between 0 and 1 s.

5. a. $A(-7, -4)$, $B(0, -2)$, $C(3, 6)$, $D(0, 3)$, $E(4, -4)$, $F(-2, -6)$, $G(4, 0)$, $H(7, 1)$, $I(-5, 2)$, and $J(-5, 4)$

    b.

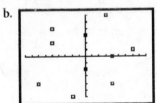

    c. *B*, *D*, and *G*

    d. I: *C* and *H*; II: *I* and *J*; III: *A* and *F*; IV: *E*

6. Scatter plot descriptions will vary. However, the location scenarios should include information such as (*positive, positive*) in Quadrant I; (*negative, positive*) in Quadrant II; (*negative, negative*) in Quadrant III; (*positive, negative*) in Quadrant IV; (0, *any number*) on *y*-axis; (*any number*, 0) on *x*-axis, and (0, 0) as the origin.

7. a. Approximate answers (the second coordinates are in millions):

    (1984, 280), (1985, 320), (1986, 340), (1987, 415), (1988, 450), (1989, 445), (1990, 440), (1991, 360), (1992, 365), (1993, 340), (1994, 345), (1995, 275), (1996, 225), (1997, 175), (1998, 160), (1999, 125), (2000, 75), (2001, 45), (2002, 30), (2003, 15)

    b. Window [1984, 2003, 1, 0, 500, 50]

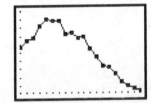

    c. Answers will vary. Shipments increased until 1988 and then decreased except for a slight increase in 1992 and 1994. The introduction of compact discs may have influenced the decrease.

8. a. Years elapsed are 0, 10, 20, 30, 35, 36, 37, 38, 39, 40, 41.

    b.

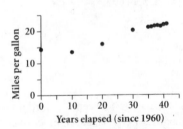

    c.

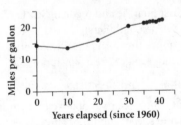

    d. Approximately 19.5 mpg

e.

Average Miles per Gallon
for All U.S. Automobiles
(since 1960)

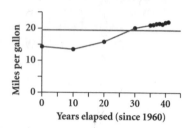

The horizontal line separates the data points that are above the mean of the averages from the data points that are below it.

f. Answers will vary.

9. a. $(-1.5, 2.6), (-3, 0), (-1.5, -2.6), (1.5, -2.6)$

b. Answers will vary.

10. a. 8:06 (The speed drops suddenly at this point.)

b. 40 mi/h   **c.** 12 min

d. Answers will vary. It seems unrealistic that Xavier's dad never fully stopped during the trip.

11. a. The **bold** values are fixed. One possibility is {**5, 12**, 14, **15**, 20, **30, 47**}.

b. The **bold** values are fixed. One possibility is {**5**, 10, **12**, 13, 14, 16, 20, **30**, 40, **47**}.

c. The **bold** values are fixed. One possibility is {**5**, 10, 12, 12, 13, 14, 16, 20, 28, 32, 40, **47**}.

12. a. The five-number summary is 476, 496, 506.5, 536, 605.

b.

Result of TIMSS

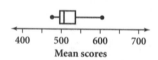

Mean scores

c. The greatest spread is between the third quartile and the maximum, that is, the right whisker. The least spread occurs between the first quartile and the median.

d. The interquartile range is $536 - 496 = 40$ points.

e. Between first quartile and median: Scotland, England, Sweden, Lithuania, United States, Australia; above the third quartile: Belgium, Japan, Taiwan, Hong Kong, Korea, Singapore

IMPROVING YOUR REASONING SKILLS

The weather glyphs show four variables: cloud coverage, wind direction, wind speed, and time. Time is definitely a numeric variable. Wind direction, cloud coverage, and wind speed, however, could be argued as either numerical or categorical. Wind direction might be assigned a compass bearing. Cloud coverage could be three categories, or be assigned a percentage (0%, 50%, 100%), or be assigned a degree number (1, 2, 3). Wind speed is also complex

because although a specific numeric wind speed would be measured (e.g., 6 knots), it would then be placed in a categorical bin (e.g., 3–7 knots). A variety of graphs can display this data, but it may be hard to find a single type of graph to display all the information.

LESSON 1.7

EXERCISES

1. a. Window: $[0, 70, 10, -10, 60, 10]$. (The lower Ymin value allows trace numbers to appear on the calculator screen without interfering with plotted points.)

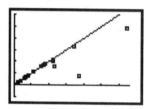

b. $y = x$

c. No. In no case is the estimated number of dinosaurs more than the actual number.

d. Yes. For five species, the estimated count is less than the actual count.

2. a. The points below the line—*B, C, E, F,* and *J*—represent Lucia's estimates.

b. The points above the line—*A, D, G, H,* and *I*—represent Malcolm's estimates.

3. Overestimates are points for which the *y*-coordinate is greater than the *x*-coordinate. These points are *B, C, D, E,* and *G*. Underestimates are points for which the *y*-coordinate is less than the *x*-coordinate. These points are *A, F, H,* and *I*.

4. a. Possible approximations are

Time	0	0.5	1.0	1.5	2.0
Distance	0	0.5	0.8	1.4	2.1

Time	2.5	3.0	3.5	4.0	4.5
Distance	2.7	3.0	3.6	3.9	4.25

b. Answers will vary. A minimum window is $[0, 5, 1, 0, 5, 1]$.

c. $y = x$

d. Increasing

5. a. Answers will vary. The more the rubber band is stretched, the farther it flies.

b. Answers will vary between 400 and 600 cm. For a point with *x*-coordinate 15 to fit the pattern in this graph, the point would need to have a *y*-coordinate between 400 and 600.

c. Answers will vary between 7 and 12 cm. For a point with y-coordinate 400 to fit the pattern in this graph, the point would need to have an x-coordinate between 7 and 12.

6. a. For such a point, the actual price is 12 and the estimated price is 16. The point is A (12, 16).

b. For such a point, the actual price is 18 and the estimated price is 13. The point is B (18, 13).

c. Point C is an overestimate of $2, point D an over-estimate of $5, and point E an overestimate of $2.

Estimated Prices vs. Actual Prices

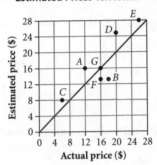

d. (*See graph for 6c.*)

e. On a horizontal line through the estimate $16 on the vertical axis

f. On a vertical line through the actual $16 on the horizontal axis

g. They are points on the line shown. These points indicate points for which *estimate = actual price*.

7. a. It shows the differences between the estimated number of each species and the actual count. This helps identify overestimates and underestimates.

b. Window: [0, 60, 10, −40, 10, 10]

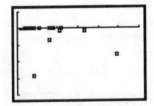

c. 5; for the points below the x-axis, the y-coordinate, *estimated number − actual number*, is less than 0, so the estimated number is less than the actual number. They represent underestimates.

d. (8, −29); the 8 is the estimated number of velociraptors; the number of velociraptors was underestimated by 29.

8. a. (−4, 1)   **b.** (−2, −5)   **c.** (1, 5)

d. Plotted points will vary. In general, they lie on the line that bisects Quadrant II and Quadrant IV. The equation $y = −x$ fits these points.

9. a. If a point lies on the line $y = x$, it means the verbal score is equal to the mathematics score.

b. These states also have high verbal scores. The verbal scores are not as high as the math scores.

c. Because more points are below the line than above it, more states had students with higher mathematics scores than verbal scores.

10. a. About 1 m/s, because the distances in meters are about equal to the times in seconds.

b. Between 0.5 and 1.0, between 2.5 and 3.0, between 3.5 and 4.0, between 4.0 and 4.5. For these intervals, the change in the distance values is less than the change in the time values.

c. Between 1.0 and 1.5, between 1.5 and 2.0, between 2.0 and 2.5. For these intervals, the change in the distance values is greater than the change in the time values.

d. Between 0 and 0.5, between 3.0 and 3.5. For these intervals, the change in the distance values is about equal to the change in the time values.

11. a. Answers will vary. The mean of the values is 125.0 cm, and the median is 125.3 cm.

b. Answers will vary. The string is longer than the stick, so you would need to measure twice or fold the string. The string will have some stretch, so it would be hard to keep it straight without stretching it. The ends of the string are never "clean" cut, so you would have to choose "the end."

c. It means that this measure is accurate within 0.2 cm.

d. Answers will vary. The range of measures is 123.3 to 126.5. This could be written 124.9 ± 1.6 cm.

12. Answers will vary.

a. The median must be equal to one of the quartiles. One possible answer is {1, 3, 3, 3, 4, 5, 6}.

b. The first and third quartiles must be the same. One possible answer is {1, 4, 4, 4, 4, 4, 7}.

c. The minimum value must be less than Q1 − 1.5 · IQR. One possible answer is {1, 6, 6, 7, 7, 8, 9}.

d. The third quartile and the maximum value must be the same. One possible answer is {1, 2, 3, 4, 5, 6, 6}.

13. a. The data values need to be organized in increasing order. The key should show an actual value from the data set.

b.

13	5 8
14	2 6 7 9
15	2 5 5 7 7 8 8
16	2 2 4 4 5 8
17	1 3 3 3 6
18	2 4

Key

13	5 means 13.5 cm

c. 18.4 − 13.5 = 4.9 cm

EXERCISES

1. Matrix [A] shows the 1992 statistics. Row 2 represents Randall Cunningham. Column 3 represents the number of touchdown passes. So, the entry in row 2, column 3, of matrix [A] tells you that Randall Cunningham threw 19 touchdown passes in 1992.

2. Steve Young made 322 pass completions in 1998.

3. 3×4

4. Answers will vary.

5. $\begin{bmatrix} 788 & 489 & 35 & 19 \\ 809 & 492 & 53 & 21 \\ 919 & 590 & 61 & 19 \end{bmatrix}$

This matrix gives the totals from the two years.

6. Yes. This result should always be true if the matrices have the same dimensions.

7. $\begin{bmatrix} -158 & -115 & -11 & -9 \\ 41 & 26 & 15 & -1 \\ 115 & 54 & 11 & 5 \end{bmatrix}$

This matrix gives the difference between the 1998 totals and the 1992 totals.

8. $([A] + [B]) \cdot \left(\frac{1}{2}\right)$

Note: The calculator expression $([A] + [B])/2$ will produce an error message because division is not defined for matrices.

9. a. $\begin{bmatrix} 8 & -5 & 4.5 \\ -6 & 9.5 & 5 \end{bmatrix}$ Add corresponding entries.

b. $\begin{bmatrix} -3 & 4 & -2.5 \\ 2 & -6 & -4 \end{bmatrix}$ Change each entry in [A] to its opposite.

c. $\begin{bmatrix} 15 & -3 & 6 \\ -12 & 10.5 & 3 \end{bmatrix}$ Multiply each entry in [A] by 3.

d. $\begin{bmatrix} 4 & -2.5 & 2.25 \\ -3 & 4.75 & 2.5 \end{bmatrix}$ Add corresponding entries and then multiply each result by $\frac{1}{2}$.

10. $[B] = \begin{bmatrix} -2 & 0 \\ 6 & -11.6 \\ 4.25 & 7.5 \end{bmatrix} - \begin{bmatrix} 2.8 & 2.4 \\ 2.5 & -9.4 \\ 1 & 6 \end{bmatrix}$

$= \begin{bmatrix} -4.8 & -2.4 \\ 3.5 & -2.2 \\ 3.25 & 1.5 \end{bmatrix}$

11. Answers will vary. Possible problem: Find the labor costs of building an item using 16 hours billed at $5.25 per hour and 30 hours billed at $8.75 per hour. The product is

$[5.25 \quad 8.75] \cdot \begin{bmatrix} 16 \\ 30 \end{bmatrix} = [5.25 \cdot 16 + 8.75 \cdot 30] =$
$[84 + 262.50] = [346.50].$

12. a. Quantity matrix: $\begin{bmatrix} 74 & 25 & 37 \\ 32 & 38 & 16 \\ 120 & 52 & 34 \end{bmatrix}$

Profit matrix: $\begin{bmatrix} 0.90 \\ 1.25 \\ 2.15 \end{bmatrix}$

The number of columns in the quantity matrix must be the same as the number of rows in the profit matrix.

b. Atlanta profit:
$74(\$0.90) + 25(\$1.25) + 37(\$2.15) = \$177.40$

Decatur profit:
$32(\$0.90) + 38(\$1.25) + 16(\$2.15) = \$110.70$

Athens profit:
$120(\$0.90) + 52(\$1.25) + 34(\$2.15) = \$246.10$

c. $\begin{bmatrix} 177.40 \\ 110.70 \\ 246.10 \end{bmatrix}; 3 \times 1$

d. The answer matrix gives the profit at each location.

Location	Profit
Atlanta	$177.40
Decatur	$110.70
Athens	$246.10

e. The error message—ERR: DIM MISMATCH— means that the dimensions of the matrices in the product don't match.

13. a. Answers will vary. The minimum must be 0 and the maximum must be 7. Also, the data value 2 must occur more frequently than any other. A sample solution is {0, 1, 2, 2, 2, 2, 3, 4, 6, 7}.

b. Answers will vary. The minimum must be 22.2 and the maximum must be 30.4. No value in the list should occur more often than any other value. A sample solution is {22.2, 24.5, 25.1, 26.2, 28.3, 28.7, 29.4, 30.4}.

14. a. The 40 leaves to the left of the stem represent Mrs. Shapiro's students. The 41 leaves to the right represent Mr. Chin's students. So, there are 40 students in Mrs. Shapiro's class and 41 in Mr. Chin's class.

b. Mrs. Shapiro's: $1.35; Mr. Chin's: $1.25.

c. 13

d. In Mrs. Shapiro's class, one student had $1.35 and one student had $1.30.

e. Answers will vary. Based on the stem plot, you might expect Mrs. Shapiro's class to have more money. There are more students with more than a dollar in her class and more with less than 50¢ in Mr. Chin's class.

f. Mr. Chin's: $20.34; Mrs. Shapiro's: $24.96.

EXERCISES

1. a. Mean: 41.5; divide the sum of the numbers by 14. Median: 40; list the numbers in order and find the mean of the two middle numbers. Mode: 36; find the number that occurs most often.

b. 27, 36, 40, 46, 58

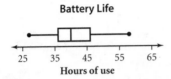

Battery Life

2. The five-number summary gives us five of the seven values. We need only fill in the blanks in this ordered data set {9, 11, –?– , 16, –?– , 21, 22}. Because the mean of the seven values is 16, the sum of the values must be 7 · 16 = 112. The values we have so far have a sum of 79, so the missing values must add to 112 − 79 or 33. The values 14 and 19 add to 33, so one possible data set is {9, 11, 14, 16, 19, 21, 22}.

3. a.

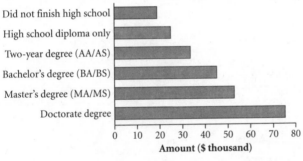

Mean Annual Wages, 1998

b. Greatest difference: from a master's degree to a doctorate; smallest difference: from not finishing high school to a high school diploma.

4. a.

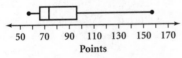

2003 NCAA Women's Tournament Top Scorers

b. Diana Taurasi, with 157 points, is an outlier.

c. Answers may vary. The measures of center are mean, 83.9; median, 73.5; and modes, 66, 74.

5. a. Mean ≈ 154; median = 121; there is no mode.

b. Bin widths may vary.

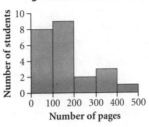

Pages Read in Current Book

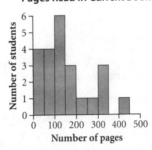

Pages Read in Current Book

c.

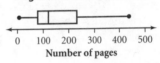

Pages Read in Current Book

d. Answers will vary. Possible answer: Most of the students questioned had read fewer than 200 pages, with a fairly even distribution between 0 and 200.

6. a.

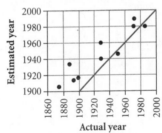

Invention Dates

b.

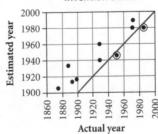

Invention Dates

c. $y = x$, where x represents actual year and y represents estimated year.

7. a. $\begin{bmatrix} 5.00 & 8.00 \\ 3.50 & 4.75 \\ 3.50 & 4.00 \end{bmatrix}$, $\begin{bmatrix} 0.50 & 0.75 \\ 0.50 & 0.25 \\ 0.50 & 0.25 \end{bmatrix}$, $[43 \quad 81 \quad 37]$

b. Add the matrix of current prices and the matrix of price increases.

$$\begin{bmatrix} 5.00 & 8.00 \\ 3.50 & 4.75 \\ 3.50 & 4.00 \end{bmatrix} + \begin{bmatrix} 0.50 & 0.75 \\ 0.50 & 0.75 \\ 0.50 & 0.25 \end{bmatrix} = \begin{bmatrix} 5.50 & 8.75 \\ 4.00 & 5.00 \\ 4.00 & 4.25 \end{bmatrix}$$

c. Multiply the attendance matrix by the new price matrix calculated in 7b.

$$[43 \quad 81 \quad 37]\begin{bmatrix} 5.50 & 8.75 \\ 4.00 & 5.00 \\ 4.00 & 4.25 \end{bmatrix} = [708.5 \quad 938.5]$$

The revenue from a matinee will be $708.50. The revenue from an evening show will be $938.50.

8. a. Kayo was jogging fastest between points A and B because she covered a lot of distance in a short period of time.

b. Kayo was not moving; perhaps she was resting.

c. Possible answer: Kayo started out jogging fast but had to rest for a few minutes. Then she jogged much slower until she had to rest again. She finally got the energy to jog all the way home at a steady pace without stopping.

9. a. 2,900,000

b. (*See graph at bottom of page.*)

c. The Ten Most Populated
U.S. Cities, 2000

```
0 | 95
1 | 14 19 22 32 52 95
2 | 90
3 | 69
4 |
5 |
6 |
7 |
8 | 01
```

Key

| 2 | 90 means 2.90 million |

d. The Ten Most Populated
U.S. Cities, 2000

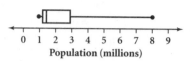

Population (millions)

e. The bar graph helps show how each city compares with the others, since they remain identified by name. The stem plot shows distribution, but also shows actual values. The box plot shows distribution and a clustering between 1 and 1.4 million, but does not show individual city names or populations.

10. a. Mean = 416.875 min

b. Median = 425 min   **c.** Mode = 480 min

TAKE ANOTHER LOOK

The picture bar graph uses both a broken vertical axis (starting at 15) and pictures with decreasing area to exaggerate the decline of green space. The normal bar graph, on the other hand, measures only acres and neglects the ratio to the increasing population, which the first bar graph does. Therefore, both of the bar graphs are engineered to persuade. Answers will depend on whether you think acres per person or total acres is a better measure.

CHAPTER 2

LESSON 2.1

EXERCISES

1. Increasing order: b, a, d, c

Decimal values:

a. $\frac{7}{8} = 0.875$ **b.** $\frac{13}{20} = 0.65$

c. $\frac{13}{5} = 2.6$ **d.** $\frac{52}{25} = 2.08$

2. a. There are fourteen 9th graders (9 + 3 + 2). Nine of the 9th graders have brown eyes, so the ratio is $\frac{9}{14}$.

b. $\frac{11}{20}$ **c.** $\frac{4}{3}$ **d.** $\frac{3}{30}$, or $\frac{1}{10}$

Chapter 1 Review, Exercise 9. b.

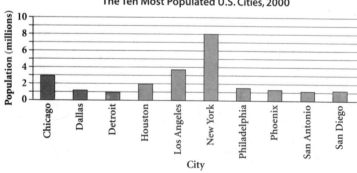

The Ten Most Populated U.S. Cities, 2000

Discovering Algebra Solutions Manual
©2007 Key Curriculum Press

3. a. $\dfrac{240 \text{ mi}}{1 \text{ h}}$

   b. 10 ppm means 10 parts per million—in this case, 10 parts capsaicin to 1,000,000 parts water. This can be written $\dfrac{10 \text{ parts capsaicin}}{1{,}000{,}000 \text{ parts water}}$, or $\dfrac{1 \text{ part capsaicin}}{100{,}000 \text{ parts water}}$.

   c. $\dfrac{350 \text{ women-owned firms}}{1000 \text{ firms}}$, or $\dfrac{7 \text{ women-owned firms}}{20 \text{ firms}}$

   d. $\dfrac{35{,}500 \text{ dollars}}{1 \text{ person}}$

4. a. To solve $\dfrac{24}{40} = \dfrac{T}{30}$ for T, multiply by 30 to undo the division.

   b. To solve $\dfrac{49}{56} = \dfrac{R}{32}$ for R, multiply by 32 to undo the division.

   c. To solve $\dfrac{M}{16} = \dfrac{87}{232}$ for M, multiply by 16 to undo the division.

5. a.
$$\frac{24}{40} = \frac{T}{30}$$
$$30 \cdot \frac{24}{40} = T \qquad \text{Multiply by 30 to undo the division.}$$
$$18 = T \qquad \text{Multiply and divide.}$$

   b. $R = 28$

   c.
$$\frac{52}{91} = \frac{42}{S}$$
$$\frac{91}{52} = \frac{S}{42} \qquad \text{Invert both sides.}$$
$$42 \cdot \frac{91}{52} = S \qquad \text{Multiply by 42 to undo the division.}$$
$$73.5 = S \qquad \text{Multiply and divide.}$$

   d. $x = 2.1$

   e.
$$\frac{M}{16} = \frac{87}{232}$$
$$M = \frac{87}{232} \cdot 16 \qquad \text{Multiply by 16 to undo the division.}$$
$$M = 6 \qquad \text{Multiply and divide.}$$

   f.
$$\frac{6}{n} = \frac{62}{217}$$
$$\frac{n}{6} = \frac{217}{62} \qquad \text{Invert both sides.}$$
$$n = \frac{217}{62} \cdot 6 \qquad \text{Multiply by 6 to undo the division.}$$
$$n = 21 \qquad \text{Multiply and divide.}$$

   g. $c = 31.2$

   h. $W = 9$

6. a. The ratio of the amount the ant can carry to the ant's weight would be equal to the ratio of the amount the student could carry to the student's weight. Let x be the amount the student could carry, and then write and solve a proportion.
$$\frac{4 \text{ g}}{1.5 \text{ g}} = \frac{x \text{ kg}}{55 \text{ kg}}$$
$$55 \cdot \frac{4}{1.5} = x \qquad \text{Multiply by 55 to undo the division.}$$
$$146.\overline{6} = x \qquad \text{Multiply and divide.}$$

The student could carry about 147 kg (about 323 lb). (Note: The proportion above is only one possibility. In this and other parts of this exercise, there are several proportions that also lead to the correct solution. For example, the ratio of the ant's weight to the student's weight is equal to the ratio of the amount the ant can carry to the amount the student can carry.)

   b. The ratio of the ant's stride to the ant's length would be equal to the ratio of the student's stride to the student's height. Let x be the length of the student's stride, and then write and solve a proportion.
$$\frac{0.84 \text{ cm}}{1.27 \text{ cm}} = \frac{x \text{ m}}{1.65 \text{ m}}$$
$$1.65 \cdot \frac{0.84}{1.27} = x \qquad \begin{array}{l}\text{Multiply by 1.65 to undo}\\\text{the division.}\end{array}$$
$$1.09 \approx x \qquad \text{Multiply and divide.}$$

The student would have strides about 1.09 m long.

   c. The ratio of the distance the ant travels to the ant's length would be equal to the ratio of the distance the student travels to the student's height. Let x be the distance the student travels, and then write and solve a proportion.
$$\frac{0.4 \text{ km}}{0.0127 \text{ m}} = \frac{x \text{ km}}{1.65 \text{ m}} \qquad \begin{array}{l}\text{Change cm to m so that}\\\text{both denominators are}\\\text{in the same unit.}\end{array}$$
$$1.65 \cdot \frac{0.4}{0.0127} = x \qquad \begin{array}{l}\text{Multiply by 1.65 to}\\\text{undo the division.}\end{array}$$
$$52 \approx x \qquad \text{Multiply and divide.}$$

The student would travel about 52 km (about 32 mi).

7. a. $\dfrac{5}{2} = \dfrac{25}{10}, \dfrac{2}{10} = \dfrac{5}{25}, \dfrac{25}{5} = \dfrac{10}{2}$

   b. $\dfrac{9}{a} = \dfrac{27}{12}, \dfrac{a}{12} = \dfrac{9}{27}, \dfrac{27}{9} = \dfrac{12}{a}$

   c. $\dfrac{k}{j} = \dfrac{m}{l}, \dfrac{j}{l} = \dfrac{k}{m}, \dfrac{m}{k} = \dfrac{l}{j}$

8. a. If 15% is withheld, Jeremy gets to keep $100\% - 15\%$, or 85%.

   b. 85% means 85 out of 100. So the ratio of Jeremy's hourly take-home wage t to his hourly wage is equal to $\dfrac{85}{100}$. You can find the value of t by writing and solving a proportion.
$$\frac{t}{7.38} = \frac{85}{100}$$
$$t = \frac{85}{100} \cdot 7.38 \qquad \begin{array}{l}\text{Multiply by 7.38 to}\\\text{undo the division.}\end{array}$$
$$t = 6.273 \qquad \text{Multiply and divide.}$$

Jeremy's hourly take-home pay is $6.27.

9. Use P to represent the number of people in the resort area during the summer. Then set up a proportion, making sure both ratios make the same comparison.

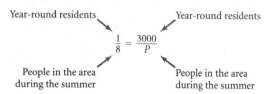

Year-round residents → → ← Year-round residents

$$\frac{1}{8} = \frac{3000}{P}$$

People in the area during the summer → ← People in the area during the summer

To solve this proportion, invert both ratios and then multiply by 3000. The number of people in the area during the summer is 24,000.

10. No matter how many servings you make, the ratio of cups of oatmeal to servings is $\frac{1}{3}$. To find the amount of oatmeal m needed for 2 servings, you can solve the proportion $\frac{1}{3} = \frac{m}{2}$. Multiplying by 2, you get $m = \frac{2}{3}$ cup. You need four times as much water as oatmeal, so you need $4 \cdot \frac{2}{3}$, or $\frac{8}{3}$, or $2\frac{2}{3}$ cups of water.

You can use the same strategy to find the amounts for 5 servings, or you can just add the amounts for 2 servings to the amounts for 3 servings. For 5 servings, you need $4 + 2\frac{2}{3} = 6\frac{2}{3}$ cups water and $1 + \frac{2}{3} = 1\frac{2}{3}$ cups oatmeal.

11. a. 3 carbon, 6 hydrogen, 1 oxygen

b. You will need 3(470), or 1410 atoms of carbon and 6(470), or 2820 atoms of hydrogen.

c. 500 molecules; use all the hydrogen atoms, 1500 carbon atoms, and 500 oxygen atoms.

12. Reading from the plot, the values are 2, 2, 4, 4, 4, 5, 5, 6, 6, 6, 6, 8, 8, 10, 10, 10, 10, 11, 11, 11, 15, 15, 16, 17. The median of these 24 values is 8, the mean of the twelfth and thirteenth values (8 and 8). Q1 is 5, the mean of the sixth and seventh values (5 and 5). Q2 is 11, the mean of the eighteenth and nineteenth values (11 and 11).

[dot plot with axis labeled 0, 4, 8, 12, 16, 20]

13. Mean: $104.9 million; median: $77.5 million; modes: $210 million, $80 million. The high incomes of Mel Gibson and Oprah Winfrey make the mean much higher than the median. The modes are meaningless for a data set this small.

14. a. $5 \cdot -4 + 8 = -20 + 8 = -12$

b. $-12 \div (7 - 4) = -12 \div 3 = -4$

c. $-3 - 6 \cdot 25 \div 30 = -3 - 150 \div 30 = -3 - 5 = -8$

d. $18 (-3) \div 81 = -\frac{2}{3}$

LESSON 2.2

EXERCISES

1. Sample answers:

a. In this proportion, 24 is the part, w is the whole, and 32 is the percent. So the proportion represents this question: 32% of what number is 24?

b. In this proportion, t is the part, 450 is the whole, and 48 is the percent. So the proportion represents this question: 48% of 450 is what number?

c. In this proportion, 98 is the part, 117 is the whole, and n is the percent. So the proportion represents this question: What percent of 117 is 98?

2. Different variables will be used.

a. In general, a percent question can be expressed by a proportion in the form $\frac{\text{part}}{\text{whole}} = \frac{\text{percent}}{100}$. In this question, we are given the percent, 125, and the part, 80. If we let d represent the whole, we can write the proportion $\frac{80}{d} = \frac{125}{100}$.

b. In this question, we are given the percent, 0.25, and the whole, 46. If we let k represent the part, we can write the proportion $\frac{k}{46} = \frac{0.25}{100}$.

c. In this question, we are given the part, 72, and the whole, 470. If we let r represent the percent, we can write the proportion $\frac{72}{470} = \frac{r}{100}$.

3. The ratio of twelfth graders to all students is equal to 17% or $\frac{17}{100}$. To find the number of twelfth graders x, write and solve a proportion.

$$\frac{x}{1582} = \frac{17}{100}$$

$$x = \frac{17}{100} \cdot 1582 \qquad \text{Multiply by 1582 to undo the division.}$$

$$x = 268.94 \qquad \text{Multiply and divide.}$$

There are 269 twelfth graders.

4. a. The ratio of tagged fish in the sample to total fish in the sample is $\frac{5}{75}$. This is approximately equal to the ratio of tagged fish in the lake, 250, to total fish in the lake, f. So, to estimate the number of fish in the lake, solve the proportion $\frac{5}{75} = \frac{250}{f}$.

$$\frac{5}{75} = \frac{250}{f}$$

$$\frac{75}{5} = \frac{f}{250} \qquad \text{Invert both sides.}$$

$$250 \cdot \frac{75}{5} = f \qquad \text{Multiply by 250 to undo the division.}$$

$$3750 = f \qquad \text{Multiply and divide.}$$

There are about 3750 fish in the lake.

b. The ratio of tagged fish in the sample to total fish in the sample should be about equal to $\frac{250}{5500}$ (the ratio of tagged fish in the lake to total fish in the lake). So, solve the proportion $\frac{250}{5500} = \frac{15}{f}$ to find the number of fish in the sample. There are about 330 fish in the sample.

5. a. Marie has won more than half of the games so far, so she should win more than 6 of the next 12 games.

  b. $\dfrac{28 \text{ games won by Maria}}{28 + 19 \text{ total games}} = \dfrac{M}{12}$; $M = 7.15$. So Marie should win 7 games.

  c. $\dfrac{19}{47} = \dfrac{30}{G}$ (Both ratios express the ratio of Tracy's wins to games played.); $G \approx 74$; they would need to play about 74 games.

6. a. Slightly fewer than 600 pieces. Sixteen ounces is almost ten times 1.69 ounces.

  b. $\dfrac{60 \text{ candy pieces}}{1.69 \text{ oz}} = \dfrac{N \text{ pieces}}{16 \text{ oz}}$; there are about 568 candies in a 1 lb bag.

  c. $\dfrac{1{,}000{,}000}{568} \approx 1761$ lb

7. Let $E =$ the total number of errors in the paper.

$$\dfrac{\text{errors found by Terry}}{\text{total errors}} = \dfrac{\text{errors found by both}}{\text{errors found be Jesse}}$$

$$\dfrac{24}{E} = \dfrac{18}{36}$$

$$E = 48$$

This method gives an estimated total of 48 errors in the paper. Of these, 18 were found by both Terry and Jesse, $24 - 18 = 6$ were found only by Terry, and $36 - 18 = 18$ were found only by Jesse. Thus, the number of errors found by at least one of them was $6 + 18 + 18 = 42$. Therefore, the estimate of the number of errors both of them missed is $48 - 42 = 6$ errors.

8. Bass $= \dfrac{360}{24} \cdot 235 = 3525$. Trout $= \dfrac{223}{15} \cdot 147 = 2185.4$. Perch $= \dfrac{208}{16} \cdot 151 = 1963$. Total $= \dfrac{791}{55} \cdot 533 = 7665.5$. These values are estimates, so the total should be close to the sum of the species totals, but not exactly equal to it.

9. a. $\dfrac{5}{3}$ **b.** $\dfrac{5}{8}$ **c.** $\dfrac{3}{8}$

10. a. When the ages are ordered, the median is between the 21st and 22nd values. Looking at the bar heights, you can see that both values are in the bin 54–56. So, the median age is 54 or 55.

  b. $2 + 3 + 3 = 8$

  c. Younger than 42, 44, 45, 66, 67, older than 69.

  d.

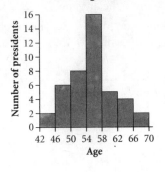

Presidents' Ages at Inauguration

11. $12 - 2 \cdot 6 - 3 = 12 - 12 - 3 = 0 - 3 = -3$. Matt is correct. Marta and Miguel did not use the order of operations. Marta did the operations from left to right, and Miguel did the subtractions before he multiplied. In the order of operations, multiplication comes first.

LESSON 2.3

EXERCISES

1. a. $x = 49.4$ **b.** $x = 40$

  c. $x \approx 216$ **d.** $x = 583.\bar{3}$

2. $\dfrac{1 \text{ mi}}{3 \text{ min } 53.43 \text{ s}} = \dfrac{1 \text{ mi}}{(3 \cdot 60 + 53.43) \text{ s}} = \dfrac{5280 \text{ ft}}{233.43 \text{ s}}$
≈ 22.62 ft/s

3. a. $\dfrac{50 \cancel{\text{m}}}{1 \cancel{\text{s}}} \cdot \dfrac{1 \text{ km}}{1000 \cancel{\text{m}}} \cdot \dfrac{60 \cancel{\text{s}}}{1 \cancel{\text{min}}} \cdot \dfrac{60 \cancel{\text{min}}}{1 \text{ h}} = 180$ km/h

  b. $0.025 \cancel{\text{day}} \cdot \dfrac{24 \cancel{\text{h}}}{1 \cancel{\text{day}}} \cdot \dfrac{60 \cancel{\text{min}}}{1 \cancel{\text{h}}} \cdot \dfrac{60 \text{ s}}{1 \cancel{\text{min}}} = 2160$ s

  c. $1200 \cancel{\text{oz}} \cdot \dfrac{1 \cancel{\text{lb}}}{16 \cancel{\text{oz}}} \cdot \dfrac{1 \text{ ton}}{2000 \cancel{\text{lb}}} = 0.0375$ ton

4. In each part, the ratio of ounces to grams is equal to 1 to 28.4 (or, equivalently, the ratio of grams to ounces is 28.4 to 1).

  a. $\dfrac{8 \text{ oz}}{x \text{ g}} = \dfrac{1 \text{ oz}}{28.4 \text{ g}}$; 227 g

  b. $\dfrac{x \text{ oz}}{50 \text{ g}} = \dfrac{1 \text{ oz}}{28.4 \text{ g}}$; 1.76 oz

  c. $\dfrac{160 \text{ oz}}{x \text{ g}} = \dfrac{1 \text{ oz}}{28.4 \text{ g}}$; 4544 g

  d. $\dfrac{x \text{ oz}}{100 \text{ g}} = \dfrac{1 \text{ oz}}{28.4 \text{ g}}$; 3.52 oz

5. In each part, the ratio of centimeters to inches is equal to 2.54 to 1 (or, equivalently, the ratio of inches to centimeters is 1 to 2.54).

  a. $\dfrac{x \text{ cm}}{62.5 \text{ in.}} = \dfrac{2.54 \text{ cm}}{1 \text{ in.}}$; about 159 cm

  b. $\dfrac{x \text{ cm}}{96 \text{ in.}} = \dfrac{2.54 \text{ cm}}{1 \text{ in.}}$; about 244 cm

  c. $\dfrac{12 \text{ cm}}{x \text{ in.}} = \dfrac{2.54 \text{ cm}}{1 \text{ in.}}$; about 4.72 in.

  d. $\dfrac{3.25 \text{ cm}}{x \text{ in.}} = \dfrac{2.54 \text{ cm}}{1 \text{ in.}}$; about 1.28 in.

6. a. $\dfrac{3 \text{ pounds}}{30 \text{ days}} = 0.1$ pound per day

  b. $\dfrac{5 \text{ pounds}}{45 \text{ days}} = 0.\bar{1}$ pound per day

  c. Crystal's cat eats more each day.

7. a. Divide the first meter measurement in the table by the first yard measurement: $\dfrac{6.3 \text{ m}}{7 \text{ yd}} = \dfrac{0.9 \text{ m}}{1 \text{ yd}}$.

  Dividing each of the other meter measurements by the corresponding yard measurement and rounding to the nearest tenth gives 1 yd ≈ 0.9 m, so a conversion factor from yards to meters is 1 yd ≈ 0.9 m.

To find a conversion factor from meters to yards, divide the yard measurements by the meter measurements. For example, $\frac{7\,\text{yd}}{6.3\,\text{m}} \approx \frac{1.1\,\text{yd}}{1\,\text{m}}$. Thus, a conversion factor from meters to yards is $1\,\text{m} \approx 1.1\,\text{yd}$.

b. Solve this proportion $\frac{0.9\,\text{m}}{1\,\text{yd}} = \frac{x\,\text{m}}{100\,\text{yd}}$. A football field is about 90 meters long.

c. Solve this proportion $\frac{0.9\,\text{m}}{1\,\text{yd}} = \frac{200\,\text{m}}{x\,\text{yd}}$. The exit is about 222 yards away.

d. Solve this proportion $\frac{0.9\,\text{m}}{1\,\text{yd}} = \frac{100\,\text{m}}{x\,\text{yd}}$, or just find half of the answer to 7c. A 100-meter dash is about 111 yards long.

e. Solve this proportion: $\frac{0.9\,\text{m}}{1\,\text{yd}} = \frac{x\,\text{m}}{15\,\text{yd}}$. You should buy 13.5 meters of fabric if you need 15 yards.

8. a.

Yards	1	2	3	4	5
Feet	3	6	9	12	15

b. 3

c. Because there are 3 feet in every yard, the ratio of feet f to yards y is 3 to 1. You can write this as the proportion $\frac{f}{y} = \frac{3}{1}$.

d. i. 450 ft   **ii.** 128 yd

9. $1500\,\text{m} \cdot \frac{1\,\text{km}}{1000\,\text{m}} \cdot \frac{1\,\text{mi}}{1.6\,\text{km}} = 0.9375\,\text{mi}$

Because 1500 meters is less than a mile, the 1-mile race is longer.

10. a. To make 120 servings, you need $120 \cdot 8$, or 960 oz of lemonade. One can of concentrate makes 64 oz, so to make 960 oz, you need $960 \div 64$, or 15 cans of concentrate. Using dimensional analysis:

$120\ \text{servings} \cdot \frac{8\ \text{oz}}{1\ \text{serving}} \cdot \frac{1\ \text{can}}{64\ \text{oz}} = 15\ \text{cans}$

b. Because 12 oz of concentrate makes 64 oz of lemonade, you need $\frac{12}{64}$, or 0.1875 oz to make 1 oz of lemonade.

c. $\dfrac{\text{number of oz of concentrate}}{\text{number of oz of lemonade}} = \dfrac{12}{64}$

d. $\frac{16}{L} = \frac{12}{64}$; $L \approx 85$ oz

11. $120\ \text{mL} \cdot \frac{1\ \text{L}}{1000\ \text{mL}} \cdot \frac{1.06\ \text{qt}}{1\ \text{L}} \cdot \frac{4\ \text{cups}}{1\ \text{qt}} = 0.5088\ \text{cup}$, or about $\frac{1}{2}$ cup

12. The Math Club has $\frac{3}{5}$ of the 20 students. If the profits are divided in proportion to the number of students in the clubs, the Math Club would get $\frac{3}{5} \cdot 480$, or $288, leaving $480 − $288, or $192 for the Chess Club.

13. Because only five values are represented in the plot, they must correspond to the values in the five-number summary: 10 cm, 22 cm, 33 cm, 41 cm, 46 cm.

From the first bullet, you know that the pygmy kingfisher has length 10 cm and the laughing kookaburra has length 46 cm.

The mean length of the five birds is 30.4. So, the second bullet indicates that the belted kingfisher is $30.4 + 2.6$, or 33 cm long. This leaves 22 cm and 41 cm.

Because the ringed kingfisher's length is closer to the median than the green kingfisher, the ringed kingfisher has length 41 cm, and the green kingfisher has length 22 cm.

IMPROVING YOUR VISUAL THINKING SKILLS

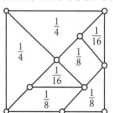

LESSON 2.4

EXERCISES

1. a. 40; find the y-value corresponding to an x-value of 25.

   b. 75; find the x-value corresponding to a y-value of 120.

2. a. 88; scroll down to find the y-value corresponding to the x-value 55.

   b. 281; scroll down to find the x-value corresponding to a y-value of about 450.

3. To change miles to kilometers, multiply by 1.6; to change kilometers to miles, divide by 1.6.

Distance (mi)	Distance (km)
2.8	4.5
7.8	12.5
650.0	1040.0
937.5	1500.0

4. a. Divide by 3.5 to undo the multiplication; $x = 4$.

   b. Divide by 8 to undo the multiplication; $x = 3.4875$.

   c. Multiply by 7 to undo the division; $x = 2.625$.

   d. Change the proportion to $\frac{x}{12} = \frac{1}{0.8}$. Then multiply by 12 to undo the division; $x = 15$.

5. a. $c = 1.25(2.5) = 3.125$, or \$3.13

   b. Substitute 5 for c to get $5 = 1.25f$. Then solve for f.

   $$5 = 1.25f$$
   $$\frac{5}{1.25} = \frac{1.25f}{1.25}$$
   $$4 = f$$

   You can buy 4 yd of fabric for \$5.

   c. \$1.25

6. a.

Market A

Ears	7	14	21	28	35	42
Cost ($)	1.25	2.50	3.75	5.00	6.25	7.50

Market B

Ears	13	26	39	52	65	78
Cost ($)	2.75	5.50	8.25	11.00	13.75	16.50

   b. For Market A, the cost per ear is \$1.25 ÷ 7, or about \$0.179. So, if x is the number of ears and y is the total cost in dollars, then $y = 0.179x$.

   For Market B, the cost per ear is \$2.75 ÷ 13, or about \$0.212. So, if x is the number of ears and y is the total cost in dollars, then $y = 0.212x$.

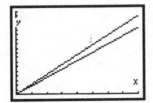

   [0, 80, 10, 0, 18, 1]

   c. Market A: \$0.18; Market B: \$0.21; these are the constants of variation in the equations, rounded to the nearest hundredth.

   d. The graph for the market with the lower rate (Market A) is less steep than the graph for the market with the higher rate.

7. a.

Vegetable	Weight (kg)	Weight (lb)
Cabbage	56	123
Summer squash	49	108
Zucchini	29	64
Kohlrabi	28	62
Celery	21	46
Radish	13	28
Cucumber	9	20
Brussels sprout	8	18
Carrot	5	11

   b. Divide each pound value by the corresponding kilogram value and find the mean or median of the values. You should find that there are about 2.2 pounds per kilogram. So, if x is the number of kilograms and y is the number of pounds, then $y = 2.2x$.

   c. Solve $6.5 = 2.2x$. The pumpkin weighs about 2.95 kg.

   d. $y = 2.2 \cdot 3600 = 7920$. The elephant weighs 7920 lb.

   e. 100 lb = $45.\overline{45}$ kg; 100 kg = 220 lb

8. a. Thu calculated $\frac{150}{93} \approx 1.61$, which is the number of kilometers per mile. In Thu's equation, x is the number of miles and y is the number of kilometers.

   b. Sabrina calculated $\frac{93}{150} = 0.62$, which is the number of miles per kilometer. In Sabrina's equation, x is the number of kilometers and y is the number of miles.

   c. Thu's equation may be more convenient because you can just multiply the number of miles by 1.61.

   d. Sabrina's equation is more convenient for converting kilometers to miles.

9. a. Answers will vary. A sample answer is to use the value of U.S. coins and bills in dollar denominations: {100, 50, 20, 10, 5, 1, 0.50, 0.25, 0.10, 0.05, 0.01}.

   b. Multiply the list by the exchange rate. For example, to convert to Japanese yen, multiply the list by 104.160. The result would be {10416, 5208, 2083.2, 1041.6, 520.8, 104.16, 52.08, 26.04, 10.416, 5.208, 1.0416}.

   c. Divide list L_2 by the exchange rate to obtain the original values.

   d. Using dimensional analysis:

   $$\frac{11.297 \text{ pesos}}{1 \text{ dollar}} \cdot \frac{1 \text{ dollar}}{0.772 \text{ euros}}$$
   $$\approx 14.633 \text{ pesos per euro}$$

   Then multiply the number of euros by this exchange rate.

10. a. Because distance and time are directly proportional, the ratio of distance to time is a constant. I walk 3 mi in 1.5 h, so the constant ratio is $\frac{3 \text{ mi}}{1.5 \text{ h}}$, or 2 mi/h. So in 1 h I can walk 2 mi.

   b. 2 h · 2 mi/h = 4 mi

   c. It takes 1 h to walk 2 mi, so it would take 3 h to walk 6 mi.

d.

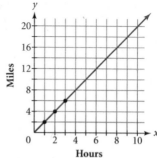

e. The constant of variation, 2 mi/h, represents the constant walking speed.

f. $d = 2t$, where d is distance traveled in miles and t is travel time in hours

11. a. $D = 5t$, where D is the distance traveled, in inches, and t is the time elapsed, in minutes.

b. The constant of variation is 5. This is the constant rate of 5 in. every min.

c. The distance traveled in 1 h (or 60 min) is $5(60) = 300$ in.

d. The perimeter of the room is $2(14 \text{ ft}) + 2(20 \text{ ft}) = 68$ ft. Convert this distance to inches: $68 \text{ ft} \cdot \frac{12 \text{ in}}{1 \text{ ft}} = 816$ in. Substitute 816 for D in the equation $D = 5t$ and solve for t.

$$D = 5t$$
$$816 = 5t$$
$$t = \frac{816}{5} = 163.2$$

It would take the bug 163.2 min, or 2.72 h, to completely "circle" the room.

e.

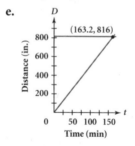

12. a. $\frac{130 \text{ km}}{1 \text{ h}} \cdot \frac{1 \text{ mi}}{1.6 \text{ km}} = 81.25$ mi/h

b. $\frac{25 \text{ mi}}{1 \text{ h}} \cdot \frac{1.6 \text{ km}}{1 \text{ mi}} = 40$ km/h

c. 65 miles per hour is 104 kilometers per hour. A speed limit sign might post 100 kilometers per hour.

13. a. To make $12 per hour, she would need to earn $36 for a 3-hour party. $36 ÷ $3.50 is about 10.3, so she would have to entertain a minimum of 11 children.

b. Solve $\frac{0.6}{3.50} = \frac{p}{100}$; $p \approx 17$, so the cost of balloons and face paint per child is about 17% of the total cost per child.

c. Solve $\frac{0.6}{x} = \frac{10}{100}$; $x = 6$, so Cecile should charge $6 per child.

14. a. $2.49 per box, 42¢ per bar, $2.99 per box, 25¢ per ounce

b. Yes; $2.49 ÷ 6 = $0.415, so the bars cost 42¢ each.

c. $\frac{2.99 \text{ dollars}}{1 \text{ box}} \cdot \frac{1 \text{ box}}{8 \text{ bars}} \cdot \frac{1 \text{ oz}}{0.25 \text{ dollar}} =$

$\frac{2.99 \text{ oz}}{2 \text{ bars}} = 1.495$ oz per bar

d. $\frac{\$2.49}{10 \text{ oz}} = \$0.249$ per oz or approximately 25¢ per oz

e. Possible answer: Both brands cost the same amount per oz. Chewy Granola Bars cost less per bar (37¢ versus 42¢), but the bars are smaller. If Marie and Tracy prefer fewer, larger bars, they should buy Crunchy Granola Bars. If they prefer more, smaller bars, they should buy Chewy Granola Bars.

LESSON 2.5

EXERCISES

1. a. $y = \frac{15}{x}$ **b.** $y = \frac{35}{x}$ **c.** $y = \frac{3}{x}$

2. Because x and y are inversely proportional, their product is constant. When $x = 3$, $y = 4$, so the constant product is $3 \cdot 4$, or 12. In 2a–d, you need to find the value such that the coordinates have a product of 12.

   a. 3   **b.** 6   **c.** 12   **d.** 0.5

3. Answers will vary. For each point, the product of the coordinates must be 20. Possible points include (4, 5), (2, 10), (5, 4), (10, 2), and (2.5, 8). Here is a graph of the points and the equation made using the window [0, 20, 2, 0, 20, 2].

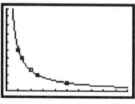

[0, 20, 2, 0, 20, 2]

4. This is not an inverse variation. The product of the quantities *time spent watching TV* and *time spent doing homework* is not a constant. It is an inverse relationship only in the sense that as one increases the other decreases, but the sum, not the product, is a constant. This is a relationship of the form $x + y = k$ or $y = k - x$, not an inverse variation of the form $xy = k$ or $y = \frac{k}{x}$.

5. a. 3 h   **b.** 2 h   **c.** 60 mi/h

6. a. Inverse variation; the x- and y-values have a constant product, 24; the equation is $y = \frac{24}{x}$, or $xy = 24$.

b. Direct variation; the ratio of y to x is constant; the equation is $y = 12x$.

c. Neither; it is not an inverse variation because some of the values are 0, and neither variable in an inverse variation can have the value 0; it is not a direct variation because the ratio of y to x is not constant $\left(\text{for example, } \frac{3.0}{3.0} = 1, \text{ while } \frac{1.5}{6} = 0.25\right)$.

d. Inverse variation; the x- and y-values have a constant product, 19.5; the equation is $y = \frac{19.5}{x}$, or $xy = 19.5$.

7. a. If x is the distance and y is the force, then $y = \frac{935}{x}$. Substitute each given distance for x to find the corresponding force: 62.$\bar{3}$ N, 93.5 N, and 187 N.

b. As you move closer to the hinge, it takes more force to open the door. When you go from 15 cm to 10 cm, the required force increases by about 31.2 N. When you go from 10 cm to 5 cm, the required force increases by 93.5 N. As you move closer, the force needed increases more rapidly. When you get very close to the hinge, the force needed becomes extremely large.

c. The curve goes up very steeply near the y-axis.

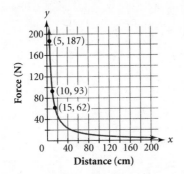
Distance (cm)

8. a. *Sid's weight · Sid's distance = Emily's weight · Emily's distance*, so $65 \cdot 4 = \text{Emily's weight} \cdot 2.5$; Emily weighs 104 lb.

b. Solve the equation $130 \cdot 4 = 104 \cdot D$ to find the distance Emily would have to sit from the center if the boys sit on the seat. Emily would have to sit 5 ft from the center. The distance from the center to the seat is only 4 ft, so she can't balance the two boys as long as they stay on the seat. However, if the boys move and Emily sits on the seat, it can be done. Solve $130 \cdot D = 104 \cdot 4$ to find the distance the boys would then have to sit from the center. They must sit 3.2 ft from the center.

9. a. If the balance point is at the center, then the weight of an unknown object will be exactly the same as the weight that balances it on the other side. If the balance point is off-center, you must know the two distances and do some calculation.

b. $15 \cdot M = 20 \cdot 7$; $M \approx 9.3$ kg

10. a. Answers will vary. In every case, the number of students times the amount should equal $10,000.

Number of students	Amount each needs to raise
100	$100
200	$50
250	$40
400	$25

b.

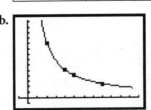

$[-50, 600, 50, -10, 140, 10]$

$y = \frac{10,000}{x}$

c. The graph should stop at $x = 500$ because there are only 500 students.

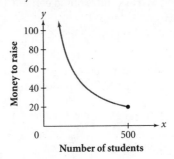
Number of students

11. a. Answers will vary. On this graph, x represents frequency and y represents tube length. As the frequency increases, the tube length decreases; this appears to be an inverse relationship.

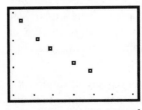

$[400, 1000, 100, 30, 90, 10]$

b. Possible answer: $y = \frac{37,227.1}{x}$, where 37,227.1 is the mean of the products of the frequencies and tube lengths.

c. $y = \frac{37,227.1}{880.0}$; $y \approx 42.3$ cm

12. a. The product of the volume and the pressure is a constant. When the pressure is 1 atm, the volume is 1 L, so the constant is $1 \cdot 1$, or 1. If the volume is 0.5 L, the pressure must be 2 atm.

 b. $0.25p = 1$; pressure is 4 atm.

 c. $v \cdot 10 = 1$; volume is 0.1 L.

 d. Answers will vary. You would have to increase the volume of the container. If you kept the same volume, you would have to suck some of the air out of the container.

 e.

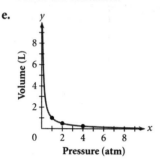

13. $s = 0.85p$; $s = 0.85(\$13.95)$; the sale price is $11.86.

14. a. Solve $\frac{5}{3} = \frac{2.5}{x}$; Mario's body should contain 1.5 lb of phosphorus.

 b. 2% of 130 lb is 2.6 lb, so Kyla's body should contain 2.6 lb of calcium. To find the amount of phosphorus, solve the proportion $\frac{5}{3} = \frac{2.6}{x}$; Kyla's body should contain 1.56 lb of phosphorus.

15. a. $\dfrac{1 \text{ apartment}}{3 \text{ gal}} \cdot 36 \text{ gal} = 12$ apartments

 b. $\dfrac{3 \text{ gal}}{\text{apartment}} \cdot 24 \text{ apartments} = 72$ gal

16. a. 1 sulfur atom, 2 hydrogen atoms, and 4 oxygen atoms

 b. There is 1 sulfur atom for every 2 hydrogen atoms, so it would take 100 sulfur atoms to combine with 200 hydrogen atoms. There are 4 oxygen atoms for every 2 hydrogen atoms. So, it would take 400 oxygen atoms to combine with 200 hydrogen atoms.

 c. Use all 400 atoms of oxygen, 200 atoms of hydrogen, and 100 atoms of sulfur to make 100 molecules of sulfuric acid.

LESSON 2.6

Activity day: There are no answers for this lesson.

LESSON 2.7

EXERCISES

1. a.

		¹1	0	6	2	²1	8	
		5				7		
		5				³3	6	
⁴5	5	7	⁵8			7		
6			⁶1	4	3	/	4	2
⁷7	9	⁸4	9			4		
		3		⁹1	0			
		3		¹⁰4				
¹¹1	1	4	8	0				
3		9		.				
1				5				
0				2				
¹²1	8	5	1	9	3			

Across:

 1. $(2/3)(159327) = 106218$

 3. $(-1 + 17{\wedge}2)/(4 + 2{\wedge}2) = 36$

 4. $4835 - 541 + 1284 = 5578$

 6. $(3 + 140)/(3*14)$ ▶ Frac $= 143/42$

 7. $8075 - 3*42 = 7949$

 9. $\sqrt{\ }(6{\wedge}2 + 8{\wedge}2) = 10$

 11. $740/(18.4 - 2.1*9) = -1480$

 12. $57{\wedge}3 = 185193$

Down:

 1. $9(-7 + 180) = 1557$

 2. $(9/2)(17/5 + 25/4)$ ▶ Frac $= 1737/40$

 4. $3 - 3(12 - 200) = 567$

 5. $9*10{\wedge}2 - 9{\wedge}2 = 819$

 8. $15 + 47(922) = 43349$

 10. $25.9058*20/4 - 89 = 40.529$

 11. $1284 - 877/0.2 = -3101$

2. Seija. Peter incorrectly added before multiplying.

3. a. First multiply 16 by 4.5. Then add 9.

 b. First divide 18 by 3. Then add 15.

 c. First square 6. Then add -5. Then multiply by 4. Then subtract the result from 3.

4.

Description	Claudia's sequence	Al's sequence
Pick the starting number.	-8.6	x
Add 5.	-3.6	$x + 5$
Multiply by 4.	-14.4	$4(x + 5)$
Subtract 12.	-26.4	$4(x + 5) - 12$
Divide by 4.	-6.6	$\dfrac{4(x + 5) - 12}{4}$
Subtract the original number.	2	$\dfrac{4(x + 5) - 12}{4} - x$

5. a. 1. Pick a number.
    2. Subtract 3.
    3. Multiply your result by 2.
    4. Add 4.
    5. Divide by 2.
    7. Add 4 or multiply by -3.

  b. Stages 6 and 7; the original number has been subtracted.

  c. Sample answer for the list {4, 11}:

```
{4,11}→L₁
                {4 11}
Ans-3
                {1 8}
Ans*2
                {2 16}
```

```
Ans+4
                {6 20}
Ans/2
                {3 10}
```

```
Ans-L₁
                {-1 -1}
Ans+4
                {3 3}
```

  d. $\dfrac{2(n - 3) + 4}{2} - n + 4$ or $-3\left[\dfrac{2(n - 3) + 4}{2} - n\right]$

6. a. Number Trick 1: Pick the starting number. Multiply by 2. Multiply by 3. Add 6. Divide by 3. Subtract your original number. Subtract your original number again.

  b. Number Trick 2: Pick the starting number. Add 2. Multiply by 3. Add 9. Subtract 15. Multiply by 2. Divide by 6 (you should have your original number).

7. a. Possible answers:

    $(3 + 2)(5) - 7 = 18$. First add 3 and 2 to get 5. Then multiply by 5 to get 25. Then subtract 7 to get 18.

    $3(2) + 5 + 7 = 18$. Multiply 3 by 2 to get 6. Then add 5 to get 11. Then add 7 to get 18.

  b. $8 - 5(6 - 7) = 13$. First subtract 7 from 6 to get -1. Then multiply by 5 to get -5. Then subtract this result from 8 to get 13.

8. a. Pick a number. Subtract 5. Multiply by 4. Add 8. Divide by 2. Subtract the original number. Add 6.

  b. Solutions will vary. The trick always produces the original number.

9. Possible solutions:

    $1 + 2 + 3 + 4 + 5 + 6 + 7 + 8 \cdot 9 = 100$;

    $-1 + 2 + 3 + 4 \cdot 5 \cdot 6 - 7 - 8 - 9 = 100$;

    $12 + 34 + 5 \cdot 6 + 7 + 8 + 9 = 100$

10. Answers will vary. Sample answer:

  a. Pick a number. Subtract 3. Multiply by 2. Add 10. Divide by 2. Subtract the original number. Subtract 6.

  b. I started with x and started applying operations. I subtracted 3, then multiplied by 2, and then subtracted 10. Because I multiplied by 2, I knew I had to undo this by dividing by 2, so I added this step. Then I subtracted the original number so that the final result would not be affected by the starting number chosen. I tested my trick, and I always ended up with 2. I added the step "Subtract 6" so that everyone would get -4.

  c. $\dfrac{2(x - 3) + 10}{2} - x - 6$

11. a. $\dfrac{308 \text{ mi}}{10.8 \text{ gal}} \approx 28.5 \text{ mpg}$

  b. $\dfrac{1 \text{ gal}}{28.5 \text{ mi}} \cdot 750 \text{ mi} \approx 26.3 \text{ gal}$

  c. $26.3 \text{ gal} \cdot \dfrac{\$2.35}{1 \text{ gal}} \approx \$61.81$

  d. Portia's gas mileage is more than 19%, or 6.5 mpg lower than the higher estimate. It is about 5%, or 1.5 mpg lower than the lower estimate.

12. a.

Length (in.)	Width (in.)
1	24
2	12
3	8
4	6
6	4
8	3
12	2
24	1

b.

Possible Boxes

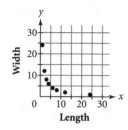

c. Inverse variation; the product of the length and the width equals a constant.

d. $l \cdot w = 24$, or $w = \frac{24}{l}$. Yes, the situation requires the dimensions to be whole numbers of inches.

13. a. Here is the scatter plot (the line is added in 13c):

Distance Traveled

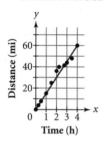

b. The cyclist traveled 60 miles in 4 hours, so the average speed was $60 \div 4$ or 15 mi/h.

c. $y = 15x$, where x is the time in hours and y is the distance in miles

d. From 1 h to 2.25 h and from 3.5 h to 4 h, the cyclist's speed is greater than the average speed, indicating that he or she may be traveling downhill. From 2.25 h to 3.5 h, the cyclist's speed is less than the average speed, indicating that he or she may be traveling uphill.

IMPROVING YOUR REASONING SKILLS

Encourage students to check their expressions for unnecessary parentheses. For example, $5 \cdot (3^2)$ can be written more simply as $5 \cdot 3^2$.

a. $5 \cdot (13 - 4)$

b. $5 \cdot 3^2$

c. $5 \cdot 13 + 5 \cdot -4$

d. $(100 + 35)/(1 + 2)$

e. $(6 + 3) \cdot 5$

f. $5 + 5 \cdot 8$

g. $5 \cdot (1 + 8)$

h. $5 \cdot 3^{\wedge}(1 + 1)$

i. $65 - 5 \cdot (3 + 1)$

j. $87 - 6 \cdot (10 - 3)$

k. $-3^2 + 54$

LESSON 2.8

EXERCISES

1. a. $-4 + (-8) = -12$

b. $(-4)(-8) = 32$

c. $-2(3 + 9) = -2(12) = -24$

d. $5 + (-6)(-5) = 5 + 30 = 35$

e. $(-3)(-5) + (-2) = 15 + (-2) = 13$

f. $\frac{-15}{3} + 8 = -5 + 8 = 3$

g. $\frac{23 - 3(4 - 9)}{-2} = \frac{23 - 3(-5)}{-2} = \frac{23 + 15}{-2}$
$= \frac{38}{-2} = -19$

h. $\frac{-4[7 + (-8)]}{8} - 6.5 = \frac{-4(-1)}{8} - 6.5$
$= \frac{4}{8} - 6.5 = 0.5 - 6.5 = -6$

i. $\frac{6(2 \cdot 4 - 5) - 2}{-4} = \frac{6(8 - 5) - 2}{-4}$
$= \frac{6(3) - 2}{-4} = \frac{18 - 2}{-4} = \frac{16}{-4} = -4$

2. a. Subtract 32.

b. Divide by 9.

c. Multiply by 9.

d. Add 32.

3. a. $2(6) + 3 = 12 + 3 = 15$

b. $2(6 + 3) = 2(9) = 18$

c. $5(6) - 13 = 30 - 13 = 17$

d. $\frac{6 + 9}{3} = \frac{15}{3} = 5$

4. a. $x = 15$. Order of operations: Start with x. Subtract 3. Divide by 2. The result is 6. Working backward: Start with 6. Multiply by 2. Add 3. The result is 15.

Equation: $\frac{x - 3}{2} = 6$

Operations on x	Undo operations	Results
		$x = 15$
$- (3)$	$+ (3)$	12
$/ (2)$	$\cdot (2)$	6

b. $x = 5$. Order of operations: Start with x. Multiply by 3. Add 7. The result is 22. Working backward: Start with 22. Subtract 7. Divide by 3. The result is 5.

Equation: $3x + 7 = 22$

Operations on x	Undo operations	Results
		$x = 5$
$\cdot (3)$	$/ (3)$	15
$+ (7)$	$- (7)$	22

c. $x = 6$. Order of operations. Start with x. Divide by 6. Subtract 20. The result is -19. Working backward: Start with -19. Add 20. Multiply by 6. The result is 6.

Equation: $\frac{x}{6} - 20 = -19$

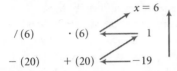

Operations on x	Undo operations	Results
		$x = 6$
$/(6)$	$\cdot (6)$	1
$-(20)$	$+(20)$	-19

5. Multiply by 60, multiply by 60 again, and then divide by 5280.

6. Justine could start with 33 and work backward, undoing each operation: Start with 33. Add 2 to get 35. Divide by 5 to get 7. Quentin picked 7.

7. a. 3

b. Start with 3 and see whether you get the answer 3.

c. 15

d. The final result is always the original number.

8. a. 8.8   **b.** 15

c. I undid the operations shown in reverse order: I multiplied by 5, then added 12, then divided by 2, and then subtracted 10.

d. $\dfrac{2(x + 10) - 12}{5}$

e. $\frac{2(x + 10) - 12}{5} = 0$. To solve this equation, work backward: Multiply by 5 to get 0. Add 12 to get 12. Divide by 2 to get 6. Subtract 10 to get -4. To check, use -4 as a starting number and work forward: Add 10 to get 6. Multiply by 2 to get 12. Subtract 12 to get 0. Divide by 5 to get 0.

9. a. 25. Add 7. Multiply by 5. Divide by 3.

b. Start with -18. Multiply by 3 to get -54. Divide by 5 to get -10.8. Subtract 7 to get -17.8.

10. a. $3(x - 5) + 8 = -14.8$

Equation: $3(x - 5) + 8 = -14.8$		
Description	**Undo**	**Result**
Pick x.		-2.6
$-(5)$	$+(5)$	-7.6
$\cdot (3)$	$/(3)$	-22.8
$+(8)$	$-(8)$	-14.8

$x = -2.6$

b. $3.5\left(\dfrac{x - 8}{4}\right) = 2.8$

Equation: $3.5\left(\dfrac{x - 8}{4}\right) = 2.8$		
Description	**Undo**	**Result**
Pick x.		11.2
$-(8)$	$+(8)$	3.2
$/(4)$	$\cdot (4)$	0.8
$\cdot (3.5)$	$/(3.5)$	2.8

$x = 11.2$

c. $\dfrac{4(x - 5) - 8}{-3} = 12$

Equation: $\dfrac{4(x - 5) - 8}{-3} = 12$		
Description	**Undo**	**Result**
Pick x.		-2
$-(5)$	$+(5)$	-7
$\cdot (4)$	$/(4)$	-28
$-(8)$	$+(8)$	-36
$/(-3)$	$\cdot (-3)$	12

$x = -2$

d. $\dfrac{4 - 3(7 + 2x)}{5} + 18.5 = -74.9$

Equation: $\dfrac{4 - 3(7 + 2x)}{5} + 18.5 = -74.9$		
Description	**Undo**	**Result**
Pick x.		75
$\cdot (2)$	$/(2)$	150
$+(7)$	$\div (7)$	157
$\cdot (-3)$	$/(-3)$	-471
$+(4)$	$-(4)$	-467
$/(5)$	$\cdot (5)$	-93.4
$+(18.5)$	$-(18.5)$	-74.9

$x = 75$

11. a. $x = -2.4$. Start with 8. Subtract 4.2 to get 3.8. Multiply by 2.5 to get 9.5. Divide by 5 to get 1.9. Subtract 4.3 to get -2.4.

b. $x = 23.6$. Start with 5.4. Add 4.3 to get 9.7. Multiply by 5 to get 48.5. Divide by 2.5 to get 19.4. Add 4.2 to get 23.6.

12. $D = 6 + 0.4(t - 5)$

   a. Substitute 60 for t in the equation and solve for D.

      $D = 6 + 0.4(60 - 5) = 6 + 0.4(55) = 6 + 22 = 28$

      After 60 min, the depth of the water is 28 in.

   b. Substitute 36 for D in the equation and solve for t.

      $36 = 6 + 0.4(t - 5)$

      Undo adding 6 by subtracting 6.

      $30 = 0.4(t - 5)$

      Undo multiplying by 0.4 by dividing by 0.4.

      $75 = t - 5$

      Undo subtracting 5 by adding 5.

      $80 = t$ or $t = 80$

      It takes 80 min until the water is 36 in. deep.

   c. $D = 6 + 0.4(t - 5)$

      First, undo adding 6 by subtracting 6.

      $D - 6 = 0.4(t - 5)$

      Next, undo multiplying by 0.4 by dividing by 0.4.

      $\dfrac{D - 6}{0.4} = t - 5$

      Finally, undo subtracting 5 by adding 5.

      $\dfrac{D - 6}{0.4} + 5 = t$ or $t = \dfrac{D - 6}{0.4} + 5$

13.

Equation: $\dfrac{3(2 - 4x)}{4} - 7 = 14$		
Description	**Undo**	**Result**
Pick x.		~~5~~2 — 6.5
$\cdot\,(-4)$	$/\,(-4) \cdot +(4)$	~~13~~ 26
~~$\cdot(2)$~~ $+ (2)$	$-\,(2) \;+(2)$	~~27~~ 28
~~$+(5)$~~ $\cdot\,(3)$	$/\,(3) \;\;-(5)$	~~81~~ 84
$/\,(4)$	$\cdot\,(4)$	21
$-\,(7)$	$+\,(7)$	14

14. a. To find the speed in miles per hour, solve the proportion $\frac{x}{200} = \frac{1}{87}$. The car travels about 2.3 miles per hour. To convert this speed to feet per second, you can use dimensional analysis:

$\dfrac{2.3 \text{ mi}}{1 \text{ h}} \cdot \dfrac{1 \text{ h}}{60 \text{ min}} \cdot \dfrac{5280 \text{ ft}}{1 \text{ mi}} \approx 202 \text{ ft/min}$

   b. To convert to centimeters per second, use dimensional analysis:

$\dfrac{202 \text{ ft}}{1 \text{ min}} \cdot \dfrac{12 \text{ in.}}{1 \text{ ft}} \cdot \dfrac{2.54 \text{ cm}}{1 \text{ in.}} \cdot \dfrac{1 \text{ min}}{60 \text{ s}} \approx 103 \text{ cm/s}$

15. a. $\dfrac{12.5 \text{ gal}}{350 \text{ mi}} \approx 0.036 \text{ gal/mi};$

$\dfrac{0.036 \text{ gal}}{1 \text{ mi}} \cdot 520 \text{ mi} \approx 19 \text{ gal}$

   b. $\dfrac{225 \text{ mi}}{10.7 \text{ gal}} \approx 21 \text{ mpg};$

$\dfrac{21 \text{ mi}}{1 \text{ gal}} \cdot 9 \text{ gal} = 189 \text{ mi}$

16. a. $\dfrac{3}{4} + \dfrac{2}{3} + \dfrac{1}{2} = \dfrac{23}{12}$, or $1\dfrac{11}{12}$ cups

   b. $\dfrac{3}{4}(\$6.98) + \dfrac{2}{3}(\$7.98) + \dfrac{1}{2}(\$4.98) = \$13.05$

IMPROVING YOUR REASONING SKILLS

This problem can be solved in several ways. By working backwards, you will realize that some numbers won't work. For example, for each child and the dog to get one cookie at the end, there must have been 7 cookies when the last child gives one to the dog and takes one-third. But 7 is not two-thirds of any number, so each child must have gotten at least 2 in the end, and so on up to 7, the smallest number that works. Another approach is to create a function and put it into a graphing calculator. At the last split, the number of cookies each child will receive can be given by the formula $y = \frac{1}{3}\left(\frac{2}{3}\left(\frac{2}{3}\left(\frac{2}{3}(x - 1) - 1\right) - 1\right) - 1\right)$. Looking at the table for this equation, you see that 79 is the first value of x that gives an integral value for y (when $x = 79$, $y = 7$).

CHAPTER 2 Review

EXERCISES

1. a. $n = 8.75$

   b. $w = 84.6$

   c. $k = 5\dfrac{1}{6}$, or $5.1\overline{6}$

2. Possible answers:

$\dfrac{7 \text{ bh}}{5 \text{ h}} = \dfrac{30 \text{ bh}}{x \text{ h}}; \dfrac{7 \text{ bh}}{30 \text{ bh}} = \dfrac{5 \text{ h}}{x \text{ h}}; \dfrac{5 \text{ h}}{7 \text{ bh}} = \dfrac{x \text{ h}}{30 \text{ bh}};$

$\dfrac{30 \text{ bh}}{7 \text{ bh}} = \dfrac{x \text{ h}}{5 \text{ h}}$

3. a. Possible points include $(2, 1)$, $(3, 1.5)$, $(4, 2)$, $(5, 2.5)$, $(6, 3)$, $(7, 3.5)$, $(8, 4)$.

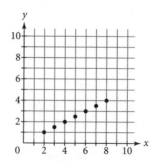

   b. All points appear to lie on a line.

4. a. $20 \text{ ells} \cdot \dfrac{3.75 \text{ ft}}{1 \text{ ell}} = 75 \text{ ft}$

   b. $\dfrac{75 \text{ ft}}{12 \text{ yr}} \cdot \dfrac{1 \text{ yr}}{12 \text{ mo}} \approx \dfrac{0.52 \text{ ft}}{1 \text{ mo}} = 0.52 \text{ ft/mo}$

5. $\frac{\text{number of shih of millett}}{\text{total number of shih}}$ should be about equal to $\frac{\text{grains of millet in sample}}{\text{total grains in sample}}$. So, you can find the amount of millet m by solving this proportion $\frac{m}{1534} = \frac{28}{254}$. You have about 169 shih of millet and about $1534 - 169$, or 1365 shih of rice.

6. a. If x represents the weight in kilograms and y represents the weight in pounds, one equation is $y = 2.2x$, where 2.2 is the data set's mean ratio of pounds to kilograms.

b. Solve the equation $30 = 2.2x$. There are about 13.6 kg in 30 lb.

c. $y = 2.2(25) = 55$. There are 55 lb in 25 kg.

7. a. About 7.5 cm

b. The plant is growing about 1.5 cm per day. To reach a height of 25 cm will take $25 \div 1.5$, or about 17 days.

c. $H = 1.5 \cdot D$

8. a. Because the product of the x- and y-values is roughly constant, it is an inverse variation.

b. One possibility: $y = \frac{45.5}{x}$, where 45.5 is the mean of the products

c. $y = \frac{45.5}{32}; y \approx 1.4$

9. a. Directly: $d = 50t$

b. Directly: $d = 1v$, or $d = v$

c. Inversely: $100 = vt$, or $t = \frac{100}{v}$

10. a. The product of the volume and the pressure is always $1.75 \cdot 1 = 1.75$. So, if the pressure is 0.8 atm, the volume is $1.75 \div 0.8$, or 2.1875 L.

b. $1.75 \div 0.75$, or $2.\overline{3}$ atm

c. $y = \frac{1.75}{x}$

d.

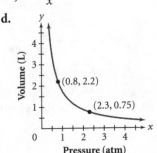

11. a. Start with a number. Double it. Subtract 1. Multiply by 3. Add 1.

b. x; $2x$; $2x - 1$; $3(2x - 1)$; $3(2x - 1) + 1$

c. $x = 4.5$; $2x = 9$; $2x - 1 = 8$; $3(2x - 1) = 24$; $3(2x - 1) + 1 = 25$

d. To find the starting value that gives a result at the last stage of 22, undo the steps listed in the answer for part a in reverse order:

Begin with the result, 22. Subtract 1 to get 21. Divide by 3 to get 7. Add 1 to get 8. Take half of 8 to get 4. Therefore, the starting value is 4.

12. To evaluate the expression $\frac{12 - 3(x + 4)}{6} + 5$ when $x = 1$, start with 1. Add 4 to get 5. Multiply by -3 to get -15. Add 12 to get -3. Divide by 6 to get -0.5. Add 5 to get 4.5.

13.

Equation: $\frac{12 - 3(x + 4)}{6} + 5 = 4$		
Description	**Undo**	**Result**
Pick x.		2
$+ (4)$	$- (4)$	6
$\cdot (-3)$	$/ (-3)$	-18
$+ (12)$	$- (12)$	-6
$/ (6)$	$\cdot (6)$	-1
$+ (5)$	$- (5)$	4

IMPROVING YOUR REASONING SKILLS

Answers will vary. One method is to work with the reciprocals of the rates stated in the problem. The information about guests and dishes translates into three ratios: $\frac{1 \text{ dish}}{2 \text{ guests}}$, $\frac{1 \text{ dish}}{3 \text{ guests}}$, and $\frac{1 \text{ dish}}{4 \text{ guests}}$. To find the total number of dishes, rewrite the ratios with a common denominator of 12 guests and add: $\frac{6 \text{ dishes}}{12 \text{ guests}} + \frac{4 \text{ dishes}}{12 \text{ guests}} + \frac{3 \text{ dishes}}{12 \text{ guests}} = \frac{13 \text{ dishes}}{12 \text{ guests}}$. So there were 13 dishes for every 12 guests. There were 65, or $13 \cdot 5$ dishes in all, so there must have been $12 \cdot 5$, or 60 guests.

TAKE ANOTHER LOOK

Answers for the first three graphs: $k = 1$, $k < 1 \left(= \frac{1}{2} \right)$, and $k > 1 (= 2)$. In the fourth graph, $k < 0 (= -1)$ because the quotient $\frac{y}{x}$ is negative for every point on the graph. In the last pair of graphs, the first set of lines is symmetric across $y = x$; the k-values are reciprocals $\left(3 \text{ and } \frac{1}{3} \right)$. The second set of lines is perpendicular; the k-values are negative reciprocals $\left(-3 \text{ and } \frac{1}{3} \right)$. The geometric relationship can be confirmed with similar triangles. If $k = 0$, the graph is the x-axis. By the definition of a direct variation, $y = 0$ is a direct variation. However, nothing is varying, so $y = 0$ would not usually be called a direct variation.

CHAPTER 3

LESSON 3.1

EXERCISES

1. a. $-2(5 - 9) + 7 = -2(-4) + 7 = 8 + 7 = 15$

b. $\dfrac{(-4)(-8)}{-5 + 3} = \dfrac{32}{-2} = -16$

c. $\dfrac{5 + (-6)(-5)}{-7} = \dfrac{5 + 30}{-7} = \dfrac{35}{-7} = -5$

2. a.

Figure #	Perimeter
1	5
2	8
3	11
4	14
5	17

b. 5 ENTER, Ans + 3 ENTER, ENTER, . . .

c. Figure 10 has a perimeter of 32.

d. Figure 15 has a perimeter of 47.

3. $-14.2, -10.5, -6.8, -3.1, 0.6, 4.3$

4. a. 3 ENTER, Ans + 6 ENTER, ENTER, . . . ;
10th term = 57

b. 1.7 ENTER, Ans − 0.5 ENTER, ENTER, . . . ;
10th term = −2.8

c. −3 ENTER, Ans * −2 ENTER, ENTER, . . . ;
10th term = 1536

d. 384 ENTER, Ans/2 ENTER, ENTER, . . . ;
10th term = 0.75, you could also use Ans * 0.5

5. a. 0 ENTER, Ans + 12.35 ENTER, ENTER, ... The
starting value is 0, the height of ground level (the
first floor). The rule "+12.35" adds the average
floor height of each of the next 85 floors
$(1050 \div 85 \approx 12.35)$.

b. 1050 ENTER, Ans + 10.875 ENTER, ENTER, ... The
starting value is the height of the 86th floor. The
rule "+10.875" adds the average floor height of
floors 86 through 102 $\left(\dfrac{1224 - 1050}{102 - 86} = 10.875\right)$.

c. When you are 531 ft above the ground, you are
43 floors up from ground level and thus on the
44th floor.

d. 1093.5 ft; 94th floor

6. a. Possible explanation: The smallest square has an
area of 1. The next larger white square has an area
of 4, which is 3 more than the smallest square. The
next larger gray square has an area of 9, which is 5
more than the 4-unit white square.

b. 1 ENTER, Ans + 2 ENTER, ENTER, . . .

c. 17, which is the value of the 9th term in
the sequence

d. 39

e. The 48th term is 95. Students might press ENTER
48 times or compute $2(48) - 1$.

7. a. The table for six figures of the L-shaped puzzle
pieces is

Figure	Toothpicks	Perimeter	Area
1	8	8	3
2	14	12	6
3	20	16	9
4	26	20	12
5	32	24	15
6	38	28	18

b. Number of toothpicks: 8 ENTER,
Ans + 6 ENTER, ENTER, . . .
Perimeter: 8 ENTER, Ans + 4 ENTER, ENTER, . . .
Area: 3 ENTER, Ans + 3 ENTER, ENTER, . . .

c. Figure 10 has 62 toothpicks, a perimeter of 44, and
an area of 30.

d. Figure 25, made from 152 toothpicks, has a
perimeter of 104 and an area of 75.

8. a. 4 m

b. The height of the 25th floor is 101 m. (One way to
find this is to notice that the height of each floor is
4 times the floor number, plus 1.) Moving from the
25th floor to the basement, the height decreases by
4 m with each floor. So the recursive routine is
101 ENTER, Ans − 4 ENTER, ENTER, ... The 19th
term represents the height of the seventh floor.
The height is 29 m.

c. 26

d. $-3 + 4(-4) = -19$ m = 19 m underground

9. a. Possible answers:
−16 ENTER, Ans + 12 ENTER, ENTER, . . . , and
2 ENTER, Ans · −2 ENTER, ENTER, . . .

b. For the first routine given in 9a, the sequence is
$\{-16, -4, 8, 20, 32, 44, 56, \ldots\}$. For the second
routine, the sequence is
$\{2, -4, 8, -16, 32, -64, 128, \ldots\}$.

c. More numbers in the sequence

10. a. $17 \cdot 7 = 119$

b. 14 (namely, $7 \cdot 15 = 105$ through $7 \cdot 28 = 196$)

c. Possible answer: There are 14 multiples of 7
between 100 and 200, and 14 multiples of 7
between 200 and 300 (namely, $7 \cdot 29 = 203$
through $7 \cdot 42 = 294$). However, there are
15 multiples of 7 between 300 and 400 (namely,
$7 \cdot 43 = 301$ through $7 \cdot 57 = 399$).

d. Possible answer: Find $7 \cdot 1, 7 \cdot 2, 7 \cdot 3$, and so on. Or start with 7 and add 7 repeatedly.

11. a. 6.8 [ENTER], Ans + 1.5 [ENTER], [ENTER], . . .

b. 7.2 [ENTER], Ans + 1.5 [ENTER], [ENTER], . . .

c. The starting terms differ. The rule is the same.

d.

Age (mo)	Weight of Baby A (lb)	Weight of Baby B (lb)
0	6.8	7.2
1	8.3	8.7
2	9.8	10.2
3	11.3	11.7
4	12.8	13.2
5	14.3	14.7
6	15.8	16.2

e. The starting weights are different, but for both babies the weight increases by 1.5 lb each month. The weight of Baby B is always 0.4 lb more than the weight of Baby A.

12. a. 1 [ENTER], Ans $\cdot$ 3 [ENTER], [ENTER], . . . ; the 9th term is 6561.

b. 5 [ENTER], Ans $\cdot$ (−1) [ENTER], [ENTER], . . . ; the 123rd term is 5.

c. −16.2 [ENTER], Ans + 1.4 [ENTER], [ENTER], . . . ; the 13th term is the first positive term.

d. −1 [ENTER], Ans $\cdot$ (−2) [ENTER], [ENTER], . . . ; the 8th term, 128, is the first to be greater than 100.

13. a. The top box plot represents Portland, the middle one San Francisco, and the bottom one Seattle.

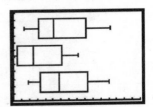

[0, 7, 0.5, 0, 12, 1]

Overall, San Francisco gets the least precipitation. The Q1-value for San Francisco is less than the minimum value of any of the other two cities, indicating that during three months of the year San Francisco gets less rain than the other two cities get in any month. The maximum value in the San Francisco plot is less than the Q3-value for each of the other plots, indicating that for three months of the year the average amount of precipitation in Seattle and Portland is greater than the average for any of the months in San Francisco.

b. You lose information about what time of year is wettest. A bar graph or scatter plot would show trends over the months of the year more clearly.

14.

Equation: $8 + 3(x − 5) = −14.8$		
Description	Undo	Result
Pick x.		− 2.6
− (5)	+ (5)	− 7.6
$\cdot$ (3)	/ (3)	− 22.8
+ (8)	− (8)	− 14.8

The solution to the equation is $x = −2.6$.

LESSON 3.2

EXERCISES

1. a. Negative; −1517
b. Positive; 472
c. Positive; $12.\overline{3}$
d. Positive; 326
e. Negative; $−3.\overline{3}$
f. Negative; −1464

2. a. 0.5, 1, 1.5, 2, 2.5, 3; 0.5 [ENTER], Ans + 0.5 [ENTER], [ENTER], [ENTER], [ENTER], [ENTER]

b. 4, 3, 2, 1, 0; 4 [ENTER], Ans −1 [ENTER], [ENTER], [ENTER], [ENTER]

c. −1, −0.75, −0.5, −0.25, 0, 0.25; −1 [ENTER], Ans + 0.25 [ENTER], [ENTER], [ENTER], [ENTER], [ENTER]

d. −1.5, 0, 1.5, 3; −1.5 [ENTER], Ans + 1.5 [ENTER], [ENTER], [ENTER]

3. 2b:

x-coordinate	y-coordinate
0	4
1	3
2	2
3	1
4	0

2d:

x-coordinate	y-coordinate
0	−1.5
1	0
2	1.5
3	3

4. a.

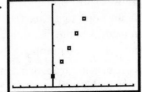

[−5, 10, 1, 0, 40, 10]

b.

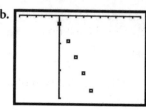

$[-5, 10, 1, 0, -30, 10]$

c. The starting point for each sequence lies on the y-axis. The x-coordinate of each starting point is 0.

d. For the recursive routine in 4a, the y-coordinates increase by 7. For the recursive routine in 4b, the y-coordinates decrease by 6.

5. a. $\{0, 0\}$ ENTER,
$\{Ans(1) + 1, Ans (2) + 2.54\}$ ENTER, ENTER, . . .

b.

In.	Cm
2	5.08
14	35.56
17	43.18

6. a. $\{0, 272\}$ ENTER,
$\{Ans(1) + 1, Ans(2) - 68\}$ ENTER, ENTER, . . .

Time (h)	Distance from San Antonio (mi)
0	272
1	204
2	136
3	68
4	0
5	−68

b.

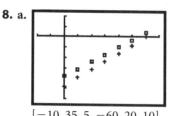

wrong size

The line is added in 6e.

c. The starting value $\{0, 272\}$ is the y-intercept $(0, 272)$ of the graph.

d. On the graph, you move right 1 unit and down 68 units to get from one point to the next. In the recursive routine, you add 1 to the first number and subtract 68 from the second number.

e. The line represents the distance from San Antonio for any time between 0 and 5 h. The points represent only distances at 1 h intervals.

f. The car is within 100 mi of San Antonio after 2.53 h have elapsed. Explanations will vary. Graphically, it is at, and after, the time which the line crosses the horizontal line $y = 100$.

g. The car takes 4 h to reach San Antonio. Answers will vary. The answer is the fourth entry in the table. Graphically, it is where the line crosses the x-axis.

7. a. Possible answer: $\{1, 1.38\}$ ENTER,
$\{Ans(1) + 1, Ans(2) + 0.36\}$ ENTER, ENTER, ...
The recursive routine keeps track of time and cost for each minute. Apply the routine until you get $\{7, 3.54\}$. A 7 min call costs \$3.54.

b. Possible answer: The graph should consist of points that lie on a line. It should include the point $(1, 1.38)$. Each subsequent point should be 1 unit to the right and 0.36 unit higher.

8. a.

$[-10, 35, 5, -60, 20, 10]$

b. The points for each submarine appear to lie on a line. The points for the USS *Dallas* lie on a steeper line, indicating that it surfaces at a faster rate.

c. Yes; the lines show the depths of the submarines at every point in time, not just for multiples of 5 s.

d. The USS *Alabama* rises 4 ft above the surface of the water when surfacing.

9. a.

Tile Edges on Perimeter

Number of tiles	Triangle	Rhombus	Pentagon	Hexagon
1	3	4	5	6
2	4	6	8	10
3	5	8	11	14
4	6	10	14	18
5	7	12	17	22
6	8	14	20	26
7	9	16	23	30
8	10	18	26	34
9	11	20	29	38
10	12	22	32	42

b. Number of tiles:
1 ENTER, Ans + 1 ENTER, ENTER, . . .
Triangle: 3 ENTER, Ans + 1 ENTER, ENTER, . . .
Rhombus: 4 ENTER, Ans + 2 ENTER, ENTER, . . .
Pentagon: 5 ENTER, Ans + 3 ENTER, ENTER, . . .
Hexagon: 6 ENTER, Ans + 4 ENTER, ENTER, . . .

To generate the sequences for all tiles simultaneously:

$\{1, 3, 4, 5, 6\}$ ENTER, $\{\text{Ans}(1) + 1, \text{Ans}(2) + 1,$
$\text{Ans}(3) + 2, \text{Ans}(4) + 3, \text{Ans}(5) + 4\}$
ENTER, ENTER, ...

c. Triangle: 52; rhombus: 102; pentagon: 152; hexagon: 202

d.

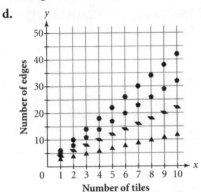

e. The points for each shape lie on a line. The leftmost point of each graph is (1, *number of sides the shape has*). The lines increase in steepness from the graph for the triangle tile to the graph for the hexagon tile.

f. No, because there must be a whole number of tiles and a whole number of edges.

10. a. Possible answer: The graph starts at (0, 5280). The points (0, 5280), (1, 4680), (2, 4080), and (3, 3480) will lie on a line. From point (3, 3480) to point (8, −1520), the points will lie on a steeper line. The bicyclist ends up 1520 ft past you.

b.

Bicyclist

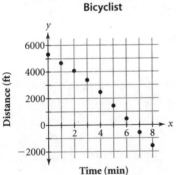

c. Answers will vary. Possible question: After how many minutes does the bicyclist pass you? Because the graph crosses the x-axis between 6 and 7, the bicyclist passes you after between 6 and 7 min.

11. a. $13.9\overline{3}$. Start with 7.2. Subtract 2.8 to get 4.4. Multiply by 3.2 to get 14.08. Add 5.4 to get 19.48. Divide by 1.2 to get $16.2\overline{3}$. Subtract 2.3 to get $13.9\overline{3}$.

b. To solve the equation $\frac{5.4 + 3.2(x - 2.8)}{1.2} - 2.3 = 3.8$, start with 3.8 and work backward, undoing the operations: Add 2.3 to get 6.1. Multiply by 1.2 to

get 7.32. Subtract 5.4 to get 1.92. Divide by 3.2 to get 0.6. Add 2.8 to get 3.4. The solution is 3.4.

12. a. $\frac{9(C + 40)}{5} - 40$

b. Add 40, multiply by 5, divide by 9, then subtract 40.

c. $\frac{5(F + 40)}{9} - 40$

13. a. $\frac{1}{2} \text{ cup} \cdot \frac{0.236 \text{ L}}{1 \text{ cup}} = 0.118 \text{ L}$, so Karen needs 0.118, or about $\frac{1}{8}$ L of water.

$1\frac{1}{2} \text{ cups} \cdot \frac{1 \text{ lb}}{4 \text{ cups}} \cdot \frac{454 \text{ g}}{1 \text{ lb}} = 170.25 \text{ g}$,

so Karen needs 170.25, or about 170 g of flour.

b. $C = \frac{5(425 + 40)}{9} - 40 = \frac{2325}{9} - 40 =$
$258.\overline{3} - 40 = 218.\overline{3}$, so 425°F is about 220°C.

14. a.

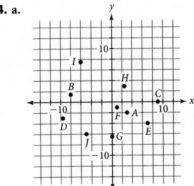

b. Quadrant I: *H*; Quadrant II: *B, I*; Quadrant III: *D, J*; Quadrant IV: *A, E, F*; x-axis: *C*; y-axis: *G*

c. If both coordinates are 0, the point is on the origin. If just the x-coordinate is 0, the point is on the y-axis. If just the y-coordinate is 0, the point is on the x-axis. If both coordinates are positive, the point is in Quadrant I. If the x-coordinate is negative and the y-coordinate is positive, the point is in Quadrant II. If both coordinates are negative, the point is in Quadrant III. If the x-coordinate is positive and the y-coordinate is negative, the point is in Quadrant IV.

LESSON 3.3

EXERCISES

1. $\{0, 4.0\}$ and $\{\text{Ans}(1) + 1, \text{Ans}(2) - 0.4\}$

2.

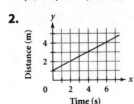

3. Start at the 0.8 m mark and walk away from the sensor at a constant rate of 0.2 m/s.

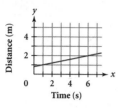

4. a. The walker starts 2.5 m away from the motion sensor and walks toward it very slowly at a rate of 1 m in 6 s.

   b. The walker starts 1 m away from the motion sensor and walks away from it at a rate of 2.5 m in 6 s.

5. a. The walker starts 6 m away from the motion sensor and walks toward it at a rate of 0.2 m/s for 6 s.

   b. The walker starts 1 m away from the motion sensor and walks away from it at a rate of 0.6 m/s for 6 s.

6. The first graph, which shows a line, better represents the walk described because the walk is a continuous process. The walker is somewhere at every possible time in the 6 s.

7. Convert 1 mi/h to ft/s.

$$\frac{1 \text{ mi}}{1 \text{ h}} \cdot \frac{1 \text{ h}}{60 \text{ min}} \cdot \frac{1 \text{ min}}{60 \text{ s}} \cdot \frac{5280 \text{ ft}}{1 \text{ mi}} = 1.4\overline{6} \text{ ft/s}$$

8. a. 4 s

   b. Away; the distance is increasing.

   c. About 0.5 m

   d. $\frac{2.9 - 0.5}{4} = 0.6$ m/s

   e. $\frac{5.5 \text{ m}}{0.6 \text{ m/s}} = 9.1\overline{6}$ s; approximately 9 s

   f. The graph is a straight line.

9.

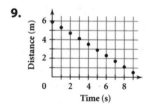

10. a. The rate is negative, so the line slopes down to the right.

   b. The rate is 0, so the line is horizontal.

   c. The line is not very steep.

11. a. ii

   b. iv

   c. iii

   d. i

12. Start walking at the 0 mark when the sensor starts, and walk 1 ft every second. Start walking at the 0 mark when the sensor starts, and walk 1 m every

second. Because a meter is longer than a foot, 1 m/s is faster.

13. a. This is not possible because the walker would have to be at more than one distance from the sensor at the 3 s mark.

   b. This is possible; the walker just stands still at about 2.5 m from the sensor.

   c. This is not possible because the walker can't be in two places at any given time.

14. a. $x = \frac{21}{5}$, or 4.2   **b.** $x = \frac{22}{9}$, or $2.\overline{4}$

   c. $\frac{x}{c} = \frac{d}{e}$

       $x = \frac{d}{e} \cdot c$ Multiply by c to undo the division.

       $x = \frac{dc}{e}$

15. a. $\dfrac{24{,}901.55 \text{ mi}}{(2 \cdot 365 + 2 \cdot 30.4 + 2) \text{ days}} \approx 31.4$ mi per day

   b. $\dfrac{31.4 \text{ mi}}{1 \text{ day}} \cdot (1.5 \cdot 365) \text{ days} \approx 17{,}191.5$ mi

   c. Let t represent the number of days, and then write and solve the proportion $\frac{1 \text{ day}}{31.4 \text{ mi}} = \frac{t}{60{,}000 \text{ mi}}$; $t \approx 1{,}911$ days or about 5.24 yr.

16. a. $\frac{175 \text{ mi}}{13.5 \text{ gal}}$, about 13 mi/gal, or about 0.077 gal/mi

   b. 13 mi/gal $\cdot$ 5 gal = 65 mi

   c. $\dfrac{1}{\frac{13 \text{ mi}}{\text{gal}}} = \dfrac{0.077 \text{ gal}}{\text{mi}}$; 0.077 gal/mi $\cdot$ 100 mi = 7.7 gal

LESSON 3.4

EXERCISES

1. a. ii   **b.** iv   **c.** iii   **d.** i

2. a. $t \approx 0.18$ h   **b.** $t \approx 0.47$ h

   c. 24 represents the initial number of miles the driver is from his or her destination.

   d. 45 means that the driver is driving at a speed of 45 mi/h.

   e.

$24 - 45t = 16$	Original equation.
$24 - 45t - 24 = 16 - 24$	To undo adding 24, subtract 24.
$-45t = -8$	Subtract.
$t = \frac{-8}{-45}$	To undo multiplying by -45, divide by -45.
$t = \frac{8}{45} = 0.1\overline{7}$	

3. a. $d \approx 38.3$ ft   **b.** $d \approx 25.42$ ft

   c. The walker started 4.7 feet away from the motion sensor.

   d. The walker was walking at a rate of 2.8 feet per second.

Discovering Algebra Solutions Manual
©2007 Key Curriculum Press

4. a. $x \approx 7.267$ **b.** $x = 11.2$

5. a. $35 + 0.8 \cdot 25 = 55$ mi

b. 50 min. One way to find this answer is to write the equation $75 = 35 + 0.8 \cdot x$ and then solve it by working backward, undoing the operations. Another way is to make a calculator graph and trace it to find the x-value corresponding to the y-value 75.

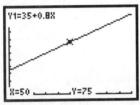

[0, 100, 10, 0, 120, 10]

6. a. The table shows that Louis burned 400 calories before beginning to run (400 is the Y1-value for X-value 0). The difference in consecutive Y1-values is 20.7, indicating that Louis burns 20.7 calories per minute while running. He wants to burn 700 calories.

b. 400 [ENTER], Ans + 20.7 [ENTER], [ENTER], . . .

c. $y = 400 + 20.7x$

d. 700 [ENTER], Ans + 0 [ENTER], [ENTER], . . .

e. $y = 700 + 0x$, or $y = 700$

f. The y-intercept of Y1, which is 400, is the number of calories burned after 0 min of running (that is, before Louis begins to run).

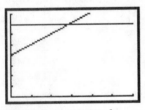

[0, 30, 5, 0, 800, 100]

g. The approximate coordinates are (14.5, 700). This means that after 14.5 min of running Louis will have burned off 700 calories.

7. a. The -300 could represent a start-up cost of $300 for equipment and expenses, the 15 could represent the amount she earns per lawn, and N could represent the number of lawns.

b. Possible questions and answers:

How many lawns will Jo have to mow to break even? To answer this question, solve $-300 + 15N = 0$. Jo must mow 20 lawns.

How much profit will Jo earn if she mows 40 lawns? To answer this question, substitute 40 for N. She would earn $-300 + 15(40)$, or $300.

c.

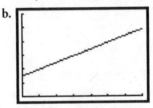

$P = -300 + 15N$	Original equation.
$P + 300 = 15N$	Undo subtracting 300 by adding 300.
$\dfrac{P + 300}{15} = N$, or $N = \dfrac{P + 300}{15}$	Undo multiplying by 15 by dividing by 15.

d. This tells you the number of lawns you have to mow to make a certain amount of profit.

8. a. The speed at 0 seconds is 5 m/s and the speed increases by 9.8 m/s every second, so the equation is $s = 5 + 9.8t$, where t is the time in seconds and s is the speed in meters per second.

b. $5 + 9.8(3) = 34.4$ m/s

c. Solve the equation $83.4 = 5 + 9.8t$. It would take 8 seconds for the object to reach a speed of 83.4 m/s.

d. Possible answer: It doesn't account for air resistance and terminal speed.

9. a. $y = 45 + 0.12x$, where x represents the dollar amount his customers spend and y represents his daily income in dollars

b.

[0, 840, 120, 0, 180, 30]

c. $y = 45 + 0.12 \cdot 312 = \$82.44$

d. Solving $45 + 0.12x = 105$ gives $x = 500$. Solving $45 + 0.12x = 120$ gives $x = 625$. So customers would have to spend between $500 and $625 in order for Manny to earn $105 to $120.

10. a. Let $x =$ the number of minutes Paula swims on Monday and $y =$ the total number of calories she burns on Monday. She burns $3.8(30) = 114$ calories biking and 6.9 calories for each minute she swims, so the equation is $y = 114 + 6.9x$.

b. Let $x =$ the number of minutes Paula jogs on Wednesday and $y =$ the total number of calories she burns on Wednesday. She burns $6.9(30) = 207$ calories swimming and 7.3 calories for each minute she swims, so the equation is $y = 207 + 7.3x$.

c. Let $x =$ the number of minutes Paula runs on Friday and $y =$ the total number of calories she burns on Friday. She burns $6.9(15) = 103.5$ calories swimming, $3.8(15) = 57$ calories biking, and 11.3 calories for each minute she runs, so the equation is $y = 160.5 + 11.3x$.

d. Monday: In her 60 min workout, Paula swims $60 - 30 = 30$ min, so $x = 30$, and $y = 114 + 6.9(30) = 321$. Therefore, she burns 321 calories.

Wednesday: In her 60 min workout, Paula jogs $60 - 30 = 30$ min, so $x = 30$, and $y = 207 + 7.3(30) = 426$. Therefore, she burns 426 calories.

Friday: In her 60 min workout, Paula runs $60 - 15 - 15 = 30$ min, so $x = 30$, and $y = 160.5 + 11.3(30) = 499.5$. Therefore, she burns 499.5 calories.

11. Possible answer: Write the percent as one ratio of a proportion. Put the part over the whole in the other ratio.

a. $\frac{8}{n} = \frac{15}{100}$, $n \approx 53.3$ **b.** $\frac{15}{100} = \frac{n}{18.95}$, $n \approx 2.8$

c. $\frac{p}{100} = \frac{326}{64}$, $p \approx 509.4$ **d.** $\frac{10}{100} = \frac{40}{n}$, $n = 400$

12. a. 22.4, 22.6, 22.1

b. $\frac{363 \text{ mi} + 342 \text{ mi} + 285 \text{ mi}}{16.2 \text{ gal} + 15.1 \text{ gal} + 12.9 \text{ gal}} = 22.3981$ mpg ≈ 22.4 mpg

c. $\frac{22.4 \text{ mi}}{1 \text{ gal}} \cdot 17.1 \text{ gal} \approx 383$ mi

d. $\frac{1 \text{ gal}}{22.4 \text{ mi}} \cdot 4230 \text{ mi} \approx 189$ gal

13. Sample explanation: For each equation, I looked for the graph with a rate of change that matched the recursive rule. I also checked that the starting value of the routine was the y-intercept of the graph.

a. ii   **b.** iv   **c.** iii   **d.** i

14. a. In 10 seconds, he cycled 140 meters, so he is riding at a rate of 14 m/s.

b.

Time (s)	Distance (m)
1	14
2	28
3	42
4	56
5	70
6	84
7	98
8	112
9	126
10	140

c. Possible routines:

0 ENTER, Ans + 14 ENTER, ENTER, . . .

or, {0, 0} ENTER,

{Ans(1) + 1, Ans(2) + 14} ENTER, ENTER, . . .

d. The points lie on a line.

e. $\frac{14 \text{ m}}{1 \text{ s}} \cdot \frac{60 \text{ s}}{1 \text{ min}} \cdot \frac{60 \text{ min}}{1 \text{ h}} = 50{,}400$ m/h. So Bjarne will ride 50,400 m, or 50.4 km, in 1 h.

15. a. The value of the expression is -4 when $y = 5$.

5	
Ans $-$ 8	-3
Ans $\cdot$ 4	-12
Ans/3	-4

b. Start with 8. Multiply by 3 to get 24. Divide by 4 to get 6. Add 8 to get 14. The solution is 14.

IMPROVING YOUR REASONING SKILLS

To see why the percentage of juice in the water is the same as the percentage of the water in the juice, think about particular amounts of liquid, such as 10 ounces of each with 1 ounce being transferred. Or use a deck of playing cards. Start with a pile of ten red cards and a pile of ten black cards. Pull out any number of red cards and mix them among the black cards. Then pull out the same number of cards from the mixed pile and put them into the red pile. Keep track of how many of each color are moving, and try it with extreme cases.

LESSON 3.5

EXERCISES

1. a.

Input	Output
20	100
-30	-25
16	90
15	87.5
-12.5	18.75

b.

L₁	L₂
0	-5.2
-8	74.8
24	-245.2
-35	344.8
-5.2	46.8

2. a. Substitute 32 for t in the given equation.

$w = -29 + 1.4t$

$w = -29 + 1.4(32) = 15.8$

At a wind speed of 40 mi/h, if the actual air temperature is 32°F, the wind chill temperature is 15.8°F.

b. Substitute -8 for w in the given equation.

$w = -29 + 1.4t$

$-8 = -29 + 1.4t$

To solve this equation, first undo subtracting 29 by adding 29.

$21 = 1.4t$

Now undo multiplying by 1.4 by dividing by 1.4.

$t = \dfrac{21}{1.4} = 15$

At a wind speed of 40 mi/h, the wind chill temperature is $-8°F$ when the actual air temperature is $15°F$.

  c. At a wind speed of 40 mi/h, the wind chill temperature changes by $1.4°$ for each change of $1°$ in actual temperature.

  d. At a wind speed of 40 mi/h, if the actual temperature is $0°F$, the wind chill temperature is $-29°F$.

3. a. The rate is negative, so the line goes from the upper left to the lower right.

  b. The rate is zero. The line is horizontal.

  c. The rate is positive, so the line goes from the lower left to the upper right.

  d. The rate for the speedier walker is greater than the rate for the person walking more slowly, so the graph for the speedier walker is steeper than the graph for the slower walker.

4. Possible answer:

```
IN OUT
      [[0  -5]
       [1  -3]
       [2  -1]
       [3   1 ]
       [4   3 ]
       [5   5 ]]
GUESS: -5+2L₁
```

5. a. In each case, the rate of change can be calculated by dividing the difference of two output values by the difference of the corresponding input values.

    i. 3.5   **ii.** 8   **iii.** -1.4

  b. The output value corresponding to an input value of 0 is the y-intercept.

    i. -6 **ii.** 1

    iii. 23; the output value for input -3 is 27.2. To get from input -3 to input 0, you add 3, so to get from output value 27.2 to the output value for 0, you must add $3 \cdot -1.4$: output $= 27.2 + 3(-1.4) = 23$.

  c. **i.** $y = -6 + 3.5x$

    ii. $y = 1 + 8x$

    iii. $y = 23 - 1.4x$

6. a. The input variable x is the temperature in °F, and the output variable y is the wind chill temperature in °F.

  b. The rate of change is 1.4. For every $10°$ increase in temperature, there is a $14°$ increase in wind chill temperature.

  c. $y = -28 + 1.4x$; for every $5°$ increase in temperature, there is a $7°$ increase in wind chill temperature, so from the point $(-5, -35)$, add $5°$ to the temperature and $7°$ to the wind chill temperature to get the y-intercept of $(0, -28)$.

  d. Both graphs show linear relationships with identical rates of change and identical y-intercepts. The graph of the points shows wind chill temperatures for temperatures of $-5°F$, $0°F$, $5°F$, $10°F$, and so on. The graph of the equation shows wind chill temperatures for every temperature. The graph of the points is *discrete* and the graph of the equation is *continuous*.

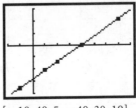

$[-10, 40, 5, -40, 30, 10]$

7. a. *Distance from sensor* $= 3.5 - 0.25 \cdot time$

  b. Rewrite the equation as $D = 3.5 - 0.25t$. Substitute 0 for D and solve for t.

$0 = 3.5 - 0.25t$

To undo adding 3.5, subtract 3.5.

$-3.5 = -0.25t$

To undo multiplying by -0.25, divide by -0.25.

$t = \dfrac{-3.5}{-0.25} = 14$

She would pass the sensor 14 s after she begins walking.

8. Because length times width gives area, 7.3 and x represent the length and width, respectively. The number 200 represents the area of the rectangle in square units. The solution is about 27.4 units. The rectangle is not drawn to scale. The length should be about 3.8 times the width.

9. a. 990 square units

  b. Possible answers:

$33x = 990$; $x = \dfrac{990}{33}$; $33x = 1584 - 594$;

$x = \dfrac{1584 - 594}{33}$

  c. The height is $990 \div 33$, or 30 units.

10. Possible answer:

```
IN OUT
      [[-3  0 ]
       [2  -5 ]
       [4  -7 ]
       [5  -8 ]
       [6  -9 ]
       [7  -10]]
GUESS: -3-L₁■
```

11. a. Start with −15. Subtract −52 (that is, add 52) to get 37. Divide by 1.6 to get 23.125. The solution is 23.125. Check:

$$-52 + 1.6(23.125) = -52 + 37 = -15.$$

b. Start with 52. Subtract 7 to get 45. Divide by −3 to get −15. The solution is −15. Check:

$$7 - 3(-15) = 7 - (-45) = 52.$$

12. a.

Hours parked	ABC Parking	Cozy Car	The Corner Lot
1	5	3	15
2	7	6	15
3	9	9	15
4	11	12	15
5	13	15	15
6	15	18	15
7	17	21	15
8	19	24	15
9	21	27	15
10	23	30	15

Possible routines:

ABC Parking: {1, 5} ENTER,
{Ans(1) + 1, Ans(2) + 2} ENTER, ENTER, . . .

Cozy Car: {1, 3} ENTER,
{Ans(1) + 1, Ans(2) + 3} ENTER, ENTER, . . .

The Corner Lot: {1, 15} ENTER,
{Ans(1) + 1, Ans(2) + 0} ENTER, ENTER, . . .

b.

Downtown Parking

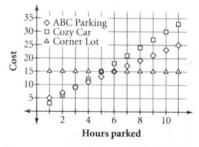

c. If you will be parking less than 3 h, Cozy Car is the best deal. On the graph, its points are below the points for the other lots for "Hours parked" values less than 3. For exactly 3 h, ABC and Cozy Car cost the same. If you will be parked between 3 and 6 h, ABC Parking is the best deal; its points are lowest for that section of the graph. For exactly 6 h, ABC and the Corner Lot cost the same. If you plan to park more than 6 h, The Corner Lot is the best deal.

d. No; because you have to pay for a whole **hour** for any fraction of the hour, the price of parking does not increase continuously.

13. a. 1 mile is 5280 feet or 1760 yards. 72 lengths is $72 \cdot 25 = 1800$ yards. So 72 lengths is more than a mile. The actual number of lengths in a mile is $1760 \div 25$, or 70.4.

b. $\dfrac{1 \text{ mi}}{40 \text{ min}} \cdot \dfrac{5280 \text{ ft}}{1 \text{ mi}} \cdot \dfrac{1 \text{ min}}{60 \text{ s}} = 2.2 \text{ ft/s}$

c. 1 kilometer ≈ 0.62 mile. There are 70.4 lengths in a mile, so there are $0.62 \cdot 70.4$, or about 44 lengths in a kilometer.

d. 40 lengths for a kilometer, about 64 lengths for a mile

14. a. $y = 6 + 1.25x$

b.

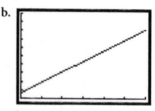

[0, 60, 10, 0, 100, 10]

c. Solve the equation $1.25x + 6 = 60$; $x = 43.2$, so Holly would have to rent 44 movies.

LESSON 3.6

EXERCISES

1. a. $2x = 6$ **b.** $x + 2 = 5$

  c. $2x - 1 = 3$ **d.** $2 = 2x - 3$

2. (*See table at bottom of next page.*)

3. a. $0.1x + 12 - 12 = 2.2 - 12$

$$0.1x = -9.8$$

$$x = -98$$

b. $\dfrac{12 + 3.12x}{3} = -100$

$$12 + 3.12x = -300$$

$$12 - 12 + 3.12x = -300 - 12$$

$$3.12x = -312$$

$$x = -100$$

4. a.

Equation: $\dfrac{3(x - 8)}{5} + 7 = 34$

Description	Undo	Result	Equation
Pick x.		53	$x = 53$
Subtract 8.	+ (8)	45	$x - 8 = 45$
Multiply by 3.	/ (3)	135	$3(x - 8) = 135$
Divide by 5.	· (5)	27	$\dfrac{3(x - 8)}{5} = 27$
Add 7.	− (7)	34	$\dfrac{3(x - 8)}{5} + 7 = 34$

Discovering Algebra Solutions Manual
©2007 Key Curriculum Press

b.

Equation: $7\left(\dfrac{2+x}{4}\right) - 5 = 16$			
Description	**Undo**	**Result**	**Equation**
Pick x.		10	$x = 10$
Add 2.	$-(2)$	12	$2 + x = 12$
Divide by 4.	$\cdot(4)$	3	$\dfrac{2+x}{4} = 3$
Multiply by 7.	$/(7)$	21	$7\left(\dfrac{2+x}{4}\right) = 21$
Subtract 5.	$+(5)$	16	$7\left(\dfrac{2+x}{4}\right) - 5 = 16$

5. a. $-\dfrac{1}{5}$ **b.** -17 **c.** 2.3 **d.** x

6. a. $\dfrac{1}{12}$ **b.** 6 **c.** 50 **d.** -2

7. a. $144x = 12$ Original equation.

$\dfrac{144x}{144} = \dfrac{12}{144}$ Divide both sides by 144.

$x = \dfrac{1}{12}$ Divide.

b. $\dfrac{1}{6}x + 2 = 8$ Original equation.

$\dfrac{1}{6}x + 2 - 2 = 8 - 2$ Subtract 2 from both sides.

$\dfrac{1}{6}x = 6$ Remove the 0 and subtract.

$6 \cdot \dfrac{1}{6}x = 6 \cdot 6$ Multiply both sides by 6.

$x = 36$ Multiply.

8. a. Add 10 to both sides. Divide both sides by 3.

b. $(5, 5)$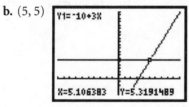

$[-10, 10, 1, -5, 20, 1]$

c. $(5, 15)$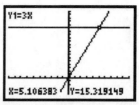

d. $(5, 5)$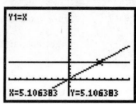

e. The lines graphed are different in each case, but the x-coordinate of the intersection is the same: $x = 5$. This illustrates that transforming the equation by doing the same thing to both sides does not change the solution.

9. a. $4 + 1.2x = 12.4$ Original equation.

$4 - 4 + 1.2x = 12.4 - 4$ Subtract 4 from both sides.

$1.2x = 8.4$ Remove the 0 and subtract.

$\dfrac{1.2x}{1.2} = \dfrac{8.4}{1.2}$ Divide both sides by 1.2.

$x = 7$ Simplify.

b. Start with 12.4. Subtract 4 to get 8.4. Divide by 1.2 to get 7.

c.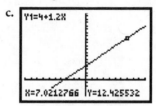

$[-10, 10, 1, -5, 20, 1]$

Lesson 3.6, Exercise 2.

Picture	Action taken	Equation
	Original equation.	$2x - 2 = 4$
$\boxed{x}\ \boxed{x}\ \ominus\ \ominus\ =\ \oplus\ \oplus\ \oplus$	Add 2 to both sides.	$2x - 2 + 2 = 4 + 2$
	Remove 0 from left side.	$2x = 6$
$\boxed{x}\ \boxed{x}\ =\ \oplus\ \oplus\ \oplus$	Divide both sides by 2.	$\dfrac{2x}{2} = \dfrac{6}{2}$
$\boxed{x}\ =\ \oplus\ \oplus\ \oplus$	Reduce.	$x = 3$

d.

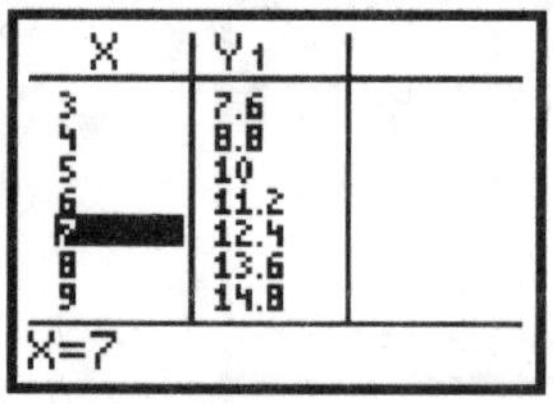

```
 X  │ Y1
 3  │ 7.6
 4  │ 8.8
 5  │ 10
 6  │ 11.2
 7  │ 12.4
 8  │ 13.6
 9  │ 14.8
────┴─────
X=7
```

10. a.

$3 + 2x = 17$	Original equation.
$3 - 3 + 2x = 17 - 3$	Subtract 3 from both sides.
$2x = 14$	Remove the 0 and subtract.
$\dfrac{2x}{2} = \dfrac{14}{2}$	Divide both sides by 2.
$x = 7$	Reduce.

b.

$0.5x + 2.2 = 101.0$	Original equation.
$0.5x + 2.2 - 2.2 = 101.0 - 2.2$	Subtract 2.2 from both sides.
$0.5x = 98.8$	Remove the 0 and subtract.
$\dfrac{0.5x}{0.5} = \dfrac{98.8}{0.5}$	Divide both sides by 0.5.
$x = 197.6$	Reduce.

c.

$x + 307.2 = 2.1$	Original equation.
$x + 307.2 - 307.2 = 2.1 - 307.2$	Subtract 307.2 from both sides.
$x = -305.1$	Remove the 0 and subtract.

d.

$2(2x + 2) = 7$	Original equation.
$\dfrac{2(2x + 2)}{2} = \dfrac{7}{2}$	Divide both sides by 2.
$2x + 2 = 3.5$	Reduce.
$2x + 2 - 2 = 3.5 - 2$	Subtract 2 from both sides.
$2x = 1.5$	Remove the 0 and subtract.
$\dfrac{2x}{2} = \dfrac{1.5}{2}$	Divide both sides by 2.
$x = 0.75$	Reduce.

e.

$\dfrac{4 + 0.01x}{6.2} - 6.2 = 0$	Original equation.
$\dfrac{4 + 0.01x}{6.2} - 6.2 + 6.2 = 0 + 6.2$	Add 6.2 to both sides.
$\dfrac{4 + 0.01x}{6.2} = 6.2$	Remove the 0 and subtract.
$\dfrac{4 + 0.01x}{6.2} \cdot 6.2 = 6.2 \cdot 6.2$	Multiply both sides by 6.2.
$4 + 0.01x = 38.44$	Multiply and reduce.
$4 - 4 + 0.01x = 38.44 - 4$	Subtract 4 from both sides.
$0.01x = 34.44$	Remove the 0 and subtract.
$\dfrac{0.01x}{0.01} = \dfrac{34.44}{0.01}$	Divide both sides by 0.01.
$x = 3444$	Reduce.

11. a. $r = \dfrac{C}{2\pi}$

b.

$A = \dfrac{1}{2}(hb)$	Original equation.
$2A = hb$	Multiply both sides by 2.
$\dfrac{2A}{b} = h$	Divide both sides by b.

c.

$P = 2(l + w)$	Original equation.
$\dfrac{P}{2} = l + w$	Divide both sides by 2.
$\dfrac{P}{2} - w = l$	Subtract w from both sides.

d. $s = \dfrac{P}{4}$

e. $t = \dfrac{d}{r}$

f.

$A = \dfrac{1}{2}h(a + b)$	Original equation.
$2A = h(a + b)$	Multiply both sides by 2.
$\dfrac{2A}{a + b} = h$	Divide both sides by $a + b$.

12. a. (*See table at bottom of page.*)

Lesson 3.6, Exercise 12. a.

Picture	Action taken	Equation
	Original equation.	$2 + 4x = x + 8$
	Subtract $1x$ from both sides.	$2 + 3x = 8$
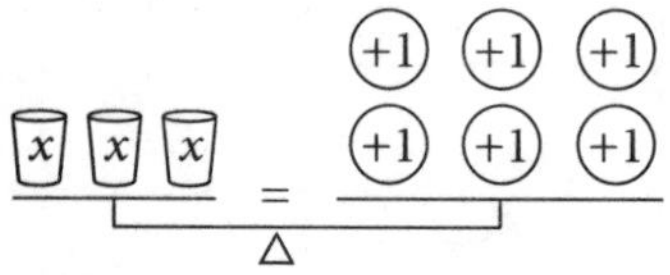 ⎡x⎤ ⎡x⎤ ⎡x⎤ = (+1)(+1)(+1) (+1)(+1)(+1)	Subtract 2 from both sides.	$3x = 6$
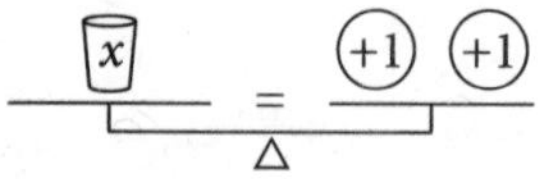 ⎡x⎤ = (+1)(+1)	Divide both sides by 3.	$x = 2$

Discovering Algebra Solutions Manual
©2007 Key Curriculum Press

b.
$$5x - 4 = 2x + 5$$
$$5x - 2x - 4 = 2x - 2x + 5$$
$$3x - 4 = 5$$
$$3x - 4 + 4 = 5 + 4$$
$$3x = 9$$
$$x = 3$$
Check: $5(3) - 4 \overset{?}{=} 2(3) + 5$
$$15 - 4 \overset{?}{=} 6 + 5$$
$$11 = 11$$

13. $\frac{\$90}{2.25} = \frac{x}{3}$, $x = \$120$

14. Sample calculator graph and equation:

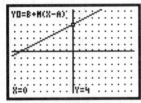

$[-9, 9, 1, -6, 6, 1]$

$y = 4 + \frac{1}{2}(x - 0)$

15. a.

Bagel Store			Grocery Store	
Bagels	**Cost ($)**		**Bagels**	**Cost ($)**
13	6.49		6	2.50
26	12.98		12	5.00
39	19.47		18	7.50
52	25.96		24	10.00
65	32.45		30	12.50
78	38.94		36	15.00
			42	17.50
			48	20.00
			54	22.50
			60	25.00

b. The line with the square markers represents the bagel store, and the lower line represents the grocery store.

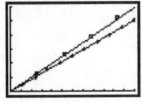

$[0, 72, 6, 0, 30, 5]$

c. Bagel store: $y = \frac{6.49}{13}x$, or $y \approx 0.50x$, where x is the number of bagels and y is the cost

Grocery store: $y = \frac{2.50}{6}x$, or $y \approx 0.42x$, where x is the number of bagels and y is the cost

d. Bagel store: about 50¢ per bagel

Grocery store: about 42¢ per bagel

These costs are the coefficients of x in the equations.

e. The grocery store, because its line is lower

f. Bernie's routine calculates each price by doubling the previous price. It works for the first two baker's dozens, because when you buy two baker's dozens, you are buying twice as much as when you buy one, so the price should double. However, if you buy three baker's dozens, the price should not be double the price for two. A correct routine would be 6.49 ENTER, Ans + 6.49 ENTER, ENTER, . . .

LESSON 3.7

IMPROVING YOUR REASONING SKILLS

Challenge students to explain the pattern. A locker is changed once for each factor of its number. For example, locker 24 is changed by students 1, 2, 3, 4, 6, 8, 12, and 24. So if a locker's number has an even number of factors, it is left closed. If a locker's number has an odd number of factors, it is left open. Those numbers with an odd number of factors are the perfect squares. The lockers left open at the end correspond to perfect squares—1, 4, 9, 16, 25, 36, 49, 64, 81, and 100. Ten lockers are left open.

Perfect squares have an odd number of factors because factors come in pairs: (1, 24), (2, 12), (3, 8), (4, 6). The square root of a perfect square (e.g., 36) is paired with itself: (1, 36), (2, 18), (3, 12), (4, 9), (6, 6). So the number of distinct factors is odd.

CHAPTER 3 Review

EXERCISES

1. a. $-x = 7$ Original equation.

     $x = -7$ Multiply both sides by -1.

b. $4.2 = -2x - 42.6$ Original equation.

     $46.8 = -2x$ Add 42.6 to both sides and remove the 0.

     $-23.4 = x$ Divide both sides by -2.

2. a. Rate: 1; y-intercept: 3; rule: add 1; equation: $y = 3 + x$

b. Rate: 0.01; y-intercept: 0; rule: add 0.01; equation: $y = 0.01x$

c. Rate: 2; y-intercept: 5; rule: add 2; equation: $y = 5 + 2x$

d. Rate: $-\frac{1}{2}$; y-intercept: 3; rule: subtract $\frac{1}{2}$; equation: $y = 3 - \frac{1}{2}x$

3. a. iii   **b.** i   **c.** ii

4. a. $y = -68.99$ **b.** $y = 4289.83$

  c. $y = 0.14032$ **d.** $y = 238{,}723$

5. a. $y = x$ **b.** $y = -3 + x$

  c. $y = -4.3 + 2.3x$ **d.** $y = 1$

6. a. The 0 represents no bookcases sold. The -850 represents a fixed cost, such as start-up costs. Ans(1) represents the previously calculated number of bookcases sold. Ans(1) + 1 represents the current number of bookcases sold, one more than the previous number. Ans(2) represents the profit for the previous number of bookcases. Ans(2) + 70 represents the profit for the current number of bookcases—the company makes $70 more profit for each additional bookcase sold.

  b. Use the x-axis to represent the number of bookcases sold and the y-axis to represent the profit. Then graph each data pair as a point, such as $(2, -710)$.

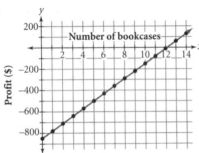

  c. A profit is made at 13 bookcases; y becomes positive between 12 and 13 bookcases.

  d. The -850, the company's profit if it sells zero bookcases, is the y-intercept; 70, the amount of profit the company makes for each bookcase sold, is the rate of change; y goes up by $70 each time x goes up by one bookcase.

  e. No; partial bookcases cannot be sold.

7. a. 3

  b.

Sections	3	4	30	50
Logs	10	13	91	151

  c. 4 ENTER, Ans + 3 ENTER, ENTER, . . .

  d. 216 m; one way to find this answer is to use the routine until you get a result of 217. The number of times you pressed ENTER, 72, is the number of fence sections. Because each section is 3 m long, the length of the fence would be 72 · 3, or 216 m.

8. a. Let v represent the value in dollars and y represent the number of years: $v = 5400 - 525y$.

  b. The rate of change is -525. In each additional year, the value of the computer system decreases by $525.

  c. The y-intercept is 5400. The original value of the computer system is $5,400.

d. By solving $5400 - 525y = 0$, you'll find that the x-intercept is about 10.3. This means that the computer system no longer has value after approximately 10.3 years.

9. a. $50 = 7.7t;\ t = \dfrac{50}{7.7} \approx 6.5$ s

  b. $50 = 5 + 6.5t;\ t = \dfrac{50 - 5}{6.5} \approx 6.9$ s

  c. Andrei wins. When Andrei finishes, his younger brother is $50 - [5 + 6.5(6.5)] \approx 2.8$ m from the finish line.

10. a. $x = 4.5$ **b.** $x = -4.1\overline{3}$ **c.** $x = 0.\overline{6}$

  d. $x = 12.8$ **e.** $x = 6.\overline{3}$

11. a. $L_2 = -5.7 + 2.3 \cdot L_1$ **b.** $L_2 = -5 - 8 \cdot L_1$

  c. $L_2 = 12 + 0.5 \cdot L_1$

12. a. $y = \frac{1}{2}x + 1$. The output value is half the input value plus 1.

x	0	1	2	3	4
y	1	1.5	2	2.5	3

  b. $y = -x$. The output value is the additive inverse (or negative) of the input value, or the sum of the input and the output value is 0.

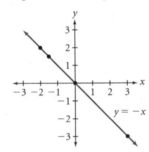

13. No, they won't fit. There are 2.54 cm in 1 in., so 210 cm equals $210 \div 2.54$, or about 82.7 in., which is about 6.89 ft.

14. a.

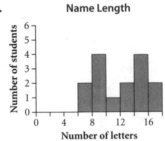

  b. Mean = 11.6 letters

15. a. $-3 \cdot 8 - 5 \cdot 6 = -24 - 30 = -54$

  b. $[-2 - (-4)] \cdot 8 - 11 = (-2 + 4) \cdot 8 - 11 = 2 \cdot 8 - 11 = 16 - 11 = 5$

  c. $7 \cdot 8 + 4 \cdot (-12) = 56 + (-48) = 8$

  d. $11 - 3 \cdot 9 - 2 = 11 - 27 - 2 = -16 - 2 = -18$

16. a. 12 ENTER, Ans + 55 ENTER, ENTER, . . .

Possible assumptions: Tom's home is 12 mi closer to Detroit than is Traverse City. He traveled at a constant speed. We are measuring highway distance.

b.

Time (h)	0	1	2	3	4	5
Distance from Traverse City (mi)	12	67	122	177	232	287

c. 55 mi/h; Tom traveled 55 miles each additional hour.

17. a. The mean number of visitors to a national park in California in 2003 was approximately 1061 thousand (or 1,061,000) visitors.

b. The minimum is 404, the first quartile is 482, the median is 738, the third quartile is 1131, and the maximum is 3379, so the five-number summary is 404, 482, 738, 1131, 3379.

c.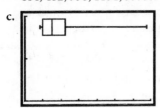

[0, 3500, 500, 0, 2, 1]

d. Yosemite is an outlier because the number of visitors to this park exceeds the third quartile, 1131, by more than 1.5 times the interquartile range: $3379 - 1131 = 2248$, and $1.5(1131 - 482) = 1.5(649) = 973.5$.

18. Use Ohm's law to solve: $i = \frac{E}{R}$, where i is in amps, E is in volts, and R is in ohms. Because $i = 18$ when $R = 4$, the value of the constant E is $18 \cdot 4 = 72$. So the equation becomes $i = \frac{72}{R}$.

a. 9 amperes   **b.** 6 ohms

19. a. $x = 3.5$. Possible solution:

$$2(x - 6) = -5$$
$$x - 6 = -2.5$$
$$x = 3.5$$

b. $2(3.5 - 6) = 2(-2.5) = -5$

20. a. $\frac{500}{6} \approx 83.3$ h   **b.** $\frac{500}{0.75 \cdot 6} \approx 111.1$ h

TAKE ANOTHER LOOK

1. a. The graph shows the change in the hiker's speed over time. The contour map shows the change in the hiker's elevation as she follows the dotted line. It also shows the horizontal distance she has traveled from her starting point.

b. The graph shows rate of change in speed as the steepness (slope) of a line. At first the speed is steadily decreasing, then it is increasing, then it remains constant. The contour map shows rate of change in elevation by the distance between the contour lines. When the lines are very close together, the elevation is changing quickly.

c. If a scale were provided, you could infer distance from the graph by estimating the average speed up to a certain point and multiplying that estimate by the time at that point. Students might refer to the formula *distance* equals *rate* (speed) times *time* ($d = rt$). You could measure distance on the contour map using the map scale.

d. Student sketches of the graph of (*distance, time*) should show three sections. In each, the graph is increasing. In the first section, the graph is a curve that is concave down, showing a steadily decreasing speed. The second section of the graph is concave up because the speed is increasing, and the third section is a steep straight line, showing a constant, fast speed.

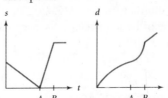

e. The contour map explains why the speed of the hiker was decreasing at the beginning, then increased until she was running, then stayed at a constant rate. First she was climbing a hill, then she was going downhill, and finally she was on level ground.

2. a. $\frac{1}{2} = 0.5$, $\frac{7}{16} = 0.4375$, $\frac{11}{125} = 0.088$, $\frac{7}{15} = 0.4\overline{6}$, $\frac{9}{22} = 0.4\overline{09}$, $\frac{11}{30} = 0.3\overline{6}$, $\frac{7}{20} = 0.35$

b. Sample answer: If the fraction is in lowest terms, and the only prime factors of the denominator are 2 and/or 5 (the factors of 10), the fraction will convert to a terminating decimal. If any prime factors of the denominator are numbers other than 2 and 5, the fraction will convert to a repeating decimal.

c. $0.25 = \frac{25}{100} = \frac{1}{4}$, $0.8 = \frac{8}{10} = \frac{4}{5}$, $0.13 = \frac{13}{100}$, $0.412 = \frac{412}{1000} = \frac{103}{250}$

d. Because $0.\overline{18}$ has two digits that repeat to the right of the decimal point, multiply by 100.

Let $F = 0.\overline{18} = 0.181818. \ldots$
Then $100F = 18.181818. \ldots$
So $100F - F = 18.181818. \ldots - 0.181818. \ldots = 18$.
Therefore, $99F = 18$, so $F = \frac{18}{99}$.

e. **i.** Because $0.\overline{32}$ has two digits that repeat to the right of the decimal point, multiply by 100.

Let $F = 0.\overline{32} = 0.323232....$
Then $100F = 32.323232....$
So $100F - F = 32.323232... - 0.323232... = 32$. Therefore, $99F = 32$, so $F = \frac{32}{99}$.

ii. Because $0.\overline{325}$ has three digits that repeat to the right of the decimal point, multiply by 1000.

Let $F = 0.\overline{325} = 0.325325325....$
Then $1000F = 325.325325325....$
So $1000F - F = 325.325325325... - 0.325325325... = 325$.
Therefore, $999F = 325$, so $F = \frac{325}{999}$.

iii. Because $0.2\overline{325}$ has four digits to the right of the decimal point before the digits start to repeat, multiply by 10,000.

Let $F = 0.2\overline{325} = 0.2325325325....$ Then $10{,}000F = 2325.325325325....$ Because the first digit in the decimal form of F does not repeat, subtract $10F = 2.325325325...$ rather than F in order to match up the decimal parts. $10{,}000F - 10F = 2325.325325325... - 2.325325325... = 2323$. Therefore, $9990F = 325$, so $F = \frac{2323}{9990}$.

IMPROVING YOUR REASONING SKILLS

The plants are not growing at the same rate. Plant 1 is growing at a rate of $20 \div 6$, or about 3.3 cm per day. Plant 2 is growing at a rate of $7 \div 6$, or about 1.2 cm per day. Plant 3 is growing at a rate of $30 \div 6$, or 5 cm per day.

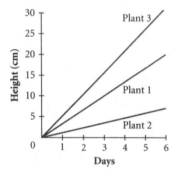

CHAPTER 4

LESSON 4.1

EXERCISES

1. The order of subtraction may vary.

a. $\frac{5-1}{3-1} = \frac{4}{2} = 2$
b. $\frac{5-3}{4-1} = \frac{2}{3}$
c. $\frac{6-2}{1-4} = \frac{4}{-3} = -\frac{4}{3}$

2. a. *Slope* $= \frac{change\ in\ y}{change\ in\ x} = \frac{7-4}{4-2} = \frac{3}{2} = 1.5$. To find another point on the line, start with a known point and add *change in x* to the x-coordinate and *change in y* to the y-coordinate. For example, if you start with $(4, 7)$, you get $(4 + change\ in\ x, 7 + change\ in\ y) = (4 + 2, 7 + 3) = (6, 10)$. So, $(6, 10)$ is on the line.

b. *Slope* $= \frac{change\ in\ y}{change\ in\ x} = \frac{5-(-1)}{2-6} = \frac{6}{-4} = \frac{3}{-2} = -1.5$. Starting with $(6, -1)$, another point on the line is $(6 + change\ in\ x, -1 + change\ in\ y) = (6 + -2, -1 + 3) = (4, 2)$.

c. *Slope* $= \frac{change\ in\ y}{change\ in\ x} = \frac{4-4}{8-(-2)} = 0$. The line is a horizontal line through $y = 4$, so any point with a y-coordinate of 4 is on the line.

d. *Slope* $= \frac{12-(-3)}{9-1} = \frac{15}{8} = 1.875$. Points will vary. One possible point is $(17, 27)$.

3. a. One way to find other points on the line is to start with $(0, 4)$ and repeatedly add 1 (the change in x) to the x-coordinate and 3 (the change in y) to the y-coordinate. Or, because $\frac{3}{1} = \frac{-3}{-1}$, you can add -1 to the x-coordinate and -3 to the y-coordinate. Two possible points are $(1, 7)$ and $(-1, 1)$. Checks: The slope between $(0, 4)$ and $(1, 7)$ is $\frac{7-4}{1-0} = \frac{3}{1}$, or 3. The slope between $(0, 4)$ and $(-1, 1)$ is $\frac{1-4}{-1-0} = \frac{-3}{-1} = \frac{3}{1}$, or 3.

b. One way to find other points on the line is to start with $(2, 8)$ and repeatedly add 1 to the x-coordinate and -5 to the y-coordinate. Or, because $-5 = \frac{5}{-1}$, you can also add -1 to the x-coordinate and 5 to the y-coordinate. Two possible points are $(3, 3)$ and $(1, 13)$. Checks: The slope between $(2, 8)$ and $(3, 3)$ is $\frac{3-8}{3-2} = \frac{-5}{1}$, or -5. The slope between $(2, 8)$ and $(1, 13)$ is $\frac{13-8}{1-2} = \frac{5}{-1}$, or -5.

c. Sample answer: $(12, 3), (4, 9)$
Checks: $\frac{3-6}{12-8} = \frac{-3}{4} = -\frac{3}{4}$ and $\frac{9-6}{4-8} = \frac{3}{-4} = -\frac{3}{4}$

d. Sample answer: $(6, 7.2), (4, 6.8)$
Checks: $\frac{7.2-7}{6-5} = \frac{0.2}{1} = 0.2$ and $\frac{6.8-7}{4-5} = \frac{-0.2}{-1} = 0.2$

4. Answers will vary.

5. a. **i.** The x-values don't change, so the slope is undefined.

ii. The y-values decrease as the x-values increase, so the slope is negative.

iii. The y-values don't change, so the slope is 0.

iv. The y-values increase as the x-values increase, so the slope is positive.

b. **i.** Using the points $(4, 0)$ and $(4, 3)$, we find the slope to be $\frac{3 - 0}{4 - 4} = \frac{3}{0}$. Because you can't divide by 0, the slope is undefined. Check: Using $(4, -8)$ and $(4, 20)$, the slope is $\frac{20 - (-8)}{4 - 4} = \frac{28}{0}$, which is undefined.

   ii. Using the points $(1, 3)$ and $(4, -3)$, we find the slope to be $\frac{-3 - 3}{4 - 1} = \frac{-6}{3} = -2$. Check: Using $(0, 5)$ and $(3, -1)$, the slope is $\frac{-1 - 5}{3 - 0} = \frac{-6}{3} = -2$.

   iii. Using the points $(-4, -5)$ and $(-3, -5)$, we find the slope to be $\frac{-5 - (-5)}{-3 - (-4)} = \frac{-5 + 5}{-3 + 4} = \frac{0}{1} = 0$. Check: Using $(1, -5)$ and $(4, -5)$, the slope is $\frac{-5 - (-5)}{4 - 1} = \frac{0}{3} = 0$.

   iv. Using the points $(0, -2)$ and $(4, 1)$, we find the slope to be $\frac{1 - (-2)}{4 - 0} = \frac{3}{4}$. Check: Using $(-4, -5)$ and $(-2, -3.5)$, the slope is $\frac{-3.5 - (-5)}{-2 - (-4)} = \frac{1.5}{2} = \frac{3}{4}$.

c. **i.** $x = 4$

   ii. $y = 5 - 2x$

   iii. $y = -5$

   iv. $y = -2 + \frac{3}{4}x$

6. a. The lines are parallel, so they have the same slope. The y-intercepts are different.

b. Line b matches the equation because it has a y-intercept of -3.

c. Line a has a y-intercept of 1 and a slope of $\frac{2}{5}$, so its equation is $y = 1 + \frac{2}{5}x$.

d. The slope, $\frac{2}{5}$, is the same in each equation. The y-intercepts, -3 and 1, are different.

7. a. Use the slope to move backward from $(40, 16.55)$; $(40 - 10, 16.55 - 0.29 \cdot 10) = (30, 13.65)$, or \$13.65 for 30 h; $(30 - 10, 13.75 - 0.29 \cdot 10) = (20, 10.75)$, or \$10.75 for 20 h.

b. Continuing the process in 7a leads to $(0, 4.95)$, or \$4.95 for 0 h. This is the flat monthly rate for Hector's Internet service.

c. $y = 4.95 + 0.29x$, where x is time in hours and y is total fee in dollars

d. Substitute 280 for x and solve for y: $y = 4.95 + 0.29(280) = 86.15$. \$86.15 for 280 h.

8. Because the line decreases from left to right, the slope is $-\frac{a}{c}$. The y-intercept is e. So the equation is $y = e - \frac{a}{c}x$, $y = e + \frac{-a}{c}x$, or $y = e + \frac{a}{-c}x$.

9. a. Slope triangles will vary. Here is one example:

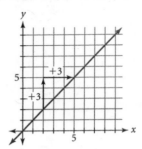

The change in y and the change in x are the same for any slope triangle.

b. Lines will vary. Here is one example:

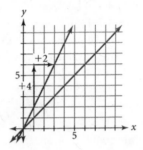

For a steeper line, the change in y is greater than the change in x. Numerically, the slope is greater than 1.

c. Lines will vary. Here is one example:

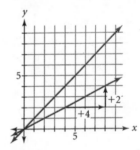

For a less steep line, the change in x is greater than the change in y. Numerically, the slope is between 0 and 1.

d. The line would decrease from left to right because the slope is negative. The line would be very steep because 15 is significantly greater than 1.

10. a. The slope between any two points is 30.

b. m/min; the slope, 30, is the number of meters the balloon rises every minute.

c. The y-intercept (the height of the balloon at 0 minutes) is 14 and the slope is 30, so the equation is $y = 14 + 30x$.

d. Substitute 8 for x: $y = 14 + 30(8) = 14 + 240 = 254$. After 8 min, the balloon will be 254 m high.

e. Solve $500 = 14 + 30x$ to find the time when the balloon reaches 500 m:

$$500 = 14 + 30x$$

$$500 - 14 = 14 - 14 + 30x$$

$$486 = 30x$$

$$\frac{486}{30} = \frac{30x}{30}$$

$$16.2 = x$$

The balloon reaches 500 m in 16.2 min, so it is at a height of 500 m or less between 0 and 16.2 min.

11. a. **i.** Line 2 is a better choice. A majority of points are closer to line 2 than to line 1.

ii. Line 4 is a better choice. Line 3 passes through or is close to a number of points, but there are too many points above this line and too few below it. Even though line 4 does not intercept any points, it is the better choice because there are about the same number of points above it as below it.

b. Answers will vary but should show the general direction of the points and have about as many points above the line as below it. Sample answers:

i.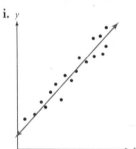

ii.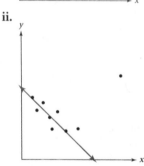

c. Answers will vary. The line should reflect the direction of the data, and about the same number of points should be above the line as below it.

12. a. Use the formula for the area of a triangle, $A = 0.5bh$, with $b = 18.3$ and $h = 7.4$:
$A = 0.5(18.3)(7.4) = 67.7 \text{ cm}^2$.

b. Use $b = 18.3 - 0.1 = 18.2$ and $h = 7.4 - 0.1 = 7.3$:
$A = 0.5(18.2)(7.3) = 66.4 \text{ cm}^2$.

c. Use $b = 18.3 + 0.1 = 18.4$ and $h = 7.4 + 0.1 = 7.5$:
$A = 0.5(18.4)(7.5) = 69.0 \text{ cm}^2$.

d. $67.7 \pm 1.3 \text{ cm}^2$

13. Answers will vary. The sum of the ages must be 50, and the middle value must be 6. One possible set of ages is {3, 3, 6, 16, 22}. Other sets are possible.

14. a. $L_2 = 2.5(L_1 + 14)$; {27.5, 32.5, 40, 55, 60}

b. $L_3 = \dfrac{(L_2 - 35)}{2.5}$, or $L_3 = \dfrac{L_2}{2.5} - 14$

15. a. 85%   **b.** 150%   **c.** 6.5%   **d.** 107%

16. 3. Combine like terms.

4. Subtract 3 from both sides.

6. Divide both sides by 5.

LESSON 4.2

EXERCISES

1. a. No; although this line goes through four points, too many points are below the line.

b. No; although the slope of the line shows the general direction of the data, too many points are below the line.

c. Yes; about the same number of points is above the line as below the line, and the slope of the line shows the general direction of the data.

d. No; although the same number of points is above and below the line, the slope of the line doesn't show the direction of the data very well.

2. Vertical; $x = 2$

3. a. $y = -2 + \dfrac{2}{3}x$

b. $y = 2 - \dfrac{2}{3}x$

c. $x = -3$

d. $y = 3$

4. a. There is a linear pattern.

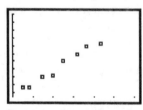

[0, 36, 6, 120, 1200, 100]

b. Answers will vary. Using the points (8, 376) and (19, 684), the slope is 28.

c. The slope represents the number of quarters Penny saves per month.

d. $y = 28x$; the line needs to move up (the y-intercept needs to increase).

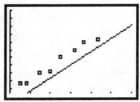

[0, 36, 6, 150, 1200, 50]

e. Answers will vary. A possible equation is $y = 152 + 28x$.

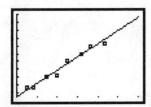

f. The y-intercept represents the number of quarters Penny's grandmother gave her.

g. Answers depend on the line students find. On her 18th birthday, Penny will have been saving for 36 months. Using the equation $y = 152 + 28x$, she will have $152 + 28(36)$, or 1160 quarters. The prediction may not be reliable because it extrapolates 10 months beyond the data.

5. a. The number of representatives depends on the population.

b. Let x represent the population in millions, and let y represent the number of representatives.

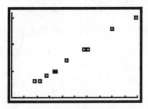

[0, 10, 1, 0, 16, 5]

c. Answers will vary. Two possible points are $(2.8, 4)$ and $(6.1, 9)$. The slope between these points is approximately 1.5. The equation $y = 1.5x$ appears to fit the data with a y-intercept of 0. The slope represents the number of representatives per 1 million people. The y-intercept means that a state with no population would have no representatives.

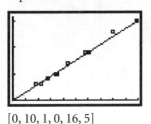

[0, 10, 1, 0, 16, 5]

d. The equation $y = 1.5x$ gives $y = 1.5(33.9) = 50.85$, or 51 representatives. (For 2001–2010, California actually has 53 representatives.)

e. The equation $y = 1.5x$ gives $8 = 1.5x$; $x = \frac{8}{1.5} \approx 5.3$; about 5.3 million. (The estimated population of Minnesota in the 2000 census was 4.9 million.)

f. A direct variation is a reasonable model because a state with no population would have no representatives, so the line should go through the origin.

6. a. No; each state has two senators regardless of its population.

b. $y = 2$, where x represents population in millions and y represents the number of senators

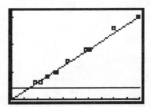

c. The graph is a horizontal line because there's no change in y, the number of senators, as x, the state population, changes.

7. a. Slope $= \dfrac{y_2 - y_1}{x_2 - x_1} = \dfrac{4.4 - 3.4}{4.5 - 2} = 0.4$ m/s

b. 2.6 m. Possible explanation: As the time decreases by 1 s, the distance decreases by 0.4 m. So after 1 s she is $3.4 - 0.4$, or 3 m away, and after 0 s she is $3 - 0.4$, or 2.6 m away.

c. $y = 2.6 + 0.4x$

8. a. The slope is negative because the distance decreases as the time increases.

b. The y-intercept represents the start distance for the walk. The x-intercept represents the elapsed time when the walker reaches the sensor.

c. Answers will vary. Quadrant II could indicate walking before you started timing. Quadrant IV could indicate that the walker walks past you (the distances behind you are considered negative).

9. a. Answers will vary. Sample answer: $y = -8 + 4x$

b. Answers will vary. Sample answer: $y = -2x$

c. $y = 6 + x$ **d.** $y = 10$

10. a. All the lines have a slope of 3, so they are all parallel.

b. All the lines cross the y-axis at 5 (excluding the y-axis itself); they radiate around the point $(0, 5)$.

c. All the lines are parallel to the x-axis, or horizontal.

d. All the lines are parallel to the y-axis, or vertical.

11. a. Neither; the *x*- and *y*-values do not have a constant product or a constant ratio.

  b. Inverse variation; the *x*- and *y*-values have a constant product. The equation is $y = \frac{100}{x}$.

  c. Direct variation; the *x*- and *y*-values have a constant ratio. The equation is $y = -2.5x$.

  d. Direct variation; the *x*- and *y*-values have a constant ratio. The equation is $y = \frac{1}{13}x$.

12. a. $8 - 12m = 17$
  $$-12m = 9$$
  $$m = -0.75$$

  b. $2r + 7 = -24$
  $$2r = -31$$
  $$r = -15.5$$

  c. $-6 - 3w = 42$
  $$-3w = 48$$
  $$w = -16$$

13. a. Mean: $24.8\overline{6}$; median: 21

  b. Mean: 44.5; median: 40

  c. Mean: approximately 140.1; median: 145

  d. Mean: 85.75; median: 86.5

IMPROVING YOUR VISUAL THINKING SKILLS

The second abacus shows 84. The third shows 71,545. 27,059 would look like this:

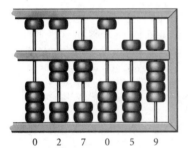

0   2   7   0   5   9

LESSON 4.3

EXERCISES

1. a. The equation $y = 3 + 4(x - 5)$ is in point-slope form $y = y_1 + m(x - x_1)$, where *m* is the slope and (x_1, y_1) is a point on the line. So the slope is 4, and (5, 3) is a point on the line.

  b. Slope 2; point $(-3.1, 1.9)$

  c. Slope -3.47; point $(7, -2)$

  d. Slope -1.38; point $(2.5, 5)$

2. a. Point-slope form is $y = y_1 + m(x - x_1)$, where *m* is the slope and (x_1, y_1) is the point. Using slope 3 and point (2, 5), we get the equation $y = 5 + 3(x - 2)$.

  b. $y = -4 - 5(x - 1)$

3. a. $\dfrac{13 - (-1)}{5 - (-2)} = \dfrac{14}{7} = 2$

  b. $y = -1 + 2(x + 2)$

  c. $y = 13 + 2(x - 5)$

  d. The graphs coincide, and the tables are identical.

4. a. Any pair of points can be used to find the slope. Using the first two points in the table, $(5, -15)$ and $(10, -8.5)$, gives

  $$\text{slope} = \frac{y_2 - y_1}{x_2 - x_1} = \frac{-8.5 - (-15)}{10 - 5} = \frac{6.5}{5} = 1.3.$$

  The data are exactly linear, so any two points will give this slope.

  b. Answers will vary. Using the point $(5, -15)$, the equation is $y = -15 + 1.3(x - 5)$.

  c. Answers will vary. Using the point $(20, 4.5)$, the equation is $y = 4.5 + 1.3(x - 20)$.

  d. The two equations should give the same graph and table.

  e. Substitute 0 for *x* in your equation from 4b or 4c and solve for *y*. Using the equation obtained in 4b, $y = -15 + 1.3(0 - 5) = -15 + 1.3(-5) = -15 - 6.5 = -21.5$. This means that when the actual temperature is 0°F with a wind speed of 20 mi/h, the wind chill temperature is -21.5°F. In the graph of this data, -21.5 is the *y*-intercept.

5. Answers will vary.

6. Segment *a* has slope 1. Two points on the segment are $(0, 0.5)$ and $(2, 2.5)$, so two possible equations are $y = 0.5 + 1(x - 0)$ and $y = 2.5 + 1(x - 2)$.

  Segment *b*: $y = 2.5 - 0.75(x - 2)$ or $y = 1 - 0.75(x - 4)$

  Segment *c*: $y = 1 + 1(x - 4)$ or $y = 3 + 1(x - 6)$

7. a. $\overline{AD}$: $y = 2 + 0.2(x + 1)$ or $y = 3 + 0.2(x - 4)$
  $\overline{BC}$: $y = -2 + 0.2(x + 3)$ or $y = -1 + 0.2(x - 2)$
  $\overline{AB}$: $y = 2 + 2(x + 1)$ or $y = -2 + 2(x + 3)$
  $\overline{DC}$: $y = 3 + 2(x - 4)$ or $y = -1 + 2(x - 2)$

  b. The slopes are the same; the coordinates of the points are different.

  c. Quadrilateral *ABCD* appears to be a parallelogram. In 7b, we found that $\overline{AD}$ and $\overline{BC}$ have the same slope, which means they are parallel. $\overline{AB}$ and $\overline{DC}$ both have slope 2, so they are also parallel.

8. a. The data appear linear.

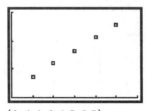

  [0, 6, 1, 0, 1.5, 0.5]

  b. The slope, $0.23 per ounce, is the cost for each additional ounce after the first.

Discovering Algebra Solutions Manual
©2007 Key Curriculum Press

c. Answers will vary; Using the point $(1, 0.37)$, we get the equation $y = 0.37 + 0.23(x - 1)$.

d. $y = 0.37 + 0.23(10 - 1) = 0.37 + 0.23(9)$
$= 0.37 + 2.07 = 2.44$. So the cost of mailing a 10 oz letter is $2.44.

e. The rates are given for weights not exceeding the given weights, so a letter weighing 3.5 oz would cost the same as a 4 oz letter, or $1.06. A letter weighing 9.1 oz would cost the same as a 10 oz letter, or $2.44.

f. No; a continuous line includes points whose x-values are not whole numbers and whose y-values are not possible rates.

9. a. The data are approximately linear.

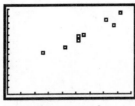

$[0, 45, 5, 0, 650, 50]$

b. Answers will vary. Using the points $(28, 450)$ and $(13, 310)$, the equation is $y = 310 + 9.3(x - 13)$.

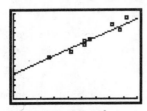

$[0, 45, 5, 0, 650, 50]$

c. Substitute 41 for x in the equation obtained in 9b to obtain $y = 310 + 9.3(41 - 13) = 570.4$. This model predicts that a Hardee's Country Steak Biscuit has approximately 570 calories.

d. The actual data point lies above the line $y = 310 + 9.3(x - 13)$. If a point lies above the line, the sandwich has more calories than the model predicts.

e. Answers will vary. Using $y = 310 + 9.3(x - 13)$ as a model, three points are above the line, two points are on the line, and three points are below the line.

f. Answers will vary. The line $y = 310 + 9.3(x - 13)$ appears to be a good fit.

g. Answers will vary. Using $y = 310 + 9.3(x - 13)$, a sandwich with 0 g of fat would have approximately 189 calories. This makes sense because not all calories in food come from fat.

10. a. $y = 205 + 1.8(x - 1990)$ or
$y = 214 + 1.8(x - 1995)$

b. and **c.**

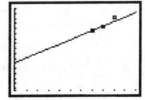

$[1955, 2010, 5, 85, 250, 10]$

The point $(2000, 223)$ is somewhat close to the line, but the predicted value is too low.

d.

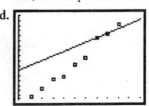

$[1955, 2010, 5, 85, 250, 10]$

e. The data are generally linear, but the line doesn't fit them very well. A line with a steeper slope would be a better fit.

f. Answers will vary. The line $y = 200 + 3.7$ $(x - 1990)$ gives a reasonable fit.

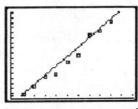

$[1955, 2010, 5, 85, 250, 10]$

g. Answers will vary depending on the equation chosen for 10f. Using $y = 200 + 3.7(x - 1990)$ gives an estimate of 274 million tons of trash in 2010.

11. a. Because volume and temperature are directly proportional, their ratio is constant. So $\frac{280}{3.5} = \frac{330}{x}$; $x = 4.125$, so the volume of gas is 4.125 L.

b. 180 K; you can find this by solving the proportion $\frac{280}{3.5} = \frac{x}{2.25}$.

12. a. The slope is -1. The change in x from the given point $(3, 1)$ to $\left(5, \square\right)$ is 2. $\frac{Change\ in\ y}{Change\ in\ x} = -1$, so the change in y must be -2. The point is $(5, 1 - 2)$ or $(5, -1)$.

b. The slope is undefined. The line is vertical. So the x-coordinate of every point on the line is 2. The point is $(2, 3)$.

c. The slope is $-\frac{5}{2}$. The change in y from the given point $(-2, 2)$ to $\left(\square, -3\right)$ is -5, so the change in x must be 2. The point is $(-2 + 2, -3)$ or $(0, -3)$.

13.

$4x + 3 = 2x + 7$	Original equation.
$4x - 2x + 3 = 2x - 2x + 7$	Subtract $2x$ from both sides.
$2x + 3 = 7$	Combine like terms.
$2x + 3 - 3 = 7 - 3$	Subtract 3 from both sides.
$2x = 4$	Combine like terms.
$\dfrac{2x}{2} = \dfrac{4}{2}$	Divide both sides by 2.
$x = 2$	Reduce.

LESSON 4.4

EXERCISES

1. a. Rewrite the first expression:
$3 - 3(x + 4) = 3 - 3x - 12 = -3x - 9$.
The expressions are not equivalent. The second expression needs to be changed to $-3x - 9$.

b. Rewrite the first expression:
$5 + 2(x - 2) = 5 + 2x - 4 = 2x + 1$.
The expressions are equivalent.

c. Rewrite the second expression:
$2 + 5(x - 1) = 2 + 5x - 5 = 5x - 3$.
The expressions are equivalent.

d. The second expression is equivalent to $-2x + 8$, so the expressions are not equivalent. You can change the second expression to $-2(x + 4)$ or $2(-x - 4)$.

2. a.

$y = 14 + 3(x - 5)$	Original equation.
$y = 14 + 3x - 15$	Distribute the 3.
$y = -1 + 3x$	Add.

b.

$y = -5 - 2(x + 5)$	Original equation.
$y = -5 - 2x - 10$	Distribute the -2.
$y = -15 - 2x$	Subtract.

c.

$6x + 2y = 24$	
$6x - 6x + 2y = 24 - 6x$	Subtract $6x$ from both sides.
$2y = 24 - 6x$	Subtract.
$\dfrac{2y}{2} = \dfrac{24 - 6x}{2}$	Divide both sides by 2.
$y = 12 - 3x$	Divide.

3. a.

$3x = 12$	Original equation.
$x = 4$	Division property.

b.

$-x - 45 = 47$	Original equation.
$-x = 92$	Addition property.
$x = -92$	Multiplication property.

c.

$x + 15 = 8$	Original equation.
$x = -7$	Subtraction property.

d.

$\dfrac{x}{4} = 28$	Original equation.
$x = 112$	Multiplication property.

4. a. $3(x - 2) = 3(x) + 3(-2) = 3x - 6$

b. $-4(x - 5) = -4(x) + (-4)(-5) = -4x + 20$

c. $-2(x + 8) = -2(x) + (-2)(8) = -2x - 16$

5. a. $(-5, 25)$

b. Solve the equation $15 = 25 - 2(x + 5)$:

$$15 = 25 - 2(x + 5)$$
$$-10 = -2(x + 5)$$
$$-10 = -2x - 10$$
$$0 = -2x$$
$$0 = x$$

6. a. Solve $y = 3(x + 8)$ for x. Two possible solutions are shown.

$y = 3(x + 8)$	Original equation.
$\dfrac{y}{3} = x + 8$	Divide by 3.
$\dfrac{y}{3} - 8 = x$, or $x = \dfrac{y}{3} - 8$	Subtract 8 from both sides.

$y = 3(x + 8)$	Original equation.
$y = 3x + 24$	Distributive property.
$y - 24 = 3x + 24 - 24$	Subtraction property (subtract 24 from both sides).
$y - 24 = 3x$	Combine like terms.
$\dfrac{y - 24}{3} = \dfrac{3x}{3}$	Division property (divide both sides by 3).
$\dfrac{y - 24}{3} = x$, or $x = \dfrac{y - 24}{3}$	Reduce.

b. Solve $\dfrac{y - 3}{x - 4} = 10$ for y.

$\dfrac{y - 3}{x - 4} = 10$	Original equation.
$y - 3 = 10(x - 4)$	Multiplication property (multiply both sides by $x - 4$).
$y = 3 + 10(x - 4)$,	Addition property (add 3 to both sides).
or $y = -37 + 10x$	Distributive property, reduce.

Discovering Algebra Solutions Manual
©2007 Key Curriculum Press

c. Solve $4(2y - 5) - 12 = x$ for y. Two possible solutions are shown.

$4(2y - 5) - 12 = x$	Original equation.
$4(2y - 5) = x + 12$	Addition property (add 12 to both sides).
$2y - 5 = \dfrac{x + 12}{4}$	Division property (divide both sides by 4).
$2y = \dfrac{x + 12}{4} + 5$	Addition property (add 5 to both sides).
$y = \dfrac{\dfrac{x + 12}{4} + 5}{2}$, or $y = \dfrac{1}{8}x + 4$	Division property (divide both sides by 2).
$4(2y - 5) - 12 = x$	Original equation.
$8y - 20 - 12 = x$	Distributive property.
$8y - 32 = x$	Combine like terms.
$8y = x + 32$	Addition property (add 32 to both sides).
$y = \dfrac{x + 32}{8}$, or $y = \dfrac{1}{8}x + 4$	Division property (divide both sides by 8).

7. a. $3(x - 4)$ **b.** $-5(x - 4)$ **c.** $4(8 + x)$

   d. $-7(x + 4)$

8. a. $y = 5(2 + x)$ **b.** $y = 5(x + 2)$

   c. The y_1-value is missing, which means it is zero; $y = 0 + 5(x + 2)$.

   d. $(-2, 0)$; this is the x-intercept.

9. a. Equations i and ii are equivalent. You can verify this by rewriting them in intercept form. Both equations are equivalent to $y = 24 - 2x$.

   b. Equations i and iii are equivalent. Both are equivalent to $y = -5 + 4x$.

   c. Equations ii and iii are equivalent. Both are equivalent to $y = 49 + 5x$.

   d. Equations i and iii are equivalent. Both are equivalent to $y = 14 + 6x$.

10. a. $x = 2$; the point $(2, 0)$ is the x-intercept.

   b. $y = 3$; the point $(0, 3)$ is the y-intercept.

   c.

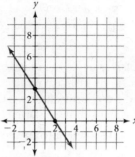

   d. The slope is $-\frac{3}{2}$. The equation is $y = 3 - \frac{3}{2}x$.

   e.

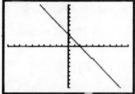

   $[-10, 10, 1, -10, 10, 1]$

   The two lines are the same, so the equations are equivalent.

   f.

$3x + 2y = 6$	Original equation.
$2y = 6 - 3x$	Subtract $3x$ from both sides.
$y = 3 - \dfrac{3}{2}x$	Divide both sides by 2.

11. a. -4.4 **b.** $y = -4.4 - 4.2(x - 2)$

   c. -0.5 **d.** $y = 6.1 - 4.2(x + 0.5)$

   e. Answers will vary. You could rewrite each equation in slope-intercept form. Both are equivalent to $y = 4 - 4.2x$.

   f. The point $(4, -12)$ is not on the line; $(-3, 16.6)$ is on the line. Possible answer: Substitute the x- and y-values into the equation and check whether you get a true statement when you evaluate the equation. Or, substitute the given x-value into the equation, evaluate, and see whether it is equivalent to the given y-value.

12. a. The slope is $\frac{17.75 - 15.20}{23 - 20} = 0.85$. Using the point $(20, 15.20)$, we get the equation $y = 15.20 + 0.85(x - 20)$.

   b. $y = 15.20 + 0.85(25 - 20)$; \$19.45

   c. The equation is used to model the bill only when she is logged on for more than 15 h. Substituting 15 for x gives the flat rate of \$10.95 for all amounts of time less than or equal to 15 h.

   d. Solve $23.70 = 15.20 + 0.85(x - 20)$: $x = 30$. So Dorine was logged on for 30 h.

13. a. Answers will vary depending on which point students use. Possible equations are
$y = 568 + 4.6(x - 5)$, $y = 591 + 4.6(x - 10)$,
$y = 614 + 4.6(x - 15)$, and
$y = 637 + 4.6(x - 20)$.

b. $y = 545 + 4.6x$

c. The slope represents the number of calories burned per minute. The y-intercept represents the number of calories Avery burned from the time she went to sleep Friday night until she started hiking.

d. Yes; it is equivalent to the slope-intercept equation $y = 545 + 4.6x$.

e. The point (60, 821) tells you that if Avery hikes for 60 minutes, she will have burned a total of 821 calories since she went to sleep Friday night.

14. a. One point on the line is (0, 15); other answers are possible. The slope is 0.45/min.

b. $y = 15 + 0.45x$

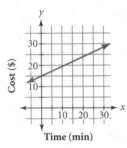

Time (min)

c. The line will be parallel to the original line, but 5 units higher.

d. The line will be parallel to the original line, but 15 units lower (passing through the origin).

e. The line will be steeper than the original line, but will have the same y-intercept.

15. a. This graph shows the slope triangles for 15a and 15b:

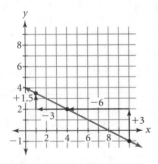

$$\frac{change\ in\ y}{change\ in\ x} = \frac{1.5}{-3} = -0.5$$

b. $\frac{change\ in\ y}{change\ in\ x} = \frac{3}{-6} = -0.5$

c. The sides of the slope triangle for 15b are twice as long, but the slopes are equal.

d. You would get a larger triangle with side lengths in the same ratio and the same slope.

16. $z = \frac{3.8 + 5.4}{0.2} - 6.2$; $z = 39.8$

LESSON 4.5

EXERCISES

1. a. $y = 1 + 2(x - 1)$ or $y = 5 + 2(x - 3)$

b. $y = 3 + \frac{2}{3}(x - 1)$ or $y = 5 + \frac{2}{3}(x - 4)$

c. $y = 6 - \frac{4}{3}(x - 1)$ or $y = 2 - \frac{4}{3}(x - 4)$

2. Estimates will vary. The answers show the equations in intercept form.

a. $y = -1 + 2x$

b. $y = \frac{7}{3} + \frac{2}{3}x$, or $y = 2.\overline{3} + 0.\overline{6}x$

c. $y = \frac{22}{3} - \frac{4}{3}x$, or $y = 7.\overline{3} - 1.\overline{3}x$

3. a. 3   **b.** -4 **c.** 6

The x-intercept of $y = b(x - x_1)$ is x_1.

4. a. Answers will vary. Using the points (1982, 341) and (1996, 363) gives the equation $y = 341 + 1.6(x - 1982)$, where x is the year and y is the concentration of CO_2 in ppm.

b. Answers will vary, but all graphs should look approximately like this:

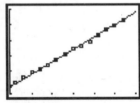

[1975, 2005, 5, 325, 380, 10]

c. Answers will vary. The equation $y = 341 + 1.6(x - 1982)$ gives 402 ppm.

d. Answers will vary. Using the equation in 4a gives an x-intercept of about 1769. This value is found by substituting 0 for y in the equation $y = 341 + 1.6(x - 1982)$ and solving for x:

$$0 = 341 + 1.6(x - 1982)$$

$$-341 = 1.6(x - 1982)$$

$$\frac{-341}{1.6} = x - 1982$$

$$x = \frac{-341}{1.6} + 1982 \approx 1769$$

This x-intercept represents the year when the concentration of CO_2 would have been 0 ppm. This does not make sense because plants depend on CO_2, so there has been some concentration of CO_2 as long as there have been plants. The model is limited; it cannot be extended much before or after the time period of the data.

e. The slope represents the average rate of change, so the typical change in CO_2 concentration is about 1.6 ppm per year.

5. a.

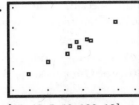

[10, 45, 5, 40, 120, 10]

b. Answers will vary. Using the points (20, 67) and (31.2, 88.6) gives a slope of approximately 1.9, and a possible equation is $y = 67 + 1.9(x - 20)$.

c. One possible answer:

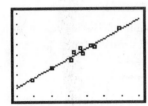

d. The slope is $\frac{212 - 32}{100 - 0}$, or 1.8. The possible equations are $y = 32 + 1.8(x - 0)$ and $y = 212 + 1.8(x - 100)$.

e. Answers will vary. The sample equation in 5b gives $y = 29 + 1.9x$. The equations in 5d both give $y = 32 + 1.8x$. The equations are not equivalent.

f. It is possible, but the difference could also be the result of measurement error or faulty procedures.

6. a.

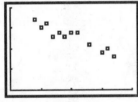

[0, 20, 5, 0, 20, 5]

b. Answers will vary. Using (13, 11) and (8, 14), we get the equation $y = 11 - 0.6(x - 13)$ or $y = 14 - 0.6(x - 8)$.

c. Answers will vary. Here is the graph of the equation in 6b:

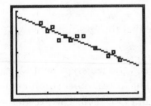

d. Answers will vary. Using $y = 11 - 0.6(x - 13)$ gives a concentration of dissolved oxygen of 17.6 ppm.

e. Answers will vary. Solving $12 = 11 - 0.6(x - 13)$ gives a temperature of about 11.3°C.

7. a. Using the point (11, 14) and the slope −0.6, the equation is $y = 14 - 0.6(x - 11)$.

b. Using the point (7, 13) and the slope −0.6, the equation is $y = 13 - 0.6(x - 7)$.

c. First equation (from Exercise 6):

$y = 11 - 0.6(x - 13)$

$y = 11 - 0.6x + 7.8$

$y = 18.8 - 0.6x$

Second equation:

$y = 14 - 0.6(x - 11)$

$y = 14 - 0.6x + 6.6$

$y = 20.6 - 0.6x$

Third equation:

$y = 13 - 0.6(x - 7)$

$y = 13 - 0.6x + 4.2$

$y = 17.2 - 0.6x$

d. The equation has prediction accuracy within 1.8 ppm.

8. a. First find the slope of the line:

$$\text{slope} = \frac{y_2 - y_1}{x_2 - x_1} = \frac{30 - 47}{67 - 79} = \frac{-17}{-12} \approx 1.4$$

Using the point (67, 30) and the slope 1.4, the equation is $y = 30 + 1.4(x - 67)$.

b.

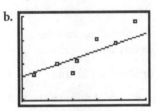

[60, 85, 5, 0, 70, 10]

c. Equations will vary. The graph with a larger y_1-value is parallel but higher, and the graph with a smaller y_1-value is parallel but lower.

d. Equations will vary. The graphs pass through point (67, 30), but the one with a larger value of b is steeper, and the one with a smaller value of b is less steep.

e. Possible equation: $y = 26 + 2(x - 67)$

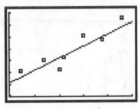

[60, 85, 5, 0, 70, 10]

9. a. The number of biscuits decreases by 3 each day, so the slope is −3.

b. Using the point (10, 106) and slope −3, we find the equation $y = 106 - 3(x - 10)$.

c. The box will be empty on the 46th day. You can find this by solving the equation $y = 106 - 3(x - 10)$ or by reasoning that it will take 36 days to eat the 106 biscuits that remain in the box. Because there were 106 biscuits on the 10th day, it takes a total of $36 + 10$ or 46 days to finish the box.

d. The y-intercept, 136, is the number of biscuits that were in the box when it was new.

10.

Description	Undo	Equation
Pick y.		$y = \dfrac{12 - 2x}{-3} - 1$, or $y = -5 + \dfrac{2x}{3}$
$+ 1$	-1	$y + 1 = \dfrac{12 - 2x}{-3}$, or $y + 1 = -4 + \dfrac{2x}{3}$
$\cdot (-3)$	$/ (-3)$	$-3(y + 1) = 12 - 2x$
$+ 2x$	$- 2x$	$2x - 3(y + 1) = 12$

11. a. $\dfrac{1}{10}t + \dfrac{1}{8}t = 1$ Original equation.

$\dfrac{4}{40}t + \dfrac{5}{40}t = 1$ Change fractions to have a common denominator.

$\dfrac{9}{40}t = 1$ Add fractions.

$9t = 40$ Multiply by 40 to undo the division.

$t = \dfrac{40}{9}$ Divide by 9 to undo the multiplication.

$t = 4.\overline{4}$, or about 4 h 27 min

b. Let t represent the number of minutes the bathtub is filling (and draining).

$\dfrac{1}{30}t - \dfrac{1}{45}t = 1$ Original equation.

$\dfrac{3}{90}t - \dfrac{2}{90}t = 1$ Find a common denominator.

$\dfrac{1}{90}t = 1$ Subtract.

$t = 90$ Multiply by 90 to undo the division.

It takes 90 minutes to fill the tub.

LESSON 4.6

EXERCISES

1. a. 166, 405, 623, 1052, 1483

b. 204, 514, 756, 1194, 1991

c.

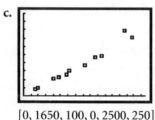

[0, 1650, 100, 0, 2500, 250]

d. The slope will be positive because as the flying distance increases so does the driving distance.

e. To make the rectangle, draw the vertical lines $x = 405$ and $x = 1052$, and the horizontal lines $y = 514$ and $y = 1194$. The Q-points are $(405, 514)$ and $(1052, 1194)$.

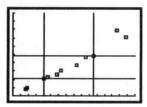

f. The slope is approximately 1.05. The equation is $y = 1194 + 1.05(x - 1052)$ or $y = 514 + 1.05(x - 405)$.

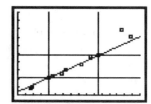

g. About 1054 miles; you can find this by substituting 919 for x in the equation or by tracing the graph.

h. About 535 miles; you can find this by substituting 651 for y in the equation and solving for x or by tracing the graph.

2. a. $y = 10 + 0.5(32 - 28)$; 12 grams of saturated fat

b. $15 = 10 + 0.5(x - 28)$

$5 = 0.5x - 14$

$19 = 0.5x$

$38 = x$; 38 grams of fat

3. a. For the x-values: $Q1 = 5$, $Q3 = 10$
For the y-values: $Q1 = 4$, $Q3 = 9$
Use a graph to see that the Q-points are $(5, 4)$ and $(10, 9)$.

b. For the x-values: $Q1 = 3$, $Q3 = 8$
For the y-values: $Q1 = 2$, $Q3 = 8$
Use a graph to see that the Q-points are $(3, 8)$ and $(8, 2)$.

4. a. Let x represent years, and let y represent winning time in minutes. The five-number summary for x is 1952, 1962, 1976, 1990, 2000. The five-number summary for y is 27.12, 27.5, 27.78, 28.65, 29.46. The Q-points are $(1962, 28.65)$ and $(1990, 27.5)$. The slope of the line through these two points is about -0.0411, so the possible equations are $y = 28.65 - 0.0411(x - 1962)$ and $y = 27.5 - 0.0411(x - 1990)$.

Discovering Algebra Solutions Manual
©2007 Key Curriculum Press

b.

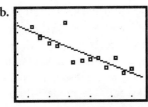

[1945, 2005, 10, 26, 30, 0.5]

c. The slope, -0.0411, means that the winning time decreases an average of 0.0411 min (2.47 s) each year.

d. The prediction is 26.92 min, which is 0.16 min (9.6 s) less than the actual winning time.

e. Answers will vary. However, there is a physical limit to how fast a person can run. Eventually the times will have to level off.

5. Answers will vary. Q1 and Q3 for the x-values should be 4 and 12, respectively, and Q1 and Q3 for the y-values should be 28 and 47, respectively. If we create a data set with seven values, the quartiles will be the second and sixth values. The x-values can be 2, 4, 6, 8, 10, 12, 14. The y-values can be 22, 28, 30, 35, 42, 47, 53. Now we have to match up the x- and y-values so that one of the Q-points, say (12, 47), is in the data set and the other is not. One possible pairing is {(2, 22) (4, 30) (6, 28) (8, 35) (10, 42) (12, 47) (14, 53)}.

6. iv. Possible explanation: The y-values decrease as the x-values increase, so the slope of the line of fit must be negative, which narrows the choices to iii and iv. If you fit a line to the data using Q-points, the Q-points would be (11, 1.3) and (6, 2.2). The slope of the line through these points is -0.18. Equation iv is the equation of the line through these Q-points, so it is the best fit.

7. a. The Q-points for this data set are (4, 1.3) and (12, 6.3). The slope of the line through these points is 0.625, so the equation is $y = 1.3 + 0.625(x - 4)$ or $y = 6.3 + 0.625(x - 12)$.

b. The elevator is rising at a rate of 0.625 second per floor.

c. Substituting 60 for x gives a y-value of 36.3. So the elevator passes the 60th floor at 36.3 seconds after 2:00, or approximately 2:00:36.

d. Substituting 45 for y and solving gives an x-value of 73.92, so the elevator will be almost at the 74th floor.

8. a. The Q-points for this data set are (92, 1.3) and (84, 6.3). The slope of the line through these points is -0.625, so the equation is $y = 1.3 - 0.625(x - 92)$ or $y = 6.3 - 0.625(x - 84)$.

b. The elevator is moving down at a rate of 0.625 second per floor.

c. Substituting 10 for x gives a y-value of 52.55. So the elevator passes the 10th floor after 52.55 seconds, or at approximately 2:00:53.

d. Substituting 34 for y and solving gives an x-value of 39.68, so the elevator will be between the 39th and 40th floors.

9. a. Answers will vary.

b. At 28.8 s, or at about 2:00:29, the elevators will pass at the 48th floor. One way to find this answer is to make a calculator table of both $y = 1.3 + 0.625(x - 4)$ and $y = 1.3 - 0.625(x - 92)$. When x is 48, the y-value for both equations is 28.8.

10. a. {0, 370} ENTER , {Ans(1) + 1, Ans(2) − 54} ENTER , ENTER , . . .

Time (h)	Distance from Mt. Rushmore (mi)
0	370
1	316
2	262
3	208
4	154
5	100
6	46

b.

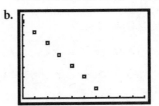

[0, 10, 1, 0, 400, 50]

c.

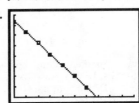

The line represents the distance from Mt. Rushmore at any time during the trip. The line lets you find the distance at any time; the points show the distance only at 1-hour intervals.

d. The slope is -54, which means that the distance from Mt. Rushmore decreases by 54 miles each hour.

e. The car will reach the Wall Drug Store after about 5.4 hours, or about 5 hours 24 minutes. You can find this by solving the equation $80 = 370 - 54x$ or by finding the x-value on the graph corresponding to the y-value 80.

f. The car will reach Mt. Rushmore in just under 7 hours. You can find this answer by solving the equation $0 = 370 - 54x$ or by finding the x-value on the graph corresponding to the y-value 0.

11. The size and cost are almost directly proportional. The 4 oz bottle costs $0.22 per oz, the 7.5 oz bottle costs $0.22 per oz, and the 18 oz bottle costs $0.2217 per oz. If you change the price of the 18 oz bottle to $3.96, then it also will cost exactly $0.22 per oz.

12. Answers will vary. Sample answer: To convert an equation from point-slope form to slope-intercept form, use the distributive property and then simplify. For example, to convert the equation $y = 4 + 2(x - 3)$ to slope-intercept form, use the distributive property to rewrite it as $y = 4 + 2x - 6$. Then simplify the equation and write it in the form $y = mx + b$. You get $y = 2x - 2$. You can check that the equations are equivalent by making a graph or a table. If the equations are equivalent, the graphs will be identical and the values in the table will be equal.

LESSON 4.7

EXERCISES

1. a. $(6, 6)$

 b. $(5, 9)$

 c. $y = 9 - 3(x - 5)$

 d. $y = 24 - 3x$

 e. $(8, 0)$

2. a. $x = 10$

 b. $x = -7.5$

 c. $x = 2.5$

 d. $x = 41.5$

3. a.
$2x + 5y = 18$	Original equation.
$5y = 18 - 2x$	Subtract $2x$ from both sides.
$y = \dfrac{18 - 2x}{5}$	Divide both sides by 5.

 or $y = 3.6 - 0.4x$

 b.
$5x - 2y = -12$	Original equation.
$-2y = -12 - 5x$	Subtract $5x$ from both sides.
$y = \dfrac{-12 - 5x}{-2}$	Divide both sides by -2.
$y = \dfrac{12 - 5x}{2},$	

 or $y = 6 + 2.5x$

4. a. Let x represent years, and let y represent distance in meters. The Q-points are $(1964, 61.00)$ and $(1992, 68.82)$. The slope of the line through these points is about 0.28, so the equation is $y = 61.00 + 0.28(x - 1964)$ or

$y = 68.82 + 0.28(x - 1992)$. The slope, 0.28, means that the winning distance increases an average of 0.28 m, or 28 cm, each year. The y-intercept, -489 m, is meaningless in this situation because it would indicate that a negative distance was the winning distance in year 0. The model cannot predict that far from the data range.

 b. Using the equation $y = 61.00 + 0.28(x - 1964)$ with $x = 1912$ gives 46.44 m. The predicted distance is 1.23 m more than the actual distance of 45.21 m.

 c. To find the year using the equation $y = 61.00 + 0.28(x - 1964)$, solve $80 = 61.00 + 0.28(x - 1964)$.

$80 = 61.00 + 0.28(x - 1964)$	Original equation.
$19.00 = 0.28(x - 1964)$	Subtract 61.00 from both sides.
$67.86 \approx x - 1964$	Divide both sides by 0.28.
$2032 \approx x$	Add 1964 to both sides and round off.

 The model predicts that the winning distance will pass 80 m in the 2032 Summer Olympics.

5. a. Let x represent the distance from Los Angeles in miles, and let y represent elapsed time in minutes. The Q-points are $(411.5, 1439)$ and $(1181.5, 273)$. The slope of the line through these points is about -1.51, so the equation is $y = 1439 - 1.51(x - 411.5)$ or $y = 273 - 1.51(x - 1181.5)$. The slope means that the elapsed time increases 1.51 minutes each time the distance decreases by 1 mile.

 b. Approximately 1758 min, or 29 h 18 min, by the first equation, or approximately 1755 min, or 29 h 15 min, by the second equation.

 c. You can find this by solving $600 = 1439 - 1.51(x - 411.5)$ or $600 = 273 - 1.51(x - 1181.5)$. The first equation gives about 967 mi, and the second gives about 965 mi. Here is the solution for the first equation:

$600 = 1439 - 1.51(x - 411.5)$	Original equation.
$-839 = -1.51(x - 411.5)$	Subtract 1439 from both sides.
$555.6 \approx x - 411.5$	Divide both sides by -1.51.
$967.1 \approx x$	Add 411.5 to both sides.

 You are about 967 mi from Los Angeles.

Discovering Algebra Solutions Manual
©2007 Key Curriculum Press

6. a. $4t + 6\left(t - \dfrac{1}{2}\right) = 7$

b. $4t + 6\left(t - \dfrac{1}{2}\right) = 7$ Original equation.

$4t + 6t - 3 = 7$ Distributive property.

$10t - 3 = 7$ Add.

$10t = 10$ Add 3 to undo the subtraction.

$t = 1$ Divide by 10 to undo the multiplication.

Check: $4(1) + 6\left(1 - \dfrac{1}{2}\right) \overset{?}{=} 7$

$4 + 6(0.5) \overset{?}{=} 7$

$4 + 3 \overset{?}{=} 7$

$7 = 7$

Ellen jogged for 1 h and Eric jogged for $\dfrac{1}{2}$ h.

c. Let r represent the rate of the propeller airplane in km/h. Then $5r$ is the rate of the jet airplane.

$2.25(5r) - 2.25r = 1170$ Original equation.

$11.25r - 2.25r = 1170$ Multiply.

$9r = 1170$ Subtract.

$r = 130$ Divide by 9.

The velocity of the propeller airplane is 130 km/h; the velocity of the jet airplane is 5(130), or 650 km/h.

7. $\dfrac{50 \text{ grains}}{3.24 \text{ grams}} = \dfrac{x \text{ grains}}{1 \text{ gram}}$; 15.4321 grains per gram

8. The balance illustrates the equation $4x + 2 = x + 7$.

$4x + 2 = x + 7$ Original equation.

$4x - x + 2 = x - x + 7$ Subtract x from both sides.

$3x + 2 = 7$ Combine like terms.

$3x + 2 - 2 = 7 - 2$ Subtract 2 from both sides.

$3x = 5$ Combine like terms.

$\dfrac{3x}{3} = \dfrac{5}{3}$ Divide both sides by 3.

$x = \dfrac{5}{3}$, or $1.\overline{6}$ Reduce.

IMPROVING YOUR REASONING SKILLS

Here is a scatter plot of the data:

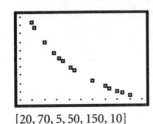

$[20, 70, 5, 50, 150, 10]$

This is the graph of an inverse variation, so the equation should be in the form $xy = k$ or $y = \dfrac{k}{x}$, where k is a constant. To find k, you can find the product of each pair of x- and y-values and calculate the mean. This gives $k = 3599.51 \approx 3600$, so the equation is $y = \dfrac{3600}{x}$. This equation fits the points very well.

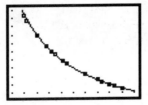

To predict the time a driver traveling 45 mi/h would need for the trip, substitute 45 for x. The result is about 80 min. To find the travel speed required to complete the trip in 70 min, substitute 70 for y and solve for x. The result is about 51.4 mi/h.

LESSON 4.8

Activity day: There are no answers for this lesson.

CHAPTER 4 Review

EXERCISES

1. $-3 = \dfrac{4 - 10}{x_2 - 2}$

$-3(x_2 - 2) = -6$

$x_2 - 2 = 2$

$x_2 = 4$

2. a. Slope: -3; y-intercept: -4

b. Slope: 2; y-intercept: 7

c. Slope: 3.8; y-intercept: -2.4

3. Line a has slope -1, y-intercept 1, and equation $y = 1 - x$.

Line b has slope 2, y-intercept -2, and equation $y = -2 + 2x$.

4. a. $y = 13.6(x - 1902) + 158.2$ Original equation.

$y = 13.6x - 25{,}867.2 + 158.2$ Distribute the 13.6.

$y = 13.6x - 25{,}709$ Add.

b. The y-coordinate of the point with x-coordinate 10 is -37. Using slope -5.2 and the point $(10, -37)$, you get the equation $y = -37 - 5.2(x - 10)$.

5. a. $(-4.5, -3.5)$

b. $y = 2x + 5.5$

c. $y = 2(x + 2.75)$; the x-intercept is -2.75.

d. The *x*-coordinate is 5.5. The equation is
$y = 16.5 + 2(x - 5.5)$.

e. Answers will vary. Possible methods are graphing, using a calculator table, and putting all equations in intercept form.

6. a. $4 + 2.8x = 51$

$2.8x = 47$

$x \approx 16.8$

b. $38 - 0.35x = 27$

$-0.35x = -11$

$x \approx 31.4$

c. $11 + 3(x - 8) = 41$

$3(x - 8) = 30$

$x - 8 = 10$

$x = 18$

d. $220 - 12.5(x - 6) = 470$

$-12.5(x - 6) = 250$

$x - 6 = -20$

$x = -14$

7. a. $y = 12{,}600 - 1{,}350x$

b. The slope is $-1{,}350$; the car's value decreases by $1,350 each year.

c. The *y*-intercept is 12,600; Karl paid $12,600 for the car.

d. The *x*-intercept is $9\frac{1}{3}$; in $9\frac{1}{3}$ years, the car will have no monetary value.

8. a. $43 = 30 + 0.375(x - 36)$

b. $x \approx 71$ s

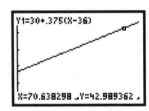

$[0, 80, 10, 0, 50, 10]$

c. $43 = 30 + 0.375(x - 36)$

$13 = 0.375(x - 36)$

$34.\overline{6} = x - 36$

$70.\overline{6} = x$

9. a. 1956, 1966, 1980, 1994, 2004; 1.76, 1.875, 1.97, 2.025, 2.06

b. The Q-points are (1966, 1.875) and (1994, 2.025).

c. $y = 1.875 + 0.00536(x - 1966)$ or
$y = 2.025 + 0.00536(x - 1994)$

d. Answers will vary. There are more points above the line than below the line.

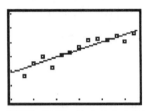

$[1950, 2005, 10, 1.6, 2.2, 0.1]$

e. Using $y = 1.875 + 0.00536(x - 1966)$, the predicted winning height for the year 2012 is 2.12 m.

10. a. $y = 2.25 + 0.13(x - 1976.5)$ or
$y = 4.025 + 0.13(x - 1990.5)$

b. The slope means that the minimum hourly wage increased about $0.13 per year.

c. Using $y = 2.25 + 0.13(x - 1976.5)$ with $x = 2010$ gives the prediction $6.61; using the equation $y = 4.025 + 0.13(x - 1990.5)$ gives the prediction $6.56.

d. Using $y = 2.25 + 0.13(x - 1976.5)$ with $y = 1.00$ gives the prediction 1967.

11. a. The equation is $y = a + bx$, where b is the slope and a is the *y*-intercept.

b. Use the points to find the slope. If the points are (x_1, y_1) and (x_2, y_2), then the slope is $\frac{y_2 - y_1}{x_2 - x_1} = b$. Use the slope and one of the points to write the equation. Using the point (x_1, y_1) gives the equation $y = y_1 + b(x - x_1)$.

TAKE ANOTHER LOOK

The rate of change of a curve (other than a straight line) is not constant. In general, you can't find the slope of a curve at a point by finding the slope of a line between two points on the curve, no matter how close together those points are. The average rate of change over the *x*-interval from 3 to 3.25 is not the same as from 3.25 to 3.5.

The average rate of change between the points (8, 1.5) and (8.5, 1.4) is -0.2. The average rate of change between (3, 4) and (3.5, 3.4) is -1.2. This tells us that the rate of change of the *y*-values is slower on the "wings" of the curve than at the portion of the graph nearest the origin.

The equation of the line through the points (8, 1.5) and (8.5, 1.4) is $y = 1.5 - 0.2(x - 8)$.

LESSON 5.1

EXERCISES

1. a. $(-15.6, 0.2)$ is a solution because
$47 + 3(-15.6) = 0.2$ and $8 + 0.5(-15.6) = 0.2$.

b. $(-4, 23)$ is not a solution because $23 \neq 12 + (-4)$.

c. $(2, 12.3)$ is not a solution because
$12.3 \neq 4.5 + 5(2)$. You can also tell that the
ordered pair is not a solution because the
equations represent parallel lines, which
never intersect.

2. a. For one of the lines, the y-values increase as the
x-values increase. For the other line, the y-values
decrease as the x-values increase. Only table iv fits
these conditions.

b. For both lines, the y-values increase as the x-values
increase. Only table iii fits these conditions.

c. One of the lines is horizontal, so the y-values are
constant. Only table i fits these conditions.

d. For both lines, the y-values decrease as the x-values
increase. Only table ii fits these conditions.

3. a. $(8, 7)$. This is an exact solution because it satisfies
both equations.

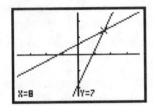

$[-18.8, 18.8, 5, -12.4, 12.4, 5]$

b. $(1.5, 0.5)$. This is an exact solution because it
satisfies both equations.

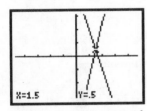

$[-4.7, 4.7, 1, -3.1, 3.1, 1]$

4. a. $(3.4, 15.5)$

X	Y1	Y2
3	14.5	17.9
3.1	14.75	17.3
3.2	15	16.7
3.3	15.25	16.1
3.4	15.5	15.5
3.5	15.75	14.9
3.6	16	14.3

X=3.4

b. $(7.3, -5.6)$

X	Y1	Y2
7	-5	-4.7
7.1	-5.2	-5
7.2	-5.4	-5.3
7.3	-5.6	-5.6
7.4	-5.8	-5.9
7.5	-6	-6.2
7.6	-6.2	-6.5

X=7.3

5. a. $y = 3 - 2x$. Substituting 1 for x gives
$y = 3 - 2(1) = 1$. Substituting $(1, 1)$ into the
original equation gives $4(1) + 2(1) = 6$. So,
$(1, 1)$ satisfies both forms of the equation.

b. $y = -4 + 0.4x$. Substituting 1 for x gives
$y = -4 + 0.4(1) = -3.6$. Substituting $(1, -3.6)$
into the original equation gives
$2(1) - 5(-3.6) = 20$. So, $(1, -3.6)$ satisfies both
forms of the equation.

6. a. Let P represent profit in dollars, and let N represent
the number of "hits." Profit is income minus
expenses. The income is the \$2.50 per "hit," and the
expenses are the \$12,000 spent on setup and
supplies. So, the equation for profit is
$P = 2.5N - 12,000$, or $P = -12,000 + 2.5N$.

b. P represents profit in dollars, and N represents
the number of "hits" to the website. \$5,000 is
Widget.kom's start-up cost, and \$1.60 is the
amount its advertisers pay per hit. Because
Widget.kom spent less in start-up costs, its website
might be less attractive to advertisers, hence the
lower rate.

c. When $N = 7778$, $P \approx 7445$ in both equations.

X	Y1	Y2
7775	7437.5	7440
7776	7440	7441.6
7777	7442.5	7443.2
7778	7445	7444.8
7779	7447.5	7446.4
7780	7450	7448
7781	7452.5	7449.6

X=7778

d. Graphing windows will vary. The graphs below
are in the window
$[0, 14100, 1000, -15000, 15000, 6000]$.

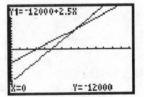

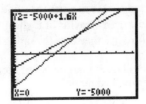

e. The intersection point is about (7778, 7445). This point can be found from the table. The point is fairly accurate. Substituting 7778 for *N* gives a *P*-value of 7445 in one equation and of 7444.8 in the other. These *P*-values are very close to each other.

f. The coordinates of the intersection point indicate that for 7778 hits, both companies make a profit of about $7,445.

7. a. $P = -5000 + 2.5N$

b.

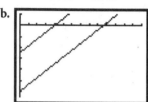

[0, 7000, 500, −13000, 2000, 2000]

c. The line for Sally's company (Gadget.kom) is parallel to and above the line for Gizmo.kom, indicating that Gadget.kom will always profit more than Gizmo.kom from the same number of hits.

d. To find the *x*-intercept, solve the equation $0 = -5000 + 2.5N$ to obtain $N = 2000$. This solution means that Sally will break even at 2000 hits, and after 2000 hits, Sally will have earned back her start-up cost.

8. a. The rate of change for University College is $30 per credit hour. The tuition for 1 credit is $55, so the fixed fees must be 55 − 30, or $25. So the equation for University College is $y = 25 + 30x$, where *x* is the number of credits and *y* is the tuition.

The rate of change for State College is $32 per credit hour. The tuition for 1 credit is $47, so the fixed fees must be 47 − 32, or $15. So, the equation for State College is $y = 15 + 32x$, where *x* is the number of credits and *y* is the tuition. The system is
$$\begin{cases} y = 25 + 30x \\ y = 15 + 32x \end{cases}$$

b. (5, 175). Check: $175 = 25 + 30(5)$, $175 = 15 + 32(5)$.

c. Answers will vary.

d. When a student takes 5 credit hours, the tuition at either college is $175.

e. For more than 5 credits, it is cheaper to attend University. For fewer than 5 credits, it is cheaper to attend State. For 5 credits, they cost the same.

9. a. $\begin{cases} d = 9 - t & \text{Drill team member's distance} \\ & \text{from 0 yd mark} \\ d = 3 + 0.5t & \text{Tuba player's distance from} \\ & \text{0 yd mark} \end{cases}$

b. (4, 5). After 4 s, the tuba player bumps into the drill team member at the 5 yd mark.

10. a. The equations give winning times of 28.239 min and 28.2398 min. The difference is 0.0008.

b. The equations give winning times of 26.7594 min and 26.7602 min. The difference is 0.0008.

c.

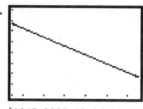

[1945, 2005, 10, 26, 30, 0.5]

d. $\begin{cases} y = 109.2882 - 0.0411x \\ y = 109.289 - 0.0411x \end{cases}$

The graph in 10c appears to show one line. However, the *y*-values are 0.0008 unit apart. Even though the two lines are not identical, they are well within the accuracy of the model, so you could say they represent the same model.

11. a. To have exactly one solution, the lines need to have different slopes, so *b* can have any value except −5, and *a* can have any value.

b. To have no solutions, the lines must be parallel— that is, they must have the same slope—but they must have different *y*-intercepts. So, *b* must be −5 and *a* can have any value but 2.

c. To have infinitely many solutions, the lines must be identical, so $a = 2$ and $b = -5$.

12. All answers are calculated using previous answers stored as unrounded values, and given with three- or four-place accuracy. Answers will vary slightly if intermediate rounding is used.

a. The length of a 5-lap race is 5(2.5 mi) = 12.5 mi.

Spirit of the Tri-Cities:
$$t = \frac{d}{r} = \frac{12.5 \text{ mi}}{145.000 \text{ mi/h}} \approx 0.0862 \text{ h}$$
Convert this time to minutes:
$$0.0862 \text{ h} \cdot \frac{60 \text{ min}}{1 \text{ h}} \approx 5.172 \text{ min.}$$

Miss B:
$$t = \frac{d}{r} = \frac{12.5 \text{ mi}}{163.162 \text{ mi/h}} \approx 0.0766 \text{ h}$$
Convert this time to minutes:
$$0.0766 \text{ h} \cdot \frac{60 \text{ min}}{1 \text{ h}} \approx 4.597 \text{ min.}$$

b. *Spirit of the Tri-Cities:* $5.172 \text{ min} \cdot \frac{4.3 \text{ gal}}{\text{min}} \approx$ 22.241 gal, using stored, unrounded values

Miss B: $4.597 \text{ min} \cdot \frac{4.3 \text{ gal}}{\text{min}} \approx 19.766$ gal, using stored, unrounded values

c. Use proportions to calculate the number of miles that each hydroplane can go on 43 gal of fuel.

Spirit of the Tri-Cities:

$\frac{12.5 \text{ mi}}{22.241 \text{ gal}} = \frac{x \text{ mi}}{43 \text{ gal}}$; $x \approx 24.167$. Or, because the hydroplane uses 4.3 gal/min, it can go 10 min on 43 gal. So, it can go $10 \text{ min} \cdot \frac{145.000 \text{ mi}}{1 \text{ h}} \cdot \frac{1 \text{ h}}{60 \text{ min}} \approx$ 24.167 mi on one tank of fuel.

Miss B: $\frac{12.5 \text{ mi}}{19.766 \text{ gal}} = \frac{x \text{ mi}}{43 \text{ gal}}$; $x \approx 27.194$, using stored, unrounded values. Or, in 10 min it can go $10 \text{ min} \cdot \frac{163.162 \text{ mi}}{1 \text{ h}} \cdot \frac{1 \text{ h}}{60 \text{ min}} \approx 27.194$ mi on one tank of fuel.

d. *Spirit of the Tri-Cities:* $\frac{12.5 \text{ mi}}{22.241 \text{ gal}} \approx 0.562$ mpg. Or, using dimensional analysis, $\frac{145.000 \text{ mi}}{1 \text{ h}} \cdot \frac{1 \text{ min}}{4.3 \text{ gal}} \cdot \frac{1 \text{ h}}{60 \text{ min}} \approx 0.562$ mpg.

Miss B: $\frac{12.5 \text{ mi}}{19.766 \text{ gal}} \approx 0.632$ mpg. Or, using dimensional analysis, $\frac{163.162 \text{ mi}}{1 \text{ h}} \cdot \frac{1 \text{ min}}{4.3 \text{ gal}} \cdot \frac{1 \text{ h}}{60 \text{ min}} \approx$ 0.632 mpg.

13. In 13a–e, other methods may be used.

a. $0.75x = 63.75$ Original equation.

$\frac{0.75x}{0.75} = \frac{63.75}{0.75}$ Divide both sides by 0.75.

$x = 85$

Check: $0.75(85) = 63.75$

b. $18.86 = -2.3x$ Original equation.

$\frac{18.86}{-2.3} = \frac{-2.3x}{-2.3}$ Divide both sides by -2.3.

$-8.2 = x$, or $x = -8.2$

Check: $18.86 = -2.3(-8.2)$

c. $6 = 12 - 2x$ Original equation.

$2x + 6 = 12$ Add $2x$ to both sides.

$2x = 6$ Subtract 6 from both sides.

$x = 3$ Divide both sides by 2.

Check: $6 \stackrel{?}{=} 12 - 2(3)$; $6 \stackrel{?}{=} 12 - 6$; $6 = 6$

d. $9 = 6(x - 2)$ Original equation.

$9 = 6x - 12$ Distributive property.

$21 = 6x$ Add 12 to both sides.

$x = \frac{21}{6} = \frac{7}{2}$, or 3.5

Check: $9 \stackrel{?}{=} 6(3.5 - 2)$; $9 \stackrel{?}{=} 6(1.5)$; $9 = 9$

e. $4(x + 5) - 8 = 18$ Original equation.

$4x + 20 - 8 = 18$ Distributive property.

$4x + 12 = 18$ Combine like terms.

$4x = 6$ Subtract 12 from both sides.

$x = \frac{6}{4} = \frac{3}{2}$, or 1.5

Check: $4(1.5 + 5) - 8 \stackrel{?}{=} 18$; $4(6.5) - 8 \stackrel{?}{=} 18$; $26 - 8 \stackrel{?}{=} 18$; $18 = 18$

14. The balance represents the equation $2x + 9 = 6x + 1$.

$2x + 9 = 6x + 1$ Original equation.

$2x - 2x + 9 = 6x - 2x + 1$ Subtract $2x$ from both sides.

$9 = 4x + 1$ Combine like terms.

$9 - 1 = 4x + 1 - 1$ Subtract 1 from both sides.

$8 = 4x$ Combine like terms.

$\frac{8}{4} = \frac{4x}{4}$ Divide both sides by 4.

$x = 2$ Reduce.

15. a. $\begin{bmatrix} 1 & -11 \\ -6 & 8 \end{bmatrix}$

b. $\begin{bmatrix} 13 & -1 \\ 7 & 8 \end{bmatrix}$

16. a. $y = 5x - 2$

b. $y = 0.8 - 1.4x$

c. $y = 1.5 + 3x$

IMPROVING YOUR GEOMETRY SKILLS

1.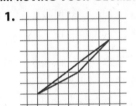

2.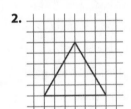

3.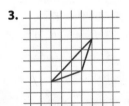

4.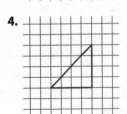

5. This is not possible; the sides would be parallel and therefore would never meet. The sides of a triangle must meet at a vertex.

EXERCISES

1. Stage 3: Add 2.5t to both sides. Stage 5: Divide both sides by 4.

2. a. $(-2, 34)$ is not a solution because it satisfies only the first equation.

b. $(4.25, 19.25)$ is a solution because $19.25 = 32 - 3(4.25)$ and $19.25 = 15 + 4.25$.

c. $(2, 12.3)$ is not a solution because it satisfies only the second equation. You can also tell that the ordered pair is not a solution because the equations represent parallel lines, which never intersect.

3. Solution steps will vary. Sample solutions are given.

a.
$14 + 2x = 4 - 3x$	Original equation.
$14 + 5x = 4$	Add 3x to both sides.
$5x = -10$	Subtract 14 from both sides.
$x = -2$	Divide both sides by 5.

b.
$7 - 2y = -3 - y$	Original equation.
$7 - y = -3$	Add y to both sides.
$-y = -10$	Subtract 7 from both sides.
$y = 10$	Multiply both sides by -1.

c.
$5d = 9 + 2d$	Original equation.
$3d = 9$	Subtract 2d from both sides.
$d = 3$	Divide both sides by 3.

d.
$12 + t = 4t$	Original equation.
$12 = 3t$	Subtract t from both sides.
$4 = t$	Divide both sides by 3.

4. Solution steps will vary. A sample solution is given.

$y = 25 + 30x$	Original first equation.
$15 + 32x = 25 + 30x$	Substitute $15 + 32x$ (from the second equation) for y.
$15 + 2x = 25$	Subtract 30x from both sides.
$2x = 10$	Subtract 15 from both sides.
$x = 5$	Divide both sides by 5.

To find y, substitute 5 for x in either equation: $y = 25 + 30(5) = 175$. The solution is $(5, 175)$. Check: $175 = 25 + 30(5)$, $175 = 15 + 32(5)$.

5. a. $5x + 2(4 - 3x) = 5x + 8 - 6x = -x + 8$

b. $7x - 2(4 - 3x) = 7x - 8 + 6x = 13x - 8$

6. Solution steps will vary. Sample solutions are given.

a.
$y = 4 - 3x$	Original first equation.
$2x - 1 = 4 - 3x$	Substitute $2x - 1$ (from the second equation) for y.
$-1 = 4 - 5x$	Subtract 2x from both sides.
$-5 = -5x$	Subtract 4 from both sides.
$1 = x$	Divide both sides by -1.

To find y, substitute 1 for x in either equation: $y = 4 - 3(1) = 1$. The solution is $(1, 1)$. Check: $1 = 4 - 3(1)$, $1 = 2(1) - 1$.

b. Solve the second equation for x: $x = 1 - 3y$. Now substitute $1 - 3y$ for x in the first equation and solve for y.

$2x - 2y = 4$	Original first equation.
$2(1 - 3y) - 2y = 4$	Substitute $1 - 3y$ for x.
$2 - 6y - 2y = 4$	Apply the distributive property.
$2 - 8y = 4$	Combine $-6y$ and $-2y$.
$-8y = 2$	Subtract 2 from both sides.
$y = -\dfrac{1}{4}$	Divide both sides by -8.

To find x, substitute $-\frac{1}{4}$ for y in either equation: $x + 3\left(-\frac{1}{4}\right) = 1$, so $x = 1 + \frac{3}{4} = \frac{7}{4}$. Check: $2(1.75) - 2(-0.25) = 4$, $1.75 + 3(-0.25) = 1$.

7. a. Solution steps will vary. A sample solution is given.

$P = -5{,}000 + 1.6N$	Original second equation.
$-12{,}000 + 2.5N = -5{,}000 + 1.6N$	Substitute $-12{,}000 + 2.5N$ for P.
$-12{,}000 + 0.9N = -5{,}000$	Subtract 1.6N from both sides.
$0.9N = 7{,}000$	Add 12,000 to both sides.
$N = \dfrac{70{,}000}{9} = 7{,}777\frac{7}{9}$	Multiply both sides by 10 and then divide both sides by 9.

To find P, substitute $\frac{70{,}000}{9}$ for N in either equation:

$$P = -12{,}000 + 2.5\left(\frac{70{,}000}{9}\right) = 7{,}444\frac{4}{9}$$

b. The approximate solution, $N \approx 7778$ and $P \approx 7445$, is more meaningful because it is not possible to have a fractional number of website hits.

8. a. The first equation states that the total admission price for two adults and three students is $13.50.

b. $\begin{cases} 2x + 3y = 13.50 \\ 3x + 2y = 16.50 \end{cases}$

First, solve the first equation for y.

$$2x + 3y = 13.50$$
$$2x + 3y - 2x = 13.50 - 2x$$
$$3y = 13.50 - 2x$$
$$\frac{3y}{3} = \frac{13.50 - 2x}{3}$$
$$y = \frac{13.50 - 2x}{3}$$

Substitute $\frac{13.50 - 2x}{3}$ for y in the second equation, and solve for x.

$$3x + 2y = 16.50$$

$$3x + 2\left(\frac{13.50 - 2x}{3}\right) = 16.50$$

$$3x + \frac{2(13.50 - 2x)}{3} = 16.50$$

$$\frac{9x}{3} + \frac{27 - 4x}{3} = 16.50$$

$$\frac{9x + 27 - 4x}{3} = 16.50$$

$$\frac{5x + 27}{3} = 16.50$$

$$5x + 27 = 49.50$$

$$5x = 22.5$$

$$x = 4.5$$

To find the corresponding y-value, substitute 4.5 for x in one of the two original equations.

$$2x + 3y = 13.50$$

$$2(4.5) + 3y = 13.50$$

$$9 + 3y = 13.50$$

$$3y = 4.50$$

$$y = 1.5$$

c. An adult ticket costs $4.50, and a student ticket costs $1.50.

9. a. $A + C = 200$ **b.** $8A + 4C = 1304$

c. The system is $\begin{cases} A + C = 200 \\ 8A + 4C = 1304 \end{cases}$. To solve this system, you could rewrite the first equation as $A = 200 - C$, and then substitute $200 - C$ for A in the second equation and solve for C. The solution to the system is $A = 126$ and $C = 74$. The theater sold 126 adult tickets and 74 child tickets.

10. a. The first walker starts at the 0.5 m mark and walks away at 0.75 m/s. The second walker starts at the 2.5 m mark and walks away at 0.75 m/s.

b. Both equations are already solved for d. Substitute $2.5 + 0.75t$ for d in the first equation.

$$2.5 + 0.75t = 0.5 + 0.75t$$

$$2.5 + 0.75t - 0.75t = 0.5 + 0.75t - 0.75t \qquad \text{Subtract } 0.75t \text{ from both sides.}$$

$$2.5 = 0.5 \qquad \text{Combine like terms.}$$

This false result indicates that the original system has no solution.

c. This means that the walkers will never meet.

11. a. $\begin{cases} d = 35 + 0.8t \\ d = 1.1t \end{cases}$; $t = 116\frac{2}{3}$, $d = 128\frac{1}{3}$. The pickup passes the sports car roughly 128 miles from Flint after approximately 117 minutes.

b. $\begin{cases} d = 220 - 1.2t \\ d = 1.1t \end{cases}$; $t \approx 95.7$, $d \approx 105.2$. The minivan meets the pickup truck about 105 miles from Flint after approximately 96 minutes.

c. $\begin{cases} d = 220 - 1.2t \\ d = 35 + 0.8t \end{cases}$; $t = 92.5$, $d = 109$. The minivan meets the sports car 109 miles from Flint after 92.5 minutes.

d. $220 - 1.2t = 2(35 + 0.8t)$; $t \approx 53.6$ min. The minivan is twice as far from Flint after about 53.6 minutes. At that time, the minivan is about 156 miles from Flint, and the sports car is about 78 miles from Flint.

12. a. Women:

The Q-points are (1976, 71.16) and (1996, 67.73).

This gives a slope of $\frac{67.73 - 71.16}{1996 - 1976} = \frac{-3.43}{20} = -0.1715$.

Line of fit: $y = 71.16 - 0.1715(x - 1976)$ or $y = 67.73 - 0.1715(x - 1996)$

Men:

The Q-points are (1976, 63.44) and (1996, 60.60).

This gives a slope of $\frac{60.60 - 63.44}{1996 - 1976} = \frac{-2.84}{20} = -0.142$.

Line of fit: $y = 63.44 - 0.142(x - 1976)$ or $y = 60.60 - 0.142(x - 1996)$

b. Form a system of equations from the first of each pair of equations given above for women and men:

$$\begin{cases} y = 71.16 - 0.1715(x - 1976) \\ y = 63.44 - 0.142(x - 1976) \end{cases}$$

To solve this system by substitution, substitute $63.44 - 0.142(x - 1976)$ for y in the first equation, and solve for x.

$$63.44 - 0.142(x - 1976) = 71.16 - 0.1715(x - 1976)$$

$$63.44 - 0.142x + 280.592 = 71.16 - 0.1715x + 338.884$$

$$344.032 - 0.142x = 410.044 - 0.1715x$$

$$0.0295x + 344.032 = 410.044$$

$$0.0295x = 66.012$$

$$x \approx 2238$$

Now, substitute 2238 for x in either of the original equations of the system, and solve for y.

$$y = 71.16 - 0.1715(x - 1976)$$

$$y = 71.16 - 0.1715(2238 - 1976)$$

$$y \approx 26.23$$

c.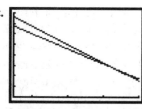

[1950, 2300, 100, 0, 80, 10]

d. The solution means that in the year 2238 (more than 200 years from now), both men and women will swim this race in 26.23 s. This is not likely. The model might be a good fit for the data, but extrapolating that far in the future produces predictions that are unlikely to come true.

13. Let x = the number of pounds of sour cherry worms, and let y = the number of pounds of sour lime bugs.

The total amount of candy in the mix is to be 20 lb, so $x + y = 20$.

The store manager's total cost of the mix is to be $65, so $2.50x + 3.50y = 65$.

Therefore, a system of equations that models this problem is

$$\begin{cases} x + y = 20 \\ 2.50x + 3.50y = 65 \end{cases}$$

To solve this system by the substitution method, first solve the first equation for y. (You could just as easily solve it for x.)

$y = 20 - x$

Substitute $20 - x$ for y in the second equation, and solve for x.

$2.50x + 3.50(20 - x) = 65$

$2.50x + 70 - 3.50x = 65$

$-x + 70 = 65$

$-x = -5$

$x = 5$

Now substitute 5 for x in the first original equation, and solve for y.

$x + y = 20$

$5 + y = 20$

$y = 15$

The manager should include 5 lb of sour cherry worms and 15 lb of sour lime bugs in the mix.

14. f represents liters of fruit juice, s represents liters of soda

$$\begin{cases} f + s = 10 \\ 0.65f + 0.05s = 0.33(10) \end{cases}$$

$f = 4\frac{2}{3}$, $s = 5\frac{1}{3}$; $4\frac{2}{3}$ L of bottled fruit juice and $5\frac{1}{3}$ L of natural orange soda

15. a. Every point on a horizontal line has the same y-coordinate, so the equation of a horizontal line through $(3, -4.5)$ is $y = -4.5$.

b. Every point on a vertical line has the same x-coordinate, so the equation of a vertical line through $(3, -4.5)$ is $x = 3$.

16. a. $\dfrac{520 \text{ ft}}{43 \text{ s}} \approx 12.1$ ft/s

b. $605 \text{ ft} \cdot \dfrac{1 \text{ s}}{12.1 \text{ ft}} \approx 50$ s

c. The initial height of the elevator is 100 ft and the elevator travels at 12.1 ft/s, so the equation for the height, y, after x seconds is $y = 100 + 12.1x$. To find the number of seconds it will take to get to the observation deck, solve the equation $520 = 100 + 12.1x$.

17. a. $2\frac{1}{6}$ **b.** $\frac{2}{3}$

c. $\frac{1}{6}$ **d.** $\frac{97}{60}$, or $1\frac{37}{60}$

18. a. i   **b.** iii   **c.** ii

LESSON 5.3

EXERCISES

1. a. $y = \dfrac{10 - 5x}{2}$, or $y = \dfrac{10}{2} - \dfrac{5}{2}x = 5 - \dfrac{5}{2}x$

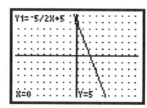

[-9.4, 9.4, 1, -6.2, 6.2, 1]

b. $y = \dfrac{30 - 15x}{6}$, or $y = \dfrac{30}{6} - \dfrac{15}{6}x = 5 - \dfrac{5}{2}x$

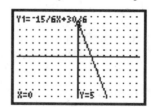

The graphs are the same because multiplying both sides of an equation by the same number results in an equivalent equation.

2. a. Substitute 6 for x and a for y and solve for a.

$5(6) - 2a = 10$

$30 - 2a = 10$

$-2a = -20$

$a = 10$

Discovering Algebra Solutions Manual
©2007 Key Curriculum Press

b. Substitute -4 for x and b for y and solve for b.

$$5(-4) - 2b = 10$$
$$-20 - 2b = 10$$
$$-2b = 30$$
$$b = -15$$

c. Substitute 25 for y and c for x and solve for c.

$$5c - 2(25) = 10$$
$$5c - 50 = 10$$
$$5c = 60$$
$$c = 12$$

d. Substitute -5 for y and d for x and solve for d.

$$5d - 2(-5) = 10$$
$$5d + 10 = 10$$
$$5d = 0$$
$$d = 0$$

3. a. Add the equations to eliminate x. You get $-5y = 5$, so $y = -1$. To find x, you can substitute -1 for y in either equation and solve for x. The result is $x = -\frac{5}{2}$, or -2.5. So, the solution is $(-2.5, -1)$.

b. You can eliminate y by multiplying the first equation by 2 and adding it to the second equation.

$$10x - 8y = 46$$
$$\underline{7x + 8y = 5}$$
$$17x = 51 \qquad \text{Add the equations.}$$
$$x = 3 \qquad \text{Divide by 17.}$$

So $x = 3$. To find y, substitute 3 for x in either equation and solve for y. The result is $y = -2$. So the solution is $(3, -2)$.

4. a. Substitution

b. Her solution is not complete. Although she correctly found the value of x, she did not substitute it into one of the original equations to find the value of y.

c. Substitute 4 for x in either of the two equations of the original system. In this case, it is easier to use the first equation.

$$y = x - 5$$
$$y = 4 - 5 = -1$$

The system has one solution, $(4, -1)$.

5. a. Multiply the first equation by -5 and the second equation by 3, or multiply the first equation by 5 and the second equation by -3.

b. Multiply the first equation by -8 and the second equation by 7, or multiply the first equation by 8 and the second equation by -7.

6. (1) You can solve both equations for y in terms of x. Then graph the resulting equations in the same window and locate the point of intersection.

(2) You can solve both equations for y in terms of x. Then make a calculator table of both equations and zoom in to find the x-value for which two y-values are the same.

(3) You can solve one equation for x in terms of y (or for y in terms of x) and then substitute the resulting expression for x (or for y) in the other equation.

(4) You can multiply both equations by numbers so that either the coefficients of x or the coefficients of y are opposites and then add the equations to eliminate a variable.

The solution is $(2, -2)$.

7. a. $(4, 2)$. Possible solution: Add the two equations to get $7x = 28$. Divide both sides by 7 to get $x = 4$. To find the value of y, substitute 4 for x in either equation. The result is $y = 2$.

b. $(3, -1)$. Possible solution: Subtract the second equation from the first to get $-2y = 2$. Divide both sides by -2 to get $y = -1$. To find the value of x, substitute -1 for y in either equation. The result is $x = 3$.

c. $(-3, -1)$. Possible solution: Subtract the second equation from the first to get $-3x = 9$. Divide both sides by -3 to get $x = -3$. To find the value of y, substitute -3 for x in either equation. The result is $y = -1$.

8.

a. $y = -3 + 0.5x$ **b.** $y = 2 - 0.75x$

c. Adding the two original equations gives $4x + 2y = 14$. Solving for y gives $y = 7 - 2x$. The graph of this equation intersects the other two lines at their intersection point.

d. The solution of the system is also a solution of the sum of the equations.

9. a. $y = 163 - x$ and $y = -33 + x$

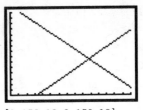

$[0, 150, 10, 0, 150, 10]$

b. Subtracting the second equation from the first gives $2y = 130$, so $y = 65$. The graph of this equation is shown as the horizontal line below.

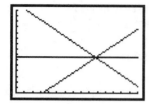

c. Adding the equations gives $2x = 196$, so $x = 98$. The graph of this equation is shown as the vertical line below.

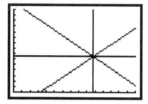

d. The four lines intersect at the same point, $(98, 65)$. The solution of the system is also a solution of the sum and difference of the equations.

10. Answers will vary. Substitute $(5, 2)$ for x and y in $4x + ay = b$ to get $20 + 2a = b$. Then find values of a and b that satisfy this equation. One possibility is $a = -3$ and $b = 14$, which gives the equation $4x - 3y = 14$.

11. a. The x-term can be eliminated either by multiplying the first equation by -3 or by multiplying the second equation by $-\frac{1}{3}$. If the first equation is multiplied by -3, the result will be $-6x + 15y = -36$.

b. Adding the equations $-6x + 15y = -36$ and $6x - 15y = 36$ gives $0 = 0$.

c. There are infinitely many solutions. (Any ordered pair that makes one of the equations in the original system true is a solution. These ordered pairs correspond to all points on the line with equation $2x - 5y = 12$.)

d. One equation is a multiple of the other.

12. a. First equation:

$$3x + 2y = 7$$

$\quad\quad 2y = 7 - 3x \quad\quad$ Subtract $3x$ from both sides.

$\quad\quad\quad y = 3.5 - 1.5x \quad$ Divide both sides by 2.

Second equation:

$$2x - y = 4$$

$\quad\quad -y = 4 - 2x \quad\quad$ Subtract $2x$ from both sides.

$\quad\quad\quad y = -4 + 2x \quad\quad$ Multiply both sides by -1.

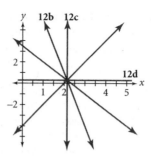

b. The sum of the two original equations is $5x + y = 11$. To solve this equation for y, subtract $5x$ from both sides to obtain $y = 11 - 5x$. This line passes through the point where the two original equations intersect.

c. Multiplying the second original equation by 2 gives $4x - 2y = 8$. Adding this new equation to the first original equation gives $7x = 15$. Solving this equation gives $x = \frac{15}{7}$. This vertical line passes through the point where the two original equations intersect.

d. Multiplying the first original equation by 2 gives $6x + 4y = 14$. Multiplying the second original equation by -3 gives $-6x + 3y = -12$. Adding these two new equations gives $7y = 2$. Solving this equation gives $y = \frac{2}{7}$. This horizontal line passes through the point where the two original equations intersect.

e. Combining the x-value found in 12c and the y-value found in 12d, the solution of the system is $\left(\frac{15}{7}, \frac{2}{7}\right)$. This is the intersection point of all the lines in 12a–d.

f. Answers will vary. If two equations intersect in a point, any combination of multiples of the two equations intersects in the same point. That's why the elimination method works.

13. a. $\begin{cases} w + p = 10 \\ 3.25w + 10.50p = 61.50 \end{cases}$

b. $w = 6$, $p = 4$. They bought 6 wallet-size pictures and 4 portrait-size pictures.

14. a. Let c represent gallons burned in the city and h represent gallons burned on the highway. Then the system is

$$\begin{cases} c + h = 11 \\ 17c + 25h = 220 \end{cases}$$

b. $c = 6.875$, $h = 4.125$. She used 6.875 gallons in the city and 4.125 gallons on the highway.

c. $\frac{17 \text{ mi}}{\text{gal}} \cdot 6.875 \text{ gal} = 116.875 \approx 117$ city mi; $\frac{25 \text{ mi}}{\text{gal}} \cdot 4.125 \text{ gal} = 103.125 \approx 103$ hwy mi

d. Check: $\begin{cases} 6.875 + 4.125 = 11 \\ 17(6.875) + 25(4.125) = 220 \\ 116.875 + 103.125 = 220 \end{cases}$

15. a. Possible answer: $\frac{5}{8}$ **b.** Possible answer: $\frac{3}{4}$

c. Possible answer: $-\frac{9}{40}$ **d.** Possible answer: $\frac{2}{3}$

Discovering Algebra Solutions Manual
©2007 Key Curriculum Press

e. Possible strategy: Rewrite the fractions with a common denominator. Then, write another fraction with the same denominator and with a numerator between the two numerators.

16. a. The rest station temperature is 14 degrees lower than the temperature at the start. The temperature falls 4 degrees for every 1000 feet, so the elevation must be $\frac{14}{4} \cdot 1000$, or 3500 feet higher than the start point. So, the elevation at the rest station is $4300 + 3500$, or 7800 feet.

The highest point is 7600 feet higher than the start, so the temperature must be $\frac{7600}{1000} \cdot 4$, or 30.4 degrees colder than at the start. The temperature at the highest point must be $78 - 30.4$, or 47.6 degrees.

b. The slope is $\frac{-4 \text{ degrees}}{1000 \text{ feet}}$, or -0.004 deg/ft. Using this slope and the point $(4300, 78)$ gives the equation $T = 78 - 0.004(E - 4300)$. In slope-intercept form, this is $T = 95.2 - 0.004E$.

The slope is the rate of change in temperature for each increase of 1 foot in elevation. The y-intercept (or here the T-intercept) is the temperature that day at sea level (an elevation of 0 feet).

c. $95.2 - 0.004(20,320)$, or about $13.9°F$

17. a. $y = -3 - 2(x - 5)$ b. $y = 7 + 2.5(x + 3)$

18. a. Walker A: $y = 0.5 + x$

Walker B: $y = 10.5$ when $x \le 1$ and $y = 10.5 - 0.5(x - 1)$, or $y = 11 - 0.5x$, when $x > 1$

b. To find the time and place where the walkers meet, form systems of equations from the individual equations for the two walkers.

For $x \le 1$, the system is

$$\begin{cases} y = 0.5 + x \\ y = 10.5 \end{cases}$$

The solution of this system is $(10, 10.5)$, but this isn't a solution for the problem because it does not satisfy the restriction $x \le 1$.

For $x > 1$, the system is

$$\begin{cases} y = 0.5 + x \\ y = 11 - 0.5x \end{cases}$$

The easiest way to solve this system is by the substitution method. Substituting $11 - 0.5x$ for y in the first equation gives $11 - 0.5x = 0.5 + x$, which leads to $x = 7$, which *does* satisfy the restriction $x > 1$. To find the corresponding value of y, substitute 7 for x in either of the original equations, giving $y = 7.5$. Therefore, the system has one solution, $(7, 7.5)$. This means that the two walkers meet 7.5 ft from the sensor, when 7 s have passed.

c. Walker B is farther from the sensor than Walker A for all times up to, but not including, 7 s.

LESSON 5.4

EXERCISES

1. a. $\begin{cases} 2x + 1.5y = 12.75 \\ -3x + 4y = 9 \end{cases}$ b. $\begin{cases} \frac{1}{2}x = \frac{1}{2} \\ -x + 2y = 0 \end{cases}$

   c. $\begin{cases} 2x + 3y = 1 \\ 2y = 0 \end{cases}$

2. a. $\begin{bmatrix} 1 & 4 & 3 \\ -1 & 2 & 9 \end{bmatrix}$ b. $\begin{bmatrix} 7 & -1 & 3 \\ 0.1 & -2.1 & 3 \end{bmatrix}$

   c. $\begin{bmatrix} 1 & 1 & 3 \\ 1 & 1 & 6 \end{bmatrix}$

3. a. $(8.5, 2.8)$ b. $\left(\frac{1}{2}, \frac{13}{16}\right)$ c. $(0, 0)$

4. Divide row 1 by 4.2. $\begin{bmatrix} 1 & 0 & 3 \\ 0 & -1 & 5.25 \end{bmatrix}$

   Multiply row 2 by -1. $\begin{bmatrix} 1 & 0 & 3 \\ 0 & 1 & -5.25 \end{bmatrix}$

   The solution is $(3, -5.25)$.

5. a. $\begin{cases} 3x + y = 7 \\ 2x + y = 21 \end{cases}$ b. $\begin{bmatrix} 3 & 1 & 7 \\ 2 & 1 & 21 \end{bmatrix}$

6.

Description	Matrix	System Equations
The matrix for $\begin{cases} 3x + 2y = 28.9 \\ 8x + 5y = 74.6 \end{cases}$	$\begin{bmatrix} 3 & 2 & 28.9 \\ 8 & 5 & 74.6 \end{bmatrix}$	
Add 8 times row 1 to -3 times row 2 and put the result in row 2.	$\begin{bmatrix} 3 & 2 & 28.9 \\ 0 & 1 & 7.4 \end{bmatrix}$	Row 3: $3x + 2y = 28.9$ $y = 7.4$
Add -2 times row 2 to row 1 and put the result in row 1.	$\begin{bmatrix} 3 & 0 & 14.1 \\ 0 & 1 & 7.4 \end{bmatrix}$	Row 4: $3x = 14.1$ $y = 7.4$
Divide row 1 by 3.	$\begin{bmatrix} 1 & 0 & 4.7 \\ 0 & 1 & 7.4 \end{bmatrix}$	Row 5: $x = 4.7$ $y = 7.4$

The solution is $(4.7, 7.4)$.

7. a.

	Adults	Children	Total (kg)
Monday	40	15	10.8
Tuesday	35	22	12.29

b. Let x represent the average weight of chips an adult eats and y represent the average weight of chips a child eats. The system is

$$\begin{cases} 40x + 15y = 10.8 \\ 35x + 22y = 12.29 \end{cases}$$

c. $\begin{bmatrix} 40 & 15 & 10.8 \\ 35 & 22 & 12.29 \end{bmatrix}$

d. Solution steps will vary.

Add -35 times row 1 to 40 times row 2 and put the result in row 2.
$$\begin{bmatrix} 40 & 15 & 10.8 \\ 0 & 355 & 113.6 \end{bmatrix}$$

Divide row 2 by 355.
$$\begin{bmatrix} 40 & 15 & 10.8 \\ 0 & 1 & 0.32 \end{bmatrix}$$

Add -15 times row 2 to row 1.
$$\begin{bmatrix} 40 & 0 & 6 \\ 0 & 1 & 0.32 \end{bmatrix}$$

Divide row 1 by 40.
$$\begin{bmatrix} 1 & 0 & 0.15 \\ 0 & 1 & 0.32 \end{bmatrix}$$

e. Each adult ate an average of about 0.15 kg (150 g) of chips, and each child ate an average of 0.32 kg (320 g) of chips.

8.

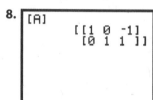

```
[A]
    [[1 0 -1]
     [0 1  1 ]]
```

9. a. Let x represent the number of small trucks and y represent the number of large trucks. The system is $\begin{cases} 5x + 12y = 532 \\ 7x + 4y = 284 \end{cases}$.

b. $\begin{bmatrix} 5 & 12 & 532 \\ 7 & 4 & 284 \end{bmatrix}$

c. Solution steps will vary.

Add 7 times row 1 to -5 times row 2 and put the result in row 2.
$$\begin{bmatrix} 5 & 12 & 532 \\ 0 & 64 & 2304 \end{bmatrix}$$

Divide row 2 by 64.
$$\begin{bmatrix} 5 & 12 & 532 \\ 0 & 1 & 36 \end{bmatrix}$$

Subtract 12 times row 2 from row 1.
$$\begin{bmatrix} 5 & 0 & 100 \\ 0 & 1 & 36 \end{bmatrix}$$

Divide row 1 by 5.
$$\begin{bmatrix} 1 & 0 & 20 \\ 0 & 1 & 36 \end{bmatrix}$$

d. Zoe should order 20 small trucks and 36 large trucks.

10. a. The variable x represents the number of grams of flour X that are used in each loaf. The variable y represents the number of grams of flour Y that are used in each loaf. The first equation adds the amount of each kind of flour (in grams) to get the total amount of flour in the loaf. The second equation adds the amounts of calcium (in milligrams) contributed by each kind of flour to get the total amount of calcium.

b. $\begin{bmatrix} 1 & 1 & 300 \\ 0.12 & 0.04 & 30 \end{bmatrix}$

c. Solution steps will vary.

Add -0.12 times row 1 to row 2.
$$\begin{bmatrix} 1 & 1 & 300 \\ 0 & -0.08 & -6 \end{bmatrix}$$

Divide row 2 by -0.08.
$$\begin{bmatrix} 1 & 1 & 300 \\ 0 & 1 & 75 \end{bmatrix}$$

Subtract row 2 from row 1.
$$\begin{bmatrix} 1 & 0 & 225 \\ 0 & 1 & 75 \end{bmatrix}$$

d. Will should mix 225 g of flour X with 75 g of flour Y.

11. a. $\begin{cases} m + t + w = 286 \\ m - t \quad\;\; = 7 \\ \quad\; t - w = 24 \end{cases}$

b. $\begin{bmatrix} 1 & 1 & 1 & 286 \\ 1 & -1 & 0 & 7 \\ 0 & 1 & -1 & 24 \end{bmatrix}$

The rows represent each equation. The columns represent the coefficients of each variable and the constants.

c. Solution steps will vary.

Subtract row 1 from row 2.
$$\begin{bmatrix} 1 & 1 & 1 & 286 \\ 0 & -2 & -1 & -279 \\ 0 & 1 & -1 & 24 \end{bmatrix}$$

Divide row 2 by -2.
$$\begin{bmatrix} 1 & 1 & 1 & 286 \\ 0 & 1 & 0.5 & 139.5 \\ 0 & 1 & -1 & 24 \end{bmatrix}$$

Subtract row 2 from row 3.
$$\begin{bmatrix} 1 & 1 & 1 & 286 \\ 0 & 1 & 0.5 & 139.5 \\ 0 & 0 & -1.5 & -115.5 \end{bmatrix}$$

Divide row 3 by -1.5.
$$\begin{bmatrix} 1 & 1 & 1 & 286 \\ 0 & 1 & 0.5 & 139.5 \\ 0 & 0 & 1 & 77 \end{bmatrix}$$

Subtract row 2 from row 1.
$$\begin{bmatrix} 1 & 0 & 0.5 & 146.5 \\ 0 & 1 & 0.5 & 139.5 \\ 0 & 0 & 1 & 77 \end{bmatrix}$$

Add -0.5 times row 3 to row 1 and row 2.
$$\begin{bmatrix} 1 & 0 & 0 & 108 \\ 0 & 1 & 0 & 101 \\ 0 & 0 & 1 & 77 \end{bmatrix}$$

d. They cycled 108 km on Monday, 101 km on Tuesday, and 77 km on Wednesday.

12. a. $\begin{bmatrix} 72 & 65 \\ 55 & 55 \\ 45 & 35 \end{bmatrix} - \begin{bmatrix} 31 & 28 \\ 26 & 24 \\ 21 & 16 \end{bmatrix} = \begin{bmatrix} 41 & 37 \\ 29 & 31 \\ 24 & 19 \end{bmatrix}$

b. If you are planning to be in the park for 3 days, then the 3-day ticket is a much better deal. The matrix showing the costs for three 1-day tickets is

$$3 \cdot \begin{bmatrix} 31 & 28 \\ 26 & 24 \\ 21 & 16 \end{bmatrix} = \begin{bmatrix} 93 & 84 \\ 78 & 72 \\ 21 & 48 \end{bmatrix}$$

Discovering Algebra Solutions Manual
©2007 Key Curriculum Press

c. The matrix showing the costs for two 1-day tickets is

$$2 \cdot \begin{bmatrix} 31 & 28 \\ 26 & 24 \\ 21 & 16 \end{bmatrix} = \begin{bmatrix} 62 & 56 \\ 52 & 48 \\ 42 & 32 \end{bmatrix}$$

These costs are less than the costs of the 3-day tickets, so if you are going for 2 days, you should buy two 1-day tickets.

13. a. 4 ENTER, Ans − 0.5, ENTER, ENTER, ...

   b. −3 ENTER, Ans + 2, ENTER, ENTER, ...

   c. 0.5 ENTER, Ans − 1, ENTER, ENTER, ...

   d. 0 ENTER, Ans + 1, ENTER, ENTER, ...

14. a. The slope is 0.75, which is the cost per drink once you've bought the mug.

   b. $y = 49.75 + 0.75(x - 33)$

   c. $y = 25 + 0.75x$. The y-intercept is the cost of buying the mug.

15. Represent the system with a column matrix.

$$\begin{bmatrix} 1 & 3 \\ -2 & 1 \\ 3 & 23 \end{bmatrix}$$

Biancheng: Multiply the left column by 3 (the top number in the right column).

$$\begin{array}{ccc} 3(1) & \rightarrow & 3 \\ 3(-2) & \rightarrow & -6 \\ 3(3) & \rightarrow & 9 \end{array}$$

Zhichu: Subtract the right column from the left column once.

$$\begin{array}{ccc} 3 - 3 & \rightarrow & 0 \\ -6 - 1 & \rightarrow & -7 \\ 9 - 23 & \rightarrow & -14 \end{array}$$

Write a new equation and solve for y: $-7y = -14$, or $y = 2$.

Substitute and solve for x: $x - 2(2) = 3$, or $x = 7$.

LESSON 5.5

EXERCISES

1. a. Multiply by 4; $12 < 28$

   b. Multiply by −3; $-15 \geq -36$

   c. Add −10; $-14 \geq x - 10$

   d. Subtract 8; $b - 5 > 7$

   e. Divide by 3; $8d < 10\frac{2}{3}$

   f. Divide by −3; $-8x \geq -10\frac{2}{3}$

2. a. Answers will vary, but the values must be > 8.

   b. Answers will vary, but the values must be > -7.

   c. Answers will vary, but the values must be < 7.92.

   d. Answers will vary, but the values must be $< \frac{120}{13} = 9\frac{3}{13} \approx 9.2308$.

3. a. $x \leq -1$ **b.** $x > 0$ **c.** $x \geq -2$

   d. $-2 < x < 1$ **e.** $0 < x \leq 2$

4. a. $3 > x$ **b.** $y \geq -2$ **c.** $z \leq 12$ **d.** $n \leq 7$

5. a. $y = \dfrac{5.2 - 3x}{4} = 1.3 - 0.75x$

   b. $y = \dfrac{2x}{3} + 5$, or $\dfrac{2x + 15}{3}$

6. Solution steps may vary.

   a.
$4.1 + 3.2x > 18$	Original inequality.
$3.2x > 13.9$	Subtract 4.1 from both sides.
$x > 4.34375 = \dfrac{139}{32}$	Divide both sides by 3.2.

   b.
$7.2 - 2.1b < 4.4$	Original inequality.
$-2.1b < -2.8$	Subtract 7.2 from both sides.
$b > 1.\overline{3}$	Divide both sides by −2.1 and reverse the inequality symbol.

   c.
$7 - 2(x - 3) \geq 25$	Original inequality.
$7 - 2x + 6 \geq 25$	Apply the distributive property.
$-2x + 13 \geq 25$	Add.
$-2x \geq 12$	Subtract 13 from both sides.
$x \leq -6$	Divide both sides by −2 and reverse the inequality symbol.

   d.
$11.5 + 4.5(x + 1.8) \leq x$	Original inequality.
$11.5 + 4.5x + 8.1 \leq x$	Apply the distributive property.
$19.6 + 4.5x \leq x$	Add.
$19.6 \leq -3.5x$	Subtract 4.5x from both sides.
$-5.6 \geq x$ or $x \leq -5.6$	Divide both sides by −3.5 and reverse the inequality symbol.

7. a.
$3x - 2 \leq 7$	Original inequality.
$3x \leq 9$	Add 2 to both sides.
$x \leq 3$	Divide both sides by 3.

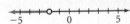

   b.
$4 - x > 6$	Original inequality.
$-x > 2$	Subtract 4 from both sides.
$x < -2$	Divide both sides by −1 and reverse the inequality symbol.

   c.
$3 + 2x \geq -3$	Original inequality.
$2x \geq -6$	Subtract 3 from both sides.
$x \geq -3$	Divide both sides by 2.

d. $10 \le 2(5 - 3x)$ Original inequality.

$10 \le 10 - 6x$ Apply the distributive property.

$0 \le -6x$ Subtract 10 from both sides.

$0 \ge x$, or $x \le 0$ Divide both sides by -6 and reverse the inequality symbol.

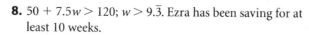

8. $50 + 7.5w > 120$; $w > 9.\overline{3}$. Ezra has been saving for at least 10 weeks.

9. a. Add 3 to both sides; $4 < 5$.

    b. Divide both sides by 2 (or multiply by 0.5); $3 > 1$.

    c. Multiply both sides by -3; $3 > -3$.

    d. Multiply both sides by 2; $0 < 6$.

10. a. $-9 < 9$ is true.

    b. $21 \ge 51$ is false.

    c. $7 < 7$ is false.

    d. $24 \ge 18$ is true.

11. a. $2x - 3 > 5x - 3x + 3$ Original inequality.

$2x - 3 > 2x + 3$ Combine like terms.

$-3 > 3$ Subtract $2x$ from both sides.

Because $-3 > 3$ is never true, the inequality has no solutions. The graph would be an empty number line, with no values marked.

b. $-2.2(5x + 3) \ge -11x - 15$ Original inequality.

$-11x - 6.6 \ge -11x - 15$ Apply the distributive property.

$-6.6 \ge -15$ Add $11x$ to both sides.

Because $-6.6 \ge -15$ is always true, every number is a solution.

12. $2.834 - 0.002 \le x \le 2.834 + 0.002$

$2.832 \le x \le 2.836$ m

13. a. $d \le 30$, where d is the number of dollars spent on CDs

    b. $h \ge 48$, where h is the height of a rider

    c. $p \ge 3$, where p is the number of people in a carpool

    d. $a \ge 17$, where a is the age of a person who will be admitted

14. a. When is the sports car 131 or more miles away from Flint?

b. $35 + 0.8x \ge 131$ Original inequality.

$35 + 0.8x - 35 \ge 131 - 35$ Subtract 35 from both sides of the inequality.

$0.8x \ge 96$ Evaluate.

$\dfrac{0.8x}{0.8} \ge \dfrac{96}{0.8}$ Divide both sides by 0.8.

$x \ge 120$ Evaluate.

The sports car is at least 131 miles from Flint when it has been traveling for at least 2 hours.

c. When is the minivan closer than the sports car to Flint?

d. $220 - 1.2x < 35 + 0.8x$ Original equation

$220 - 1.2x - 220 < 35 + 0.8x - 220$ Subtract 220 from both sides.

$-1.2x < -185 + 0.8x$ Evaluate.

$-1.2x - 0.8x < -185 + 0.8x - 0.8x$ Subtract $0.8x$ from both sides.

$-2.0x < -185$ Combine like terms.

$\dfrac{-2.0x}{-2.0} > \dfrac{-185}{-2.0}$ Divide both sides by -2.0, and reverse the inequality symbol.

$x > 92.5$ Evaluate.

The minivan is closer than the sports car to Flint after 1 h 32 min 30 s.

15. $0 \le 8 - 0.25x < 5$ Original inequality.

$-8 \le -0.25x < -3$ Subtract 8 from all parts.

$32 \ge x > 12$ Divide by -0.25 and reverse the inequalities.

Erin woke up between 13 and 32 times, inclusive.

16. a. Multiply 12 by 3.2 to get 38.4. Subtract 38.4 from 72 to get 33.6.

    b. Square 5 to get 25. Subtract 25 from 3 to get -22. Multiply -22 by 1.5 to get -33. Add -33 to 2 to get -31.

    c. Divide 21 by 7 to get 3 and divide 6 by 2 to get 3. Subtract 3 from 3 to get 0.

Discovering Algebra Solutions Manual
©2007 Key Curriculum Press

17. a. 0.37 $\boxed{\text{ENTER}}$
Ans $+$ 0.23 $\boxed{\text{ENTER}}$, $\boxed{\text{ENTER}}$, ...

Weight (oz)	Rate ($)
1	0.37
2	0.60
3	0.83
4	1.06
5	1.29
6	1.52
7	1.75
8	1.98
9	2.21
10	2.44
11	2.67

b.

Postage Costs

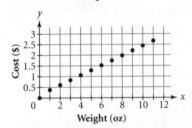

c. A line would mean that the cost would pass through each amount between the different increments. For example, if a package weighed 0.5 oz, you would pay $0.185. The line is not a useful way to show the costs because the cost increases discretely. Instead, you could draw segments for each whole ounce. Note the open and closed circles.

Postage Costs

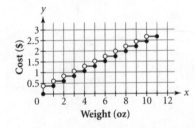

d. Because the postal rates are for ounces or fractions of ounces, the price for a 10.5 oz parcel is the same as that for an 11 oz parcel, which the table in 17a shows to be $2.67.

Without this table or using the routine, this price can also be calculated from the given U.S. postal rates: The price will be $0.37 for the first ounce + $0.23 for each of the 10 additional ounces, which is $0.37 + 10($0.23) = $2.67.

18. a. $-2(x + 8) = (-2)(x) + (-2)(8) = -2x - 16$
b. $4(0.75 - y) = 4(0.75) + 4(-y) = 3 - 4y$
c. $-(z - 5) = -1(z - 5) = (-1)(z) + (-1)(-5)$
    $= -z + 5$

LESSON 5.6

EXERCISES

1. a. iii   **b.** ii   **c.** i   **d.** iv

2. a. $84x + 7y \geq 70$ Original inequality.
    $7y \geq -84x + 70$ Add $-84x$ to both sides.
    $y \geq -12x + 10$ Divide both sides by 7.

b. $4.8x - 0.12y < 7.2$ Original inequality.
    $-0.12y < -4.8x + 7.2$ Add $-4.8x$ to both sides.
    $y > 40x - 60$ Divide both sides by -0.12 and reverse the inequality symbol.

3. a.

b.

c.

d.

4. a.–c.

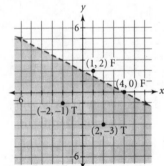

5. a.–c.

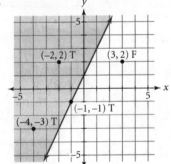

6. a.

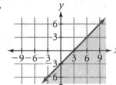

b.

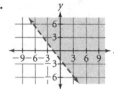

c.

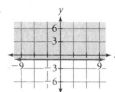

d.

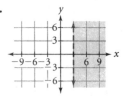

c.

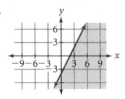

7. a. $y \le 1 - 2x$ **b.** $y < -2 + \frac{2}{3}x$

c. $y > 1 - 0.5x$ **d.** $y \ge -2 + \frac{1}{3}x$

e. $y \le 2$ **f.** $x < 2$

8. a.
$$3x - 2y = 6$$
$$3x - 2y - 3x = 6 - 3x$$
$$-2y = 6 - 3x$$
$$\frac{-2y}{-2} = \frac{6 - 3x}{-2}$$
$$y = -3 + 1.5x$$

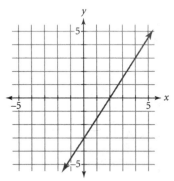

b. $(1, 3)$: $3(1) - 2(3) \le 6 \rightarrow -3 \le 6 \rightarrow$ True

$(1, -3)$: $3(1) - 2(-3) \le 6 \rightarrow 9 \le 6 \rightarrow$ False

The point $(1, 3)$ makes the statement true. Because $(1, 3)$ is above the line, you should shade above the line.

c. If the coefficient of y is negative, then shade the side opposite of what is indicated by the inequality symbol.

9. a.

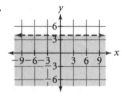

b.

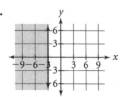

10. a. $F + 2S < 84$

b. $F + 2S = 84$

c.

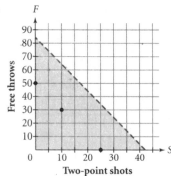

d. Answers will vary. One possible answer, indicated by dots on the graph, is $(0, 50)$, $(10, 30)$, and $(25, 0)$.

11.

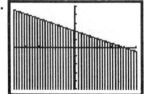

$[-5, 5, 1, -5, 5, 1]$

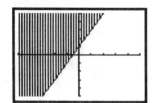

12. a. and **d.**

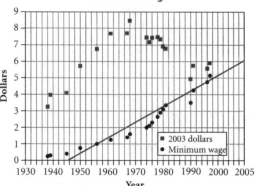

b. The data for minimum wage is more linear than the data for equivalent dollars.

Discovering Algebra Solutions Manual
©2007 Key Curriculum Press

c. Using the Q-points (1956, 1.00) and (1981, 3.35), the equation is
$y = 3.35 + 0.094(x - 1981)$,
or $y = 1.00 + 0.094(x - 1956)$,
or $y = -182.864 + 0.094x$.

e. The minimum wage has increased 9¢ every year on average. The actual dollar value was highest in 1968 and has decreased almost every year since then.

13. a. About 27 mi/h

b. Possible explanation: Because $d = r \cdot t$, and the distance was the same for both Ellie and her grandmother, you can set the product of rate and time for Ellie equal to the product of rate and time for her grandmother. If you let r represent Ellie's grandmother's speed, then $2.5(65) = 6r$.

14. a. $y = \frac{7}{3}x - \frac{22}{3}$

b. $y = -\frac{5}{4}x - 3$

IMPROVING YOUR VISUAL THINKING SKILLS

• Three planes intersect in only one point if each pair of planes intersects in a line and the three lines intersect in one point. Such a system has one solution.

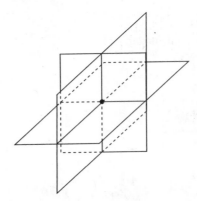

• If a system has an infinite number of solutions, the three equations might represent the same plane, but they might also represent planes that intersect in a line.

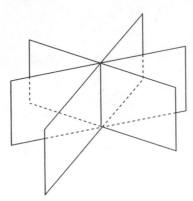

• If a system has no solutions, two of the planes might be parallel. Or two of the planes might intersect in a line and the third plane might be parallel to the line of intersection of the first two planes.

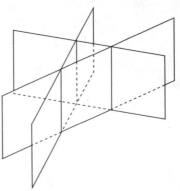

LESSON 5.7

EXERCISES

1. a. iii   **b.** i   **c.** ii

2. a. Yes. (1, 2) satisfies both inequalities.

b. No. $2 > 3$ is not true, so the first inequality is not satisfied.

c. No. $\frac{4}{3} > \frac{4}{3}$ is not true, so neither inequality is satisfied.

d. No. Because both $-3 > 5$ and $-3 > 2 - \frac{1}{2}(5)$ are false, neither inequality is satisfied.

3. a. $y \geq -x + 2$; $y \geq x - 2$

b.

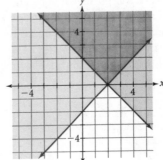

4. a.

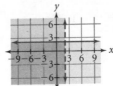

b.

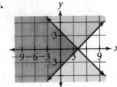

5. $\begin{cases} y > 2 - x \\ y < 2 \\ x < 3 \end{cases}$

6. a. The three inequalities are $y \geq -1250 + 0.40x$, $y \leq -1250 + 1.00x$, and $x \geq 0$.

b.

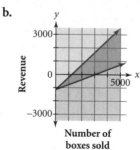

7. a. $\begin{cases} A \leq C \\ A + C \leq 75 \\ A \geq 0 \\ C \geq 0 \end{cases}$

b. All the points in the dark-shaded triangular region satisfy the system of inequalities. The point (50, 10) represents the situation in which 50 children escort 10 adults.

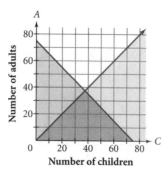

c. Answers will vary. It is possible to have all children and no adults at the restaurant. One possible additional constraint is that there must be at least one adult per five children, or $A \geq \frac{1}{5}C$. The solution for this set of constraints is shown below.

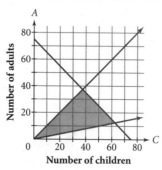

8. a. $r = 220 - a$, where a represents age in years and r represents the heart rate in beats per minute.

b. $\begin{cases} r \leq 0.90(220 - a) \\ r \geq 0.55(220 - a) \end{cases}$ or $\begin{cases} r \leq 198 - 0.09a \\ r \geq 121 - 0.55a \end{cases}$

c.

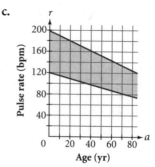

d. $a \geq 14$ and $a \leq 40$

e.

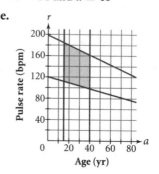

9. $x \geq 3$ and $y \geq -2 + \frac{1}{2}x$

10. $AB: y \leq \frac{2}{3}x + \frac{5}{3}$; $BC: y \leq -\frac{3}{5}x + \frac{59}{5}$;
$AC: y \geq \frac{1}{11}x + \frac{31}{11}$

11. The region is a pentagon.

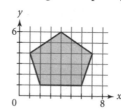

12. Region 1: $\begin{cases} y \geq 3 \\ y \geq x - 2 \\ y \leq \frac{1}{3}x + \frac{8}{3} \end{cases}$ Region 2: $\begin{cases} y \leq 3 \\ y \leq x - 2 \\ y \geq \frac{1}{3}x \end{cases}$

13. a. $713.15

b. $957.80

14. a. 4

b. 10

c. $\frac{10[(3x + 12) \div 5 - 1.4] - 10}{6}$, which simplifies to x.

15. a. $x = 6$, $y = 21$

b. $x = -2$, $y = -1$

Discovering Algebra Solutions Manual
©2007 Key Curriculum Press

16. Sample solution: Let p represent the concentration of acid in the pickling vinegar.

$$8(0.05) + 20p = 28(0.15)$$
$$p = 0.19$$

The acid concentration of the pickling vinegar is 19%.

IMPROVING YOUR REASONING SKILLS

Crows	Cries
9	729
99	970,299
999	997,002,999
9,999	999,700,029,999
99,999	999,970,000,299,999

The TI-84 Plus calculator begins rounding at 9,999 crows.

CHAPTER 5 Review

EXERCISES

1. Line a: $y = 1 - x$; line b: $y = 3 + \frac{5}{2}x$. To find the intersection point, you can solve the system using substitution:

$$y = 3 + \frac{5}{2}x \qquad \text{Original equation for line } b.$$

$$1 - x = 3 + \frac{5}{2}x \qquad \begin{array}{l}\text{Substitute } 1 - x \text{ (from the line } a \\ \text{equation) for } y.\end{array}$$

$$-2 - x = \frac{5}{2}x \qquad \text{Subtract 3 from both sides.}$$

$$-2 = \frac{7}{2}x \qquad \text{Add } x \text{ to both sides.}$$

$$-\frac{4}{7} = x \qquad \text{Multiply both sides by } \frac{2}{7}.$$

Using the equation for line a, $y = 1 - \left(-\frac{4}{7}\right) = \frac{11}{7}$.
So, the point of intersection is $\left(-\frac{4}{7}, \frac{11}{7}\right)$.

2. One way to find the point of intersection is to solve the system by elimination. Adding the equations gives $4x = 16$, so $x = 4$. Substituting 4 for x in either equation gives $y = 1$. So, the point of intersection is $(4, 1)$. Check: $3(4) - 2(1) = 10$, $(4) + 2(1) = 6$.

3. The point of intersection is $(3.75, 4.625)$.

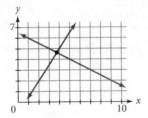

4. Solution steps may vary.

$16 + 4.3(x - 5)$ $= -7 + 4.2x$	Set the right sides of the equations equal to each other.
$16 + 4.3x - 21.5$ $= -7 + 4.2x$	Apply the distributive property.
$-5.5 + 4.3x$ $= -7 + 4.2x$	Subtract.
$0.1x = -1.5$	Add $-4.2x$ and 5.5 to both sides.
$x = -15$	Divide both sides by 0.1.
$y = -7 + 4.2(-15)$	Substitute -15 for x in the second equation and find y.
$y = -70$	Multiply and add.

The solution is $x = -15$ and $y = -70$.

5. a. The lines have the same slope but different y-intercepts (the lines are parallel).

 b. The slopes are the same and the intercepts are the same (the equations represent the same line).

 c. The lines have different slopes (the lines intersect in a single point).

6. a. $x > -1$

 b. $x < 2$

 c. $-2 \le x < 1$

7. $x \le -1$

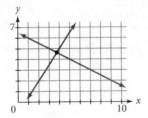

8. $\begin{cases} y \le x + 4 \\ y \le -1.25x + 8.5 \\ y \ge 1 \end{cases}$

9. a. $\dfrac{15 \text{ m} \times 12 \text{ m}}{18 \text{ min}} = 10 \text{ m}^2/\text{min};$

 $\dfrac{20 \text{ m} \times 14 \text{ m}}{40 \text{ min}} = 7 \text{ m}^2/\text{min}$

 b. No. The area of Mr. Fleming's lawn is 396 m^2. Using his plan, Harold will cut only $10 \text{ m}^2/\text{min} \cdot 10 \text{ min} + 7 \text{ m}^2/\text{min} \cdot 8 \text{ min}$, or 156 m^2.

 c. $10h + 7l = 396$

 d. $\dfrac{0.6 \text{ L}}{18 \text{ min}} = \dfrac{1}{30} \text{ L/min};$

 $\dfrac{0.6 \text{ L}}{40 \text{ min}} = \dfrac{3}{200} \text{ L/min}$

 e. $\dfrac{h}{30} + \dfrac{3l}{200} = 1.2$

 f. $l = 14.4$ min, $h = 29.52$ min; if he cuts for 29.52 min at the higher speed and 14.4 min at the lower speed, he will finish Mr. Fleming's lawn and use one full tank of gas.

10. $\begin{bmatrix} 1 & 0 & -3 \\ 0 & 1 & -8 \end{bmatrix}$

TAKE ANOTHER LOOK

If x is the number of scooters and y is the number of skateboards, then the following system describes the constraints:

$$\begin{cases} x \le 6000 \\ y \le 8000 \\ x + y \le 10{,}000 \\ x \ge 0 \\ y \ge 0 \end{cases}$$

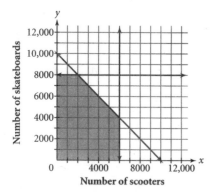

Profit: $15x + 10y$

Substituting the coordinates (6000, 4000) gives $130,000, which is the greatest possible profit.

CHAPTER 6

LESSON 6.1

EXERCISES

1. a. Starting value: 16; multiplier: 1.25; 7th term: 61.035

 b. Starting value: 27; multiplier: $\frac{2}{3}$, or $0.\overline{6}$; 7th term: $2.\overline{370}$, or $\frac{64}{27}$

2. $\{0, 100\}$ ENTER, $\{\text{Ans}(1) + 1, \text{Ans}(2) \cdot -1.6\}$ ENTER, ENTER, ... The first six terms are 100, -160, 256, -409.6, 655.36, -1048.576.

3. a. 8% increase: $\frac{108}{100}$; $1 + 0.08$

 b. 11% decrease: $\frac{89}{100}$; $1 - 0.11$

 c. 12.5% growth: $\frac{1125}{1000}$ or $\frac{112.5}{100}$; $1 + 0.125$

 d. $6\frac{1}{4}$% loss: $\frac{9{,}375}{10{,}000}$ or $\frac{93.75}{100}$; $1 - 0.0625$

 e. x% increase: $\frac{100 + x}{100}$; $1 + \frac{x}{100}$

 f. y% decrease: $\frac{100 - y}{100}$; $1 - \frac{y}{100}$

4. a. 75(1 + 0.02), or 75(1.02)

 b. 1000(1 − 0.18), or 1000(0.82)

 c. $P(1 + r)$ **d.** $75 - 75 \cdot 0.02$

 e. $80 - 80 \cdot 0.24$ **f.** $A - A \cdot r$

5. $\{0, 32\}$ ENTER, $\{\text{Ans}(1) + 1, \text{Ans}(2) \cdot 0.75\}$ ENTER, ENTER, ... Stage 2 has a shaded area of 18 square units; Stage 5 has a shaded area of 7.59375 square units.

6. a. $\{0, 20000\}$ ENTER, $\{\text{Ans}(1) + 1, \text{Ans}(2) \cdot (1 - 0.04)\}$ ENTER, ENTER, ...

 b. The 5th term, $16,986.93, represents the selling price of the car after four price reductions.

 c. 17 weeks (the18th term of the sequence)

7. a. $\{0, 7.1\}$ ENTER, $\{\text{Ans}(1) + 1, \text{Ans}(2) \cdot (1 + 0.117)\}$ ENTER, ENTER, ...

 b.

Year	Elapsed time (yr), x	Spending ($ billion), y
1970	0	7.1
1975	5	12.3
1980	10	21.5
1985	15	37.3
1990	20	64.9
1995	25	112.9
2000	30	196.3
2005	35	341.3

 c.

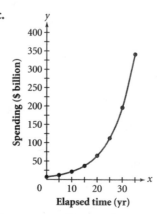

 d. Answers will vary. The graph implies a smooth, ever-increasing amount of Medicare spending, which is probably not realistic.

8. a. $\{0, 115\}$ ENTER, $\{\text{Ans}(1) + 1, \text{Ans}(2) \cdot (1 - 0.03)\}$ ENTER, ENTER, ...

 b. 12 minutes

9. a. 2 m $\cdot$ 0.85 = 1.7 m

 b. $\{0, 2\}$ ENTER, $\{\text{Ans}(1) + 1, \text{Ans}(2) \cdot 0.85\}$ ENTER, ENTER, ...

c. Approximately 0.75 m

d. Approximately 1.97 ft. (Use the recursive routine {0, 10} ENTER, {Ans(1) + 1, Ans(2) · 0.85} ENTER, ENTER, ...)

e. 19

f. Answers will vary. Sample answer: The mean of the rebound heights is 1.7 m, which is 85% of 2 m, and the median and mode are both 1.68 m, which is 84% of 2 m. However, only two of the balls tested met or exceeded 85% of the drop height, so the claim does not seem fair.

10. a. Increasing; starting value: 75; percent of increase: 2%

b. Decreasing; starting value: 1000; percent of decrease: 18%

c. Increasing; starting value: P; percent of increase: $100r\%$

d. Decreasing; starting value: 75; percent of decrease: 2%

e. Decreasing; starting value: 80; percent of decrease: 24%

f. Decreasing; starting value A; percent of decrease: $100r\%$

11. a. *(See table at bottom of page.)*

b. *(See table at bottom of page.)*

c. The graph of the first plan is linear. The graph of the second is not; its slope increases between consecutive points.

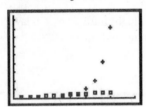

[0, 15, 3, 0, 4750, 500]

d. Possible answer: She should choose option 2 because the total donation is more than 12 times as much as with option 1.

12. a. Tamara's new hourly rate is 103.5% of her old rate. To find her new hourly rate, use the multiplier 1.035 with the initial hourly rate $7.50. $7.5(1.035) = 7.7625$. Her new hourly rate is $7.76.

b. Now her hourly rate is $100\% - 3.5\%$, or 96.5% of $7.76 (the rate you calculated in 12a). To find her new hourly rate, use the multiplier 0.965 with the hourly rate $7.76. $7.76(0.965) = 7.4884$. Now, her hourly rate is $7.49.

c. Her wage dropped by $0.01 per hour because the increase was calculated as 3.5% of $7.50, but the decrease was based on $7.76.

13. $y = -1.2(x - 600)$; y-intercept: $(0, 720)$

14. $y \approx 4.7 - 1.87(x - 2.2)$, or $y \approx -3.9 - 1.87(x - 6.8)$

15. a. i   **b.** iii   **c.** ii   **d.** iv

16. a. Let x represent minutes of use and y represent cost; $y = 50$.

b. $y = 50 + 0.35(x - 500)$

c. $y = 45$ for 600 min or less of use; $y = 45 + 0.55(x - 600)$ for more than 600 min of use.

d. First plan: $67.50; second plan: $45.00. (She pays only the flat rate of $45.00.) She should sign up for the second plan.

e. First plan: $172.50; second plan: $182.50. He should sign up for the first plan.

f. The plans cost the same for 800 min of use. A new subscriber who will use more than 800 min should choose the first plan. For a person who expects to use 800 min or less per month, the second plan is better.

LESSON 6.2

EXERCISES

1. a. 7^8 **b.** $3^4 \cdot 5^5$ **c.** $(1 + 0.12)^4$

2. a. $450(1 + 0.2) = 540$ bacteria

b. $450(1 + 0.2)^7 \approx 1612$ bacteria

Exercise 11. a.

	Jan	Feb	Mar	Apr	May	June	July	Aug	Sep	Oct	Nov	Dec
Option 1	$50	$25	$25	$25	$25	$25	$25	$25	$25	$25	$25	$25
Option 2	$1	$2	$4	$8	$16	$32	$64	$128	$256	$512	$1,024	$2,048

Exercise 11. b.

	Jan	Feb	Mar	Apr	May	June	July	Aug	Sep	Oct	Nov	Dec
Option 1	$50	$75	$100	$125	$150	$175	$200	$225	$250	$275	$300	$325
Option 2	$1	$3	$7	$15	$31	$63	$127	$255	$511	$1,023	$2,047	$4,095

3. a. ii; $y = 4(2)^x$ has starting value 4 and constant multiplier 2. This matches table ii.

b. iii; $y = 4(0.5)^x$ has starting value 4 and constant multiplier 0.5. This matches table iii.

c. iv; $y = 2(4)^x$ has starting value 2 and constant multiplier 4. This matches table iv.

d. i; $y = 2(0.25)^x$ has starting value 2 and constant multiplier 0.25. This matches table i.

4. a. iv; the starting value is 1.05, and the constant multiplier is $1 - 0.05$, or 0.95. This matches equation iv.

b. ii; the starting value is 1.05, and the constant multiplier is $1 + 0.05$. This matches equation ii.

c. i; the starting value is 0.95, and the constant multiplier is $1 + 0.05$, or 1.05. This matches equation i.

d. iii; the starting value is 0.95, and the multiplier is $1 - 0.05$, or 0.95. This matches equation iii.

5. a. a is the starting value, or the value of y when $x = 0$. In this case, $a = 1.2$. b is the ratio of consecutive y-values (or the value each y-value is multiplied by to get the next, consecutive, y-value). For this table, $b = 2$. So, the equation is $y = 1.2 \cdot 2^x$.

b. The starting value (the value of y when $x = 0$) is 500. When $x = 2$, $y = 20$, and when $x = 3$, $y = 4$, which is $0.2 \cdot 20$. So, the value of b is 0.2. The equation is $y = 500 \cdot 0.2^x$.

c. The y-values for $x = 1, 2,$ and 3 are 50, 20, and 8, respectively. Each y-value is 0.4 times the previous y-value, so the value of b is 0.4. To find the starting value, work backward: 50 (the y-value for $x = 1$) must be 0.4 times a (the y-value for $x = 0$), so $a = 50 \div 0.4 = 125$. The equation is $y = 125 \cdot 0.4^x$.

6. The number 500 represents an initial deposit of $500. The multiplier $(1 + 0.04)$ means the account earns 4% interest each year. The variable x represents the number of years since the initial deposit. The variable y represents the balance after x years.

7. Students will self-check their work as they run the program.

8. The rate of growth is 1.75% per month, so the multiplier is $(1 + 0.0175)$. An expression for the amount Stanley will owe after 4 months is $100(1 + 0.0175)(1 + 0.0175)(1 + 0.0175)$ $(1 + 0.0175)$, or $100(1 + 0.0175)^4$. Evaluating either expression gives about 107.19, so he will owe $107.19.

9. a. The rate of decrease is 20% or 0.2, so the constant multiplier is $(1 - 0.2)$. After 1 year, the truck's value will be $11,500(1 - 0.2)$, or $9,200.

b. $\{0, 11500\}$ ENTER,
$\{\text{Ans}(1) + 1, \text{Ans}(2) \cdot (1 - 0.2)\}$
ENTER, ENTER, . . .

c.

Time elapsed (yr)	Value ($)
0	11,500
1	9,200
2	7,360
3	5,888
4	4,710.40

d. $y = 11,500(1 - 0.2)^x$

e.
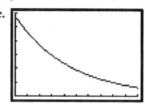

[0, 10, 1, 0, 12000, 2000]

10. a. 6 cm

b. 18 cm

c. The length of each segment is 3 times the length of the previous segment. The initial length is 2, so the length of the next segment is $2 \cdot 3 \cdot 3 \cdot 3$, or $2(3)^3$.

d. $2(3)^7 = 4,374$ and $2(3)^8 = 13,122$, so the longest segment that is less than 100 m (or 10,000 cm) has length $2(3)^7$.

11. Students will self-check their work as they run the program.

12. a. The number of layers doubles with each fold.

b. Estimates will vary.

c. Methods will vary. Eight folds gives 256 layers (512 pages), and nine folds gives 512 layers (1024 pages).

13. a. $y = 5000(1 + 0.05)^x$

b.
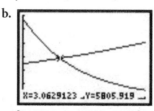

X=3.0629123 Y=5805.919

[0, 10, 1, 0, 12000, 2000]

The intersection point represents the time and the value of both cars when their value will be the same. By tracing the graph shown, students should see that both cars will be worth approximately $5,806 after a little less than 3 yr 1 mo.

14. Answers will vary. Sample answer: The first equation could model a principal of $400 to which $20 is added each time period. The second equation could model a starting balance of $400, with 5% interest added each time period. Both models have the same starting value, 400. In both models, $y = 420$ when

Discovering Algebra Solutions Manual
©2007 Key Curriculum Press

$x = 1$. For x greater than 1, y increases much more quickly in the second model.

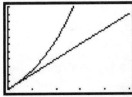

[0, 50, 10, 400, 1500, 100]

15. a. Answers will vary. Sample answer: A city has a population of 100,000. The population decreases by about 3.5% per year.

b. Sample problem based on answer given in 15a: What will be the population of the city in 7 years?

c. Sample solution based on question from 15b: $y = 100(1 - 0.035)^7 \approx 77.9$, so the population in 7 years will be about 77.9 thousand, or 77,900.

16. a.

Number of steps, x	1	2	3	4
Perimeter (cm), y	4	8	12	16

b.

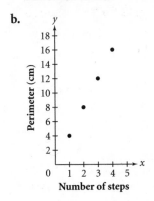

c. $y = 4x$, where y is the perimeter and x is the number of steps

d. 188 cm

e. Solving $74 = 4x$ gives $x = 18.5$. Because it is impossible to have a nonwhole number of steps, a perimeter of 74 cm is not possible.

LESSON 6.3

EXERCISES

1. a. $(5)(x)(x)(x)(x) = 5x^4$

b. $3x^4 \cdot 5x^6 = 3 \cdot 5 \cdot x^{4+6} = 15x^{10}$

c. $4x^7 \cdot 2x^3 = 4 \cdot 2 \cdot x^{7+3} = 8x^{10}$

d. $(-2x^2)(x^2 + x^4) = (-2x^2)(x^2) + (-2x^2)(x^4)$
$= -2x^{2+2} - 2x^{2+4} = -2x^4 - 2x^6$

2. a. $(3 \cdot 3 \cdot 3 \cdot 3 \cdot 3)(3 \cdot 3 \cdot 3 \cdot 3 \cdot 3 \cdot 3 \cdot 3 \cdot 3)$
$= 3^{13}$

b. $(7 \cdot 7 \cdot 7)(7 \cdot 7 \cdot 7 \cdot 7) = 7^7$

c. $(x \cdot x \cdot x \cdot x \cdot x \cdot x)(x \cdot x) = x^8$

d. $(y \cdot y \cdot y \cdot y \cdot y \cdot y \cdot y \cdot y)(y \cdot y \cdot y \cdot y \cdot y) = y^{13}$

e. $(x \cdot x \cdot y \cdot y \cdot y \cdot y)(x \cdot y \cdot y \cdot y)$
$= (x \cdot x \cdot x)(y \cdot y \cdot y \cdot y \cdot y \cdot y \cdot y) = x^3y^7$

3. a. 3^{40} **b.** 7^{12} **c.** x^{12} **d.** y^{40}

4. a. $(rt)^2 = r^2t^2$ **b.** $(x^2y)^3 = x^{2 \cdot 3}y^3 = x^6y^3$

c. $(4x)^5 = 1024x^5$

d. $(2x^4y^2z^5)^3 = 2^3x^{4 \cdot 3}y^{2 \cdot 3}z^{5 \cdot 3} = 8x^{12}y^6z^{15}$

5. Student 2 was correct. According to the order of operations, squaring should be done before multiplication.

6. a, d, and g; b and f; c and h; e has no match.

7. a, d, and g: 27,521.40084

b and f: 11,711.2344

c and h: 1060.32

e: 129,350.5839

8. a. $3x^2 \cdot 2x^4 = 3 \cdot 2 \cdot x^{2+4} = 6x^6$

b. $5x^2y^3 \cdot 4x^4y^5 = 5 \cdot 4 \cdot x^{2+4} \cdot y^{3+5} = 20x^6y^8$

c. $2x^2 \cdot 3x^3y^4 = 2 \cdot 3 \cdot x^{2+3}y^4 = 6x^5y^4$

d. $x^3 \cdot 4x^4 = 4x^{3+4} = 4x^7$

9. Enclose the -5 in parentheses.

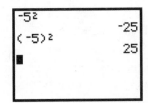

10. a. $2(3)^2 + 3(3) + 1 = 18 + 9 + 1 = 28$

b. $2(5)^2 + 3(5) + 1 = 50 + 15 + 1 = 66$

c. $2(-2)^2 + 3(-2) + 1 = 8 - 6 + 1 = 3$

d. $2(0)^2 + 3(0) + 1 = 0 + 0 + 1 = 1$

11. Possible answers:

a. $x^3 \cdot x^5 = x^8$ **b.** $(x^3)^5 = x^{15}$

c. $(3x)^5 = 3^5x^5 = 243x^5$

d. Exponents are added when you multiply two exponential expressions with the same base. Exponents are multiplied when an exponential expression is raised to a power. An exponent is distributed when a product is raised to a power.

12. a. $500(1 + 0.015)^6$; $546.72

b. $46.72

c. $500(1 + 0.015)^{12}$; $597.81

d. $51.09

e. Answers will vary. The increase is greater between 6 and 12 months because the interest each month is a percent of a greater current balance.

13. a. $x(x^3 + x^4) = x \cdot x^3 + x \cdot x^4 = x^{1+3} + x^{1+4}$
$= x^4 + x^5$

   b. $(-2x^2)(x^2 + x^4) = (-2x^2)(x^2) + (-2x^2)(x^4)$
$= -2x^{2+2} - 2x^{2+4} = -2x^4 - 2x^6$

   c. $2.5x^4(6.8x^3 + 3.4x^4)$
$= (2.5x^4)(6.8x^3) + (2.5x^4)(3.4x^4)$
$= 17x^{4+3} + 8.5x^{4+4} = 17x^7 + 8.5x^8$

14. a. $3x \cdot 5x^3 = 15x^4$ **b.** $x \cdot x^5 = x^6$

   c. $2x^3 \cdot 2x^3 = 4x^6$

   d. $3.5(x + 0.15)^4 \cdot (x + 0.15)^2$
$= 3.5(x + 0.15)^{4+2} = 3.5(x + 0.15)^6$

   e. $(2x^3)^3 = 8x^9$

   f. $\left[3(x + 0.05)^3\right]^2 = 3^2 \cdot (x + 0.05)^{3 \cdot 2}$
$= 9(x + 0.05)^6$

15. a. $4.5x - 47$

   b. $4.5x - 47 > 0$; $x > 10.\overline{4}$. He must shovel at least 11 sidewalks to pay for his equipment.

   c. $4.5x - 47 > 100$; $x > 32.\overline{6}$. He must shovel at least 33 sidewalks to pay for his expenses and buy a lawn mower.

16. a. $(5.3625, 0.70625)$

   b. $\left(\frac{65}{21}, \frac{16}{21}\right)$, or approximately $(3.095, 0.762)$

IMPROVING YOUR VISUAL THINKING SKILLS

Two pentaminos are considered the same if either can be flipped over (reflected) or turned (rotated) to match the other. The 12 distinct, or unique, pentaminos are often named after letters of the alphabet they resemble. Of these, the F, L, N, T, W, X, Y, and Z pentaminos fold into an open box.

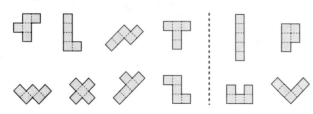

LESSON 6.4

EXERCISES

1. a. $34,000,000,000 = 3.4 \times 10,000,000,000$
$= 3.4 \times 10^{10}$

   b. $-2,100,000 = -2.1 \times 1,000,000 = -2.1 \times 10^6$

   c. $10,060 = 1.006 \times 10,000 = 1.006 \times 10^4$

2. a. $7.4 \times 10^4 = 7.4 \times 10,000 = 74,000$

   b. $-2.134 \times 10^6 = -2.134 \times 1,000,000$
$= -2,134,000$

   c. $4.01 \times 10^3 = 4.01 \times 1000 = 4010$

3. a. $12x^6$ **b.** $7y^{16}$ **c.** $2b^6 + b^5$ **d.** $10x^4 - 6x^2$

4. a. $12x^5$ **b.** $81y^{12}$ **c.** $50x^{11}$ **d.** $27m^6n^9$

5. $3.5 \times 10^7 = 3.5 \cdot 10 \cdot 10 \cdot 10 \cdot 10 \cdot 10 \cdot 10 \cdot 10$
$= 35,000,000$;

   $3.5^7 = 3.5 \cdot 3.5 \cdot 3.5 \cdot 3.5 \cdot 3.5 \cdot 3.5 \cdot 3.5$
$= 6433.9296875$

6. Because there are 3000 g in 3 kg, multiply the number of atoms in 1 g by 3000.

   $3000 \times 5.58 \times 10^{21} = 3 \times 10^3 \times 5.58 \times 10^{21}$
$= (3 \cdot 5.58) \times 10^{3+21}$
$= 16.74 \times 10^{24}$
$= 1.674 \times 10 \times 10^{24}$
$= 1.674 \times 10^{25} \text{ atoms}$

7. a. $55.5 \times 6.02 \times 10^{23} = 334.11 \times 10^{23}$
$= 3.3411 \times 10^2 \times 10^{23} = 3.3411 \times 10^{25}$

   b. $(6.02 \times 10^{23}) \times (6.02 \times 10^{23})$
$= 6.02^2 \times 10^{23+23}$
$= 36.2404 \times 10^{46}$
$= 3.62404 \times 10 \times 10^{46}$
$= 3.62404 \times 10^{47}$
$\approx 3.62 \times 10^{47}$

8. Answers will vary based on the model of calculator used.

   a. 2.5×10^2; 2.5E2

   b. 7.42×10^{12}; 7.42E12

   c. -1.8×10^1; -1.8E1

9. a. Yes; both equal 51,800,000,000.

   b. Al's answer

   c. Possible answer: 518×10^8

   d. Rewrite the number before the power of 10 in scientific notation. Then, use the multiplication property of exponents to add the exponents on the 10's. For the example given, $4.325 \times 10^2 \times 10^3$
$= 4.325 \times 10^5$.

10. a. i. 6×10^{13} **ii.** 1.3×10^9

   b. Regroup, multiply the numbers, and multiply the powers of 10 by adding the exponents.
$(2 \times 10^5)(3 \times 10^8) = 2 \times 3 \times 10^5 \times 10^8$
$= 6 \times 10^{13}$

   c. $(4 \times 10^5)(6 \times 10^7) = 4 \times 6 \times 10^5 \times 10^7$
$= 24 \times 10^{12} = 2.4 \times 10^1 \times 10^{12} = 2.4 \times 10^{13}$

11. a. 2,000,000,000; 2×10^9

   b. $365 \times 2 \times 10^9 = 730 \times 10^9 = 7.3 \times 10^2 \times 10^9$
$= 7.3 \times 10^{11}$, so Americans make 7.3×10^{11} calls per year.

12. a. Because 60 minutes $= 1.5 \cdot 40$ minutes, a person sheds $1.5 \cdot 1,000,000$ or 1.5×10^6 cells per hour.

   b. $365 \times 24 \times 1.5 \times 10^6$, or 1.314×10^{10} cells per year

13. a. 9.46×10^{12} km; 1.0×10^5 light-years

b. 9.46×10^{17} km

c. $\dfrac{9.46 \times 10^{17}}{1.27 \times 10^4} \approx 7.45 \times 10^{13}$

14. a. 3.8 is the population (in millions) in 1900, 0.017 is the annual growth rate, t is the elapsed time in years since 1900, and P is the population (in millions) t years after 1900.

b. Answer depends on the current year. The interval is $0 \le t \le (\textit{current year} - 1900)$.

c. Window settings will vary depending on the current year. Here is a graph for the years from 0 through 2000.

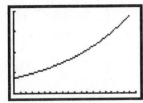

[0, 100, 5, 0, 20, 5]

d. Approximately 8.8 million

e. Answers will vary depending on the current year; $P = 3.8(1 + 0.017)^{\textit{current year} - 1900}$

15.

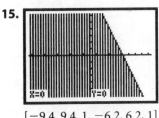

$[-9.4, 9.4, 1, -6.2, 6.2, 1]$

Improving Your Reasoning Skills

The answer is 27,682,574,402. The trick is finding a constant multiplier for the number of pairs of rats, not the number of individual rats. An exponential model is $2(7)^x$; 7 is the constant multiplier for pairs of rats (if each pair has 6 pairs of babies, then their number is increased 7 times); the 2 doubles the number of pairs, so the final answer is the number of individual rats. On a TI-83 Plus, the answer is shown in scientific notation as 2.76825744E10—the last two digits are not shown. If students subtract 27,000,000,000, the result is 682,574,402 and the final two digits are revealed.

LESSON 6.5

Exercises

1. $x^3 y$

2. a. $7^{12-4} = 7^8$

b. $x^{11-5} = x^6$

c. $\dfrac{12}{3}x^{5-2} = 4x^3$

d. $\dfrac{7}{14}x^{6-3}y^{3-1} = 0.5x^3 y^2$

3. Possible answer: $\dfrac{3^6}{3^2}$ means that there are 6 factors of 3 in the numerator and 2 factors of 3 in the

---

denominator. That is, $\dfrac{3^6}{3^2} = \dfrac{3 \cdot 3 \cdot 3 \cdot 3 \cdot 3 \cdot 3}{3 \cdot 3}$. You can rewrite this as 2 factors of $\dfrac{3}{3}$, or 1, multiplied by 4 factors of 3. That is, $\dfrac{3}{3} \cdot \dfrac{3}{3} \cdot 3 \cdot 3 \cdot 3 \cdot 3 = 1 \cdot 3 \cdot 3 \cdot 3 \cdot 3$. So $\dfrac{3^6}{3^2} = 3 \cdot 3 \cdot 3 \cdot 3 = 3^4$.

4. a. A

b. y is the current value, which is 10,000; r is the rate of appreciation, which is 10% or 0.1; and x is the number of years the value has been appreciating, which is 20. The equation is $10,000 = A(1 + 0.1)^{20}$.

c.

$10,000 = A(1 + 0.1)^{20}$	Original equation.
$\dfrac{10,000}{(1 + 0.1)^{20}} = A$	Divide both sides by $(1 + 0.1)^{20}$.
$1486.43 \approx A$	Evaluate the exponential expression and divide.

The furniture was worth about $1,486 20 years ago.

5. a. $(2x)^3 \cdot (3x^2)^4 = 8x^3 \cdot 81x^8 = 648x^{11}$

b. $\dfrac{(5x)^7}{(5x)^5} = (5x)^{7-5} = (5x)^2 = 25x^2$

c. $\dfrac{(2x)^5}{-8x^3} = \dfrac{32x^5}{-8x^3} = -4x^2$

d. $(4x^2 y^5) \cdot (-3xy^3)^3 = 4x^2 y^5 \cdot (-3)^3 x^3 y^9 = 4 \cdot (-27) \cdot x^5 y^{14} = -108x^5 y^{14}$

6. $\dfrac{1.5 \times 10^{11}}{3 \times 10^3} = 0.5 \times 10^3 = 0.5 \times 1000 = 500$. It takes 500 s, or about 8 min, for light to travel from the Sun to Earth.

7. a. $\dfrac{1.0 \times 10^8}{7.6 \times 10^5} \approx 0.132 \times 10^3 = 0.132 \times 1000 = 132$. The population density of Mexico was about 132 people per square mile.

b. $\dfrac{1.3 \times 10^8}{1.5 \times 10^5} \approx 0.867 \times 10^3 = 0.867 \times 1000 = 867$. The population density of Japan was about 867 people per square mile.

c. The population density of Japan was about 6.6 times that of Mexico.

8. a. $\dfrac{3\%}{12}$, or 0.25% per month

b. $5000(1 + 0.0025)^8 \approx 5100.88$, so they have $5,100.88.

c. $5000(1 + 0.0025)^5 \approx 5062.81$, so they would have had $5,062.81.

d. $5000(1 + 0.0025)^{10} \approx 5126.42$, so they will have $5,126.42

9. Four days earlier. Possible solution methods:

Method 1: Use a recursive routine.

{0, 864} ENTER ,
{Ans(1) + 1, Ans(2)/3} ENTER , ENTER , . . .

Method 2: Input the equation $y = 864\left(\dfrac{1}{3}\right)^x$ into a calculator. Then, look at the table to find the first x-value for which the corresponding y-value is less than 20.

10. $120,000(1 + 0.02)^{-5} \approx 108,688$, so 5 years ago the population was about 108,688.

11. a. $\frac{800,000,000}{25} = \frac{8 \times 10^8}{2.5 \times 10^1} = 3.2 \times 10^7$. An elephant lives 3.2×10^7 min or about 61 yr.

b. $\frac{800,000,000}{1150} = \frac{8 \times 10^8}{1.15 \times 10^3} = 6.96 \times 10^5$. A pygmy shrew lives 6.96×10^5 min or about 1.3 yr.

c. $\frac{800,000,000}{60} = \frac{8 \times 10^8}{6 \times 10^1} \approx 1.33 \times 10^7$. So, you would expect a human to live 1.33×10^7 min or about 25.4 yr.

12. First, convert 57,000 tons to pounds:

$57,000 \text{ tons} \cdot \frac{2000 \text{ lb}}{1 \text{ ton}} = 114,000,000 \text{ lb}$

$= 1.14 \times 10^8 \text{ lb}$

Use the fact that it takes 8 oz, or 0.5 lb, of cotton to make a T-shirt to find the number of T-shirts that can be made with 1.14×10^8 lb:

$1.14 \times 10^8 \text{ lb} \cdot \frac{1 \text{ T-shirt}}{0.5 \text{ lb}}$

$= 2.28 \times 10^8 \text{ T-shirts}$

Now figure out how many T-shirts this is for each of the 275 million people in the United States:

$\frac{2.28 \times 10^8 \text{ T-shirts}}{2.75 \times 10^8 \text{ people}} \approx 0.83 \times 10^0 \text{ T-shirts per person}$

$= 8.3 \times 10^{-1} \text{ T-shirts per person}$

13. Use dimensional analysis to find how many flowers it takes to make 1 oz of honey.

$\frac{3 \times 10^{12} \text{ flowers}}{3.3 \times 10^3 \text{ tons}} \cdot \frac{1 \text{ ton}}{2 \times 10^3 \text{ lb}} \cdot \frac{1 \text{ lb}}{16 \text{ oz}}$

$\approx 2.84 \times 10^4 \text{ flowers per oz}$

To make 8 oz of honey, it takes $8 \times 2.84 \times 10^4$, or about 2.272×10^5 flowers.

14. 14 yr

15. a. (Answers recorded to tenths.) Mercury: 4.1 cm; Venus: 10 cm; Earth: 10.5 cm; Mars: 5.6 cm; Jupiter: 117.3 cm; Saturn: 94.7 cm; Uranus: 69.3 cm; Neptune: 41.3 cm; Pluto: 2 cm; Sun: 1152 cm. One way to find these answers is to set up and solve proportions of the form $\frac{planet's\ diameter}{Pluto's\ diameter} = \frac{x \text{ cm}}{2 \text{ cm}}$, where x is the diameter of the planet in the model.

b. Possible answer: Halley should make her models much smaller because the model of Jupiter is 1 m in diameter and the model of the sun is greater than 11 m in diameter. It might be better to leave the sun out of her models altogether. If she makes Pluto with a diameter of 0.2 cm, Jupiter will be only about 12 cm in diameter.

LESSON 6.6

EXERCISES

1. a. $\frac{1}{2^3}$ **b.** $\frac{1}{5^2}$ **c.** $\frac{1.35}{10^4}$

2. a. $=$. Because $63.5 \times 10^4 = 6.35 \times 10 \times 10^4$ $= 6.35 \times 10^5$, the expressions are equal.

b. $<$. Because the powers of 10 are the same, you can just compare -5.24 to -5.2. Because $-5.24 < -5.2$, $-5.24 \times 10^{-7} < -5.2 \times 10^{-7}$.

c. $>$. Because $10^{-5} > 10^{-6}$, $2.674 \times 10^{-5} > 2.674 \times 10^{-6}$.

d. $>$. Because $10^{-4} < 10^{-3}$, $2.7 \times 10^{-4} < 2.8 \times 10^{-3}$ and $2.7 < 2.8$. Multiplying by -1 reverses the inequality symbol, so $-2.7 \times 10^{-4} > -2.8 \times 10^{-3}$.

3. a. -5; $0.0000412 = \frac{4.12}{100,000} = \frac{4.12}{10^5} = 4.12 \times 10^{-5}$

b. -4; $46 \times 10^{-5} = 4.6 \times 10^1 \times 10^{-5} = 4.6 \times 10^{-4}$

c. -4; $0.00046 = \frac{4.6}{10^4} = 4.6 \times 10^{-4}$

4. a. $45,647(1 + 0.028)^0$

b. The population 12 years ago

c. $45,647(1 + 0.028)^{-8} \approx 36,599$

d. $\frac{45,647}{(1 + 0.028)^{12}}$; $\frac{45,647}{(1 + 0.028)^8}$

5. Possible answer: A number raised to a negative power is equal to 1 over the number raised to the opposite power. So, $6^{-3} = \frac{1}{6^3} = \frac{1}{216}$. This is different from -6^3, which equals $-(6 \cdot 6 \cdot 6)$, or -216.

6. a. $(2x^3)^2(3x^4) = 12x^{10}$

b. $(5x^4)^0(2x^2) = 5^0 \cdot (x^4)^0(2x^2) = 1 \cdot x^0 \cdot 2x^2 = 2x^2$

c. $3(2x)^3(3x)^{-2} = \frac{3(2x)^3}{(3x)^2} = \frac{3 \cdot 8x^3}{9x^2} = \frac{8x}{3}$

d. $\left(\frac{2x^4}{3x}\right)^{-3} = \left(\frac{3x}{2x^4}\right)^3 = \left(\frac{3}{2x^3}\right)^3 = \frac{3^3}{(2x^3)^3}$

$= \frac{3^3}{2^3 \cdot (x^3)^3} = \frac{27}{8x^9}$

7. a. $3500(1 + 0.04)^{-4}$; approximately \$2,992

b. $250(1 + 0.04)^{-3}$; approximately \$222

c. $25(1 + 0.04)^{-5}$; approximately \$21

d. $187,000(1 + 0.04)^{-30}$; approximately \$57,656

8. a. $\frac{1.5 \times 10^5 \text{ mi}^2}{1.3 \times 10^8 \text{ people}}$

$\approx 1.2 \times 10^{-3} \text{ mi}^2 \text{ per person}$

b. $\frac{1.2 \times 10^{-3} \text{ mi}^2}{1 \text{ person}} \cdot \frac{27,878,400 \text{ ft}^2}{1 \text{ mi}^2}$

$\approx 3.35 \times 10^4 \text{ ft}^2 \text{ per person (or } 3.22 \times 10^4 \text{ ft}^2$ per person if the answer from 8a is used without rounding).

9. a. True; $\left(2^3\right)^2 = 2^3 \cdot 2^3 = 2 \cdot 2 \cdot 2 \cdot 2 \cdot 2 \cdot 2 = 2^6$

b. False; $\left(3^0\right)^4 = (1)^4 = 1$

c. False; $(10^{-2})^4 = \left(\dfrac{1}{10^2}\right)^4$

$$= \left(\dfrac{1}{10 \cdot 10}\right)\left(\dfrac{1}{10 \cdot 10}\right)\left(\dfrac{1}{10 \cdot 10}\right)\left(\dfrac{1}{10 \cdot 10}\right)$$

$$= \dfrac{1}{10^8} = 10^{-8}$$

d. True; $(5^{-3})^{-4} = \left(\dfrac{1}{5^3}\right)^{-4} = \dfrac{1}{\left(\dfrac{1}{5^3}\right)^4}$

$$= \dfrac{1}{\left(\dfrac{1}{5 \cdot 5 \cdot 5}\right)\left(\dfrac{1}{5 \cdot 5 \cdot 5}\right)\left(\dfrac{1}{5 \cdot 5 \cdot 5}\right)\left(\dfrac{1}{5 \cdot 5 \cdot 5}\right)}$$

$$= \dfrac{1}{\dfrac{1}{5^{12}}} = \dfrac{1}{5^{-12}} = 5^{12}$$

10. a. Original: 1×10^0; Abigail: 1×10^{-1}; Barbara: 1×10^{-2}; Cruz: 1×10^{-3}

b. 1×10^{-4} mi

c. Damien's string is only about 6.3 inches long, which is too short for a shoelace.

11. $36(1 + 0.5)^{4-6} = 36(1 + 0.5)^{-2}$

12. a. $1000(1 + 0.025)^2 \approx 1050.63$ and $1000(1 + 0.025)^4 \approx 1103.81$. So after 1 yr she would have \$1,050.63, and after 2 yr she would have \$1,103.81.

b. $1000(1 + 0.05)^1 = 1050$ and $1000(1 + 0.05)^2 = 1102.5$. So after 1 yr she would have \$1,050, and after 2 yr she would have \$1,102.50.

c. Possible answer: In the savings account, interest is added sooner, so the interest earns interest sooner.

13. Exponential: $y = -3(1 + 0.4)^x$, $y = 2 \cdot 3^x$; polynomial: $y = 4x^3$, $y = 2x^5 - 3x^2 + 4x + 2$, $y = 2x + 7$, $y = -6 + 2x + 3x^2$, $y = 3$; neither: $y = x^x + x^2$

14. a. The voltage is decreasing because the base, 0.957, is less than 1.

b. 9.4 is the voltage at time 0. Each second, 4.3% of the previous voltage is lost.

c.

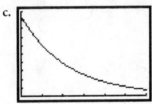

$[0, 60, 10, 0, 10, 1]$

d. $y \le 4.7$ volts when $x > 15.77$ s. Possible explanation: The exponential graph is at or below the graph of $y = 4.7$ for $x > 15.77$ s. (Note that y equals 4.7 volts at $x \approx 15.7705896$.)

15. a. **i.** 4×10^5 **ii.** 3.1×10^{10}
    iii. 1.21×10^5 **iv.** 2×10^{-4}

b. Possible answer: Divide the coefficients of the powers of 10, and then divide the powers of 10 (subtract the exponents).

c. 0.6×10^5, or 6×10^4 in scientific notation

IMPROVING YOUR REASONING SKILLS

1. Possible definition: Factors of 10 are found so the exponent on 10 is a multiple of 3; the digits, a, before 10 can represent a decimal number $1 \le a < 1000$.

2. a. 78×10^6 **b.** 9.45×10^3 **c.** 130×10^9
    d. 3.4×10^{-3} **e.** 310×10^{-3} **f.** 140×10^6

3. Answers will vary. Students should observe that engineering notation is related to the groups of three digits separated by commas in decimal numbers. That is, $n = 10^{-6}$, $\mu = 10^{-3}$, $k = 10^3$, $M = 10^6$, $G = 10^9$.

LESSON 6.7

EXERCISES

1. a. $1 + 0.15$; rate of increase: 15%

b. $1 + 0.08$; rate of increase: 8%

c. $1 - 0.24$; rate of decrease: 24%

d. $1 - 0.002$; rate of decrease: 0.2%

e. $1 + 1.5$; rate of increase: 150%

2. a. Decreasing

b. 12%

c. $y \approx 8.92$

d. The y-values approach 0.

3. $B = 250(1 + 0.0425)^t$

4. a. $108x^{18}$ **b.** $4x^5y^3$ **c.** 72   **d.** 1

    e. $\dfrac{y^4}{x^3}$ **f.** $\dfrac{1}{8x^3}$ **g.** $\dfrac{2}{x^3}$ **h.** $\dfrac{54y^6}{x^4}$

5. a. The ratios are 0.957, 0.956, 0.965, 0.964, 0.963, 0.961, 0.959, 0.958, 0.971, and 0.955.

b. approximately 0.96

c. $0.96 = 1 - 0.04$

d. $y = 47(1 - 0.04)^x$

e.

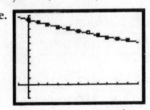

$[-1, 11, 1, -10, 50, 5]$

Adjustments to A or r are not necessary—the fit is good as is.

f. 55 min

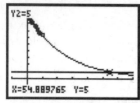

$[-10, 70, 10, -10, 50, 5]$

6. a. Possible answer: $y = 431(1 - 0.26)^x$, where 0.26 is derived from the mean ratio of about 0.74.

b. With each layer of plastic, the amount of light is reduced 26%.

c. With 9 layers, the reading would be below 30.

7. a. 50%   **b.** $y = 32(1 + 0.5)^x$

c. 243 mosquitoes; 9,342 mosquitoes; 2,727,126 mosquitoes

d. Answers will vary. Possibilities include lack of resources, overcrowding, and extermination.

8. a. $y = 2(1 + 0.5)^x$

b. $y = 2(1 + 0.5)^{0.5} \approx 2.45$; approximately 2.45 L

c. Approximately 115 L

d. After about 30.4 min, or 30 min 24 s

9. a. Possible answer: Let x represent years since 2000 and y represent median price in dollars. An equation is $y = 135,500(1 + 0.06)^x$, where 0.06 is derived from the mean ratio of about 1.06.

b–d. Answers will vary depending on year. See the table below for possible answers obtained using the model $y = 135,500(1 + 0.06)^x$. The answers for 9d are obtained by dividing the answers for 9c by 60 because 5 yr = 60 mo.

Year	9b. Median price ($)	9c. Down payment ($)	9d. Savings ($/mo)
2011	257,219	25,722	429
2012	272,653	27,265	454
2013	289,012	28,901	482
2014	306,352	30,635	511
2015	324,734	32,473	541
2016	344,218	34,422	574
2017	364,871	36,487	608

10. Note 75 above middle C (a D#) would be the highest audible note. Note -44 (an E 44 notes below middle C) would be the lowest audible note.

11. a. y gets closer and closer to 0.

b. No, because y can never equal 0. The number is just smaller than the calculator is able to represent.

c. y approaches infinity.

12. $\dfrac{1 \text{ microsecond}}{1 \text{ nanosecond}} = \dfrac{1 \times 10^{-6} \text{ seconds}}{1 \times 10^{-9} \text{ seconds}} = 1 \times 10^3$. So there are 1000 nanoseconds in a microsecond.

13. a. To estimate the tuition costs next year (one year from now), multiply each of the given tuition costs by $1 + 0.037$, or 1.037. Answers rounded to the nearest $10 are $2,970, $3,710, $8,540, $9,810, $11,840, $23,330, and $27,770.

b. To estimate the tuition costs five years from now, multiply each of the given tuition costs by $(1 + 0.037)^5$, or $(1.037)^5$. Answers rounded to the nearest $10 are $3,430, $4,290, $9,880, $11,340, $13,690, $26,980, and $32,110.

14. $5(3 \times 10^8)^2 = 5(9 \times 10^{16}) = 45 \times 10^{16}$, or 4.5×10^{17} joules

LESSON 6.8

Activity day: There are no answers for this lesson.

CHAPTER 6 Review

EXERCISES

1. a. 3^4 **b.** 3^3 **c.** 3^2 **d.** 3^{-1}

e. 3^{-2} **f.** 3^0

2. a. x^2 **b.** $\dfrac{2}{x}$ **c.** $1.23x^5$ **d.** $\dfrac{1}{3^x}$

e. 3   **f.** x^7 **g.** 3^{4x} **h.** x^2

3. a. Answers will vary. Possible answer: A $300 microwave depreciates at a rate of 15% per year. In this situation, 300 is the original price of the microwave in dollars and 0.15 is the percent decrease expressed as a decimal.

b. The years (x) for which the depreciating value of the microwave is at least $75.

c. Answers will be $x \le 8$ or $0 \le x \le 8$, depending on the situation described in 3a (negative integers may or may not make sense for the situation).

4. Answers will vary. Possible answer: $\dfrac{3^x}{3^x} = 3^{x-x} = 3^0$. Because any number divided by itself is 1, $3^0 = 1$.

5. a. $y = 200(1 + 0.4)^x$; missing value: 1505.9072

b. $y = 850(1 - 0.15)^x$

x	y
-2	1176.4706
-1	1000.0000
4	443.7053

6. a. $-2,400,000$

b. 0.000325

c. 3.714×10^{10}

d. 8.011×10^{-8}

7. $72 \cdot 365 \cdot 9365 \cdot 0.15 = 36{,}916{,}830$, so the person will spend 36,916,830 s blinking. Now, convert this to years: $36{,}916{,}830 \div 60 \div 60 \div 24 \div 365 \approx 1.17$. In scientific notation, this is 1.17×10^0 yr.

8. The equation $y = 1.00(1 + 0.03)^x$, or $y = 1.03^x$, represents the price of a can of soda x years after 2004. To find the year when this price will be equal to $2, graph $y = 1.03^x$ and $y = 2$ and find their intersection. The two graphs intersect when $x \approx 23.45$, and the price will exceed $2 thereafter. Therefore, the year in which the price will first exceed $2 is 24 yr after 2004, that is, the year 2028.

9. a. False; 3 to the power of 3 is not 9. The right side should be $27x^6$.

   b. False. You can't use the multiplication property of exponents if the bases are different. The right side should be $9 \cdot 8$, or 72.

   c. False. The exponent -2 applies only to the x. The right side should be $\frac{2}{x^2}$.

   d. False. The power property of exponents says to multiply the exponents. The right side should be $\frac{x^6}{y^9}$.

10. a. Possible answer: $y = 80(1 - 0.17)^x$, where x is the time elapsed in minutes and y is the maximum distance in centimeters. The multiplier $(1 - 0.17)$ is derived from the mean ratio of approximately 0.83.

   b. Approximately 15.0 cm   **c.** 15 min

TAKE ANOTHER LOOK

By stating the order of 10^7, the scientist is including a range of values greater than or equal to 10,000,000 cells and less than 100,000,000 cells.

If a sample grows from several hundred cells to several thousand cells, it has increased roughly by a factor of 10.

If the sample grows from several hundred cells to several hundred thousand cells, it has increased by three orders of magnitude.

If the number of cells decreases by two orders of magnitude, $\frac{1}{100}$ of the cells remain.

1. The size of a cell is greater than or equal to 0.000001 m and less than 0.00001 m.

2. The length of a cow is greater than or equal to 1 m and less than 10 m.

3. This is incorrect because the units are not equivalent (meters vs. miles).

4. This is an increase by 26 orders of magnitude.

An increase of 100% does not represent an increase in order of magnitude; an increase of 100% implies the quantity increased by a factor of 2, whereas an increase in order of magnitude implies that the quantity increased by a factor of 10.

CHAPTER 7

LESSON 7.1

EXERCISES

1. a. SBOHF   **b.** EPNBJO
   c. UBCMF   **d.** HSBQI

2. a. INPUT   **b.** OUTPUT
   c. RELATIONSHIP   **d.** RULE

3. a. A one-letter-shift code shifts A to B, B to C, C to D, and so on. This is the code given in the table in Exercise 1. Using this table, the investigation title is decoded as SECRET CODES.

   b. The coding scheme is a letter-shift of $+1$. That is, each letter is shifted to the next letter in the alphabet, and the letter Z is shifted to A.

4. a. The possible inputs are the letters on the horizontal axis that have shaded squares above them: A, B, C, E, G, H, I, K, L, M, N, O, Q, U, V, Y, Z.

   b. The possible outputs are the letters on the vertical axis that have shaded squares to their right. The outputs are all 26 letters of the alphabet.

   c. No; each of the letters B, E, G, I, K, M, and Q has more than one output.

5. a. The answer depends on whether students distinguish A.M. from P.M. If students *do not* make this distinction, the domain is: 1:00, 2:00, 3:00, 4:00, 5:00, 6:00, 7:00, 8:00, 9:00, 10:00, 11:00, 12:00. If students *do* distinguish A.M. from P.M., the domain is: 1:00 A.M., 1:00 P.M., 2:00 A.M., 2:00 P.M., and so on.

   b. Range: {0100, 0200, 0300, 0400, 0500, 0600, 0700, 0800, 0900, 1000, 1100, 1200, 1300, 1400, 1500, 1600, 1700, 1800, 1900, 2000, 2100, 2200, 2300, 2400}

   c. The answer depends on whether students distinguish A.M. from P.M. If students *do not* make this distinction, they should find that the relationship is *not* a function because each standard time corresponds to two military times. If students *do* make the distinction, they should find the relationship is a function because each standard time corresponds to a unique military time.

6. a. G   **b.** M   **c.** A   **d.** A

7. a. $L_1 = \{6, 21, 14, 3, 20, 9, 15, 14, 19\}$
   $L_2 = \{15, 30, 23, 12, 29, 18, 24, 23, 28\}$

   b. You have to subtract 26 from the numbers greater than 26. The new list L_2 is $\{15, 4, 23, 12, 3, 18, 24, 23, 2\}$.

   c. ODWLCRXWB

d.

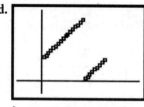

$[-10, 37, 0, -5, 31, 0]$

e. Avoid any multiple of 26, such as $0, -26, 26, -52, 52$, and so on.

8. a. $L_1 = \{1, 2, \ldots, 26\}$

b. $L_2 = \{2, 4, 6, 8, \ldots, 26, 2, 4, 6, 8, \ldots, 26\}$

c.

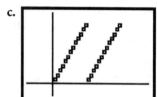

d. Sylvana will have difficulty decoding because each coded letter has two possible inputs.

9. ALGEBRA

10. a. Each input codes to a single output, but each output does not decode to a single input. There are two decoding choices for B.

b. Coding is easier.

c. Every output letter on the vertical axis should match only one input letter on the horizontal axis. Possible answer: Change the code so that D encodes as A.

11. a. Domain: $\{0, 1, -1, 2, -2\}$, range: $\{0, 1, 2\}$. This is a function because each input has exactly one output.

b. Domain: $\{1, 4, 9\}$, range: $\{1, -1, 2, -2, 3, -3\}$. This is not a function because each input has two outputs.

12. a. Double the position of the letter and add 1. If the result is greater than 26, subtract 26 until the answer is not more than 26. This number is the position of the coded letter.

b. GEIK

c. You cannot decode SPY because the letter P is not in the range.

13. The ordered pairs could represent a function because each input has a unique output. The domain is $\{-2, 0, 1, 3\}$, and the range is $\{-2, 3\}$.

14. The ordered pairs do not represent a function because the input -2 has two different outputs, 3 and 0, and the input 3 has two different outputs, 1 and -2.

15. a. Possible rule: Subtract the input letter's position from 27 to get the output letter's position.

b. Yes, each input corresponds to only one output.

c. Answers will vary.

16. TIPGKFXIRGYP must decode to CRYPTOGRAPHY (the study of coding and decoding), so C codes to T, R codes to I, Y codes to P, P codes to G, and so on. If you use position numbers for the letters, 3 codes to 20, 18 codes to 9, 25 codes to 16, 16 codes to 7, and so on. Rule: Subtract 9 from the letter's position or add 17 so that your result is between 1 and 26, inclusive. The original message is CRYPTOGRAPHY.

17. a. $28b^6$ **b.** $11a^3$ **c.** 1.75

d. $1372d^9$ **e.** Not possible   **f.** $4x^5$

18. $\dfrac{1 \text{ cal}}{4.1868 \text{ J}} = \dfrac{x \text{ cal}}{470 \text{ J}}; x = \dfrac{470}{4.1868} \approx 112 \text{ cal}$

LESSON 7.2

EXERCISES

1. a. Output values: $\{1, 3.4, 5.4, 9.32, 11.4\}$

b.

Domain x	Range y
-4	4.4
-1	2
2.4	-0.72
11	-7.6
14	-10

2.

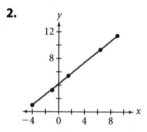

3.

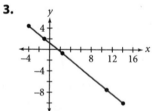

4. Both relationships are functions. Possible explanations: In the tables, every input value produces exactly one output value. Both graphs pass the vertical line test.

5. Sample answer: Start at the 2 m mark and stand still for 2 s. Walk toward the 4 m mark at 2 m/s for 1 s. Stand still for another second. Walk toward the 8 m mark at 4 m/s for 1 s. Then stand still for 3 s. Yes, the graph represents a function.

6. a. Yes; each input value has only one output value.

  b. No; many input values have two output values.

  c. No; all the points on the vertical segment have the same input value but different output values.

  d. Yes; each input value has only one output value.

  e. No; each input value has infinitely many output values.

7. a. No; Los Angeles, for example, has more than one ZIP Code (90001, 90002, . . .).

  b. Yes; each person has only one birth date.

  c. No; the same last name corresponds to many different first names. For example, if you look up the last name "Smith" in the phone book, you will see many different first names.

  d. Yes; each state has only one capital.

8. a. Graphs i, ii, iii, iv, and vi all pass the vertical line test, so they represent functions.

  b. Graphs v and vii. Graph v represents a person walking at an infinite speed, which is not possible. Graph iv shows the person in two places at once, which is not possible.

  c. Sample conclusion: It is not possible to walk a graph that does not represent a function.

9. a. This is not a function because the x-value 3 has two different y-values, 10 and 8.

  b. This is a function because each x-value corresponds to only one y-value.

  c. This is a function because each x-value corresponds to only one y-value.

10. Graphs must pass the vertical line test, pass through the points $(-2, 3)$ and $(3, -2)$, and have domain $-3 \leq x \leq 5$ and range $-4 \leq y \leq 4$. Sample graph:

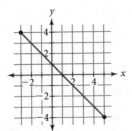

11. Graphs will not pass the vertical line test. They should include points $(-2, 3)$ and $(3, -2)$ and have the correct domain and range. Sample graph:

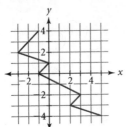

12. a. The graph is a line. This describes a function because each x-value is paired with only one y-value.

x	y
2	-1
8	1
-4	-3
-1	-2
0	$-\frac{5}{3}$
5	0

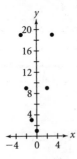

  b. This describes a function because each x-value is paired with only one y-value.

x	y
-2	9
3	19
0	1
-3	19
-1	3
± 2	9

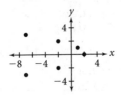

  c. This does not describe a function because there are two y-values for many x-values.

x	y
-7	± 3
1	1
-2	-2
-7	-3
-2	± 2
2	0

  d. This describes a function because each x-value is paired with only one y-value. Tables will vary. Sample table:

x	y
0	0
2	3
-2	-3
4	6
-4	-6
6	9

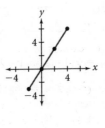

13. a. Domain: $\{-5, -4, -3, -2, -1, 0, 1, 2, 3, 4, 5\}$
  Range: $\{0, 1, 2, 3, 4, 5\}$

  b. Domain: $0 \leq x \leq 360$
  Range: $-1 \leq y \leq 1$

c. Answers may vary. Possible domain: all numbers x; possible range: all numbers y

14. a. Letters such as A, B, and C are not functions because a vertical line could intersect them in more than one point.

    b. Letters such as V and W are functions because no vertical line could intersect them in more than one point.

15. a. When $x = 10$, $y = -15$. Answers will vary. Zoom in on the table by changing the start values and the table increments (ΔTbl).

    b.

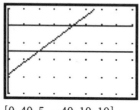

$[0, 40, 5, -40, 10, 10]$

16. a. $x = 24$

Equation: $\dfrac{4(x-7)-8}{3} = 20$		
Description	**Undo**	**Result**
Pick x.		24
$- (7)$	$+ (7)$	17
$\cdot (4)$	$/ (4)$	68
$- (8)$	$+ (8)$	60
$/ (3)$	$\cdot (3)$	20

    b. $x = 9.75$

First invert the proportion: $\dfrac{x-3}{4.5} = \dfrac{3}{2}$		
Description	**Undo**	**Result**
Pick x.		9.75
$- (3)$	$+ (3)$	6.75
$/ (4.5)$	$\cdot (4.5)$	$\dfrac{3}{2}$

17. a. $x = \dfrac{28}{11} \approx 2.55$, $y = \dfrac{29}{11} \approx 2.64$

    b. $x = -\dfrac{56}{13} \approx -4.31$, $y = -\dfrac{21}{13} \approx -1.62$

LESSON 7.3

EXERCISES

1. Answers will vary.

    a. Sample answer: The graph shows an inverse relationship that levels off. Once enough students are working, more will not help. A graph that shows a discrete function is also correct because students can be represented by whole numbers.

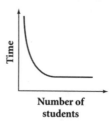

    b. Sample answer: This graph shows an inverse relationship. Eventually the price will be so high that no one will buy a T-shirt.

    c. Sample answer: Some product will be sold without any advertising. The product sold will increase as the advertising budget increases. Eventually the graph will level off because there is a limit to how much you can sell no matter how much you spend on advertising. This isn't shown on the graph.

2. a.

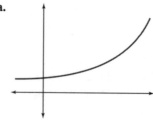

    b.

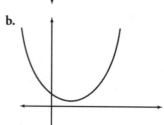

c.

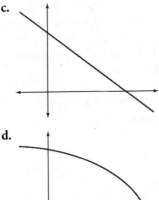

d.

3. a. $0 \leq x < 4$ **b.** $4 \leq x < 6$ **c.** $4 \leq x < 10$
   d. $6 \leq x < 12$ **e.** $0 \leq x < 12$

4. a.

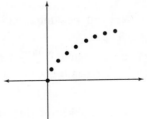

b.

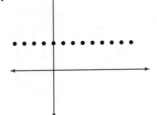

c.

d.

5. a. The reading on the scale depends on the weight of the dog, so the dog's weight is the independent variable and the reading on the scale is the dependent variable.

   b. The amount of time you spend in the plane depends on the distance you fly, so the distance between the cities is the independent variable and the amount of time in the plane is the dependent variable.

   c. The wax sticks to the candlewick each time you dip it, so the number of dips is the independent variable and the diameter of the candle is the dependent variable.

6. a. Yes; the graph passes the vertical line test, and the student cannot be at two places at the same time.

   b. $0 \leq x \leq 8$ **c.** $2 \leq y \leq 8$

   d. Before any time has elapsed, the distance is 2 m.

   e. $y = 4$; $y = 8$; $x = 2.5$

7. Answers will vary. A correct graph will consist of three line segments, each less steep than the one before it.

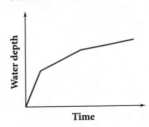

8. a. About 11:00 A.M.

   b. Between 10:10 A.M. and 10:40 A.M.

   c. Between 9:00 and 9:45 A.M. and then again after 11:00 A.M.

9. The temperature dropped slowly from midnight until 6 A.M. and was fairly constant through the morning. At about 10 A.M., the temperature began a dramatic rise for 2 h. Then the temperature continued to rise more slowly for another 7 h until 7 P.M. The temperature dropped only slightly from 7 P.M. until midnight.

10. a. Erica won in about 13.5 s.

   b. Eileen was in the lead after 60 m.

   c. They were tied at approximately 3 s, 5.5 s, from 10 to 10.5 s, and just before the end of the race.

   d. Eileen was in the lead from 0 to 3 s, from 5.5 to 10 s, and from 10.5 to about 13.2 s.

11. Graph B is correct. The graph starts at 0, which represents the turtle's starting point at the pond. The first segment of the graph represents the turtle walking at a slow, steady pace. The graph then increases quickly, representing the dog running with the turtle. The flat part of the graph represents the turtle resting after the dog drops it. The decreasing, linear segment represents the boy carrying the turtle back to the pond.

12. a. Sample answer: A ball is traveling toward the catcher; it is caught and held, then thrown back. A valid answer would also be that there is no scenario because velocity can't change instantaneously. The graph should be made up of at least three horizontal segments at heights of 0, 2, and −2.

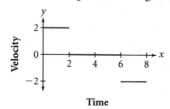

b. Sample answer: As the school bus leaves a stop, its speed increases. It travels for a while at a constant speed. Then it slows down briefly and speeds up again to a faster speed than before. It travels at a constant speed for a while, then slows down and stops as it lets some students off. It speeds up again and levels off at a constant speed.

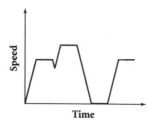

c. Sample answer: The ball is shot from shoulder level. It rises to a maximum point, goes through the hoop, and then falls to the ground.

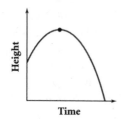

d. A sample graph is shown. The height of the grass is quite short after it has been mowed, then grows taller until it is mowed again.

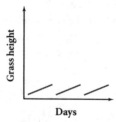

e. A sample graph is shown. The number of students and the number of buses can only be integers, so the graph is made up of dots rather than lines. After a bus is full, students get into the next bus.

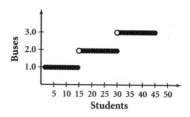

13. a. Moving away, speeding up

  b. Moving toward, speeding up

  c. Moving away, at a constant speed

  d. Moving toward, slowing down

  e. Moving toward, at a constant speed

  f. Moving away, slowing down

14. a. The slope is $\frac{10-8}{1-0} = 2$ and the y-intercept is 8, so the equation is $y = 8 + 2x$.

  b. The ratio of consecutive y-values is $\frac{10}{8} = 1.25$ and the starting value is 8, so the equation is $y = 8(1 + 0.25)^x$.

15. The equations in 15a–c can also be solved by other methods.

  a.

$$\frac{2x-4}{3} + 7 = 4 \qquad \text{Original equation.}$$

$$\frac{2x-4}{3} + 7 - 7 = 4 - 7 \qquad \text{Subtract 7 from both sides.}$$

$$\frac{2x-4}{3} = -3 \qquad \text{Subtract.}$$

$$3\left(\frac{2x-4}{3}\right) = 3(-3) \qquad \text{Multiply both sides by 3.}$$

$$2x - 4 = -9 \qquad \text{Multiply.}$$

$$2x - 4 + 4 = -9 + 4 \qquad \text{Add 4 to both sides.}$$

$$2x = -5 \qquad \text{Add.}$$

$$\frac{2x}{2} = \frac{-5}{2} \qquad \text{Divide both sides by 2.}$$

$$x = -\frac{5}{2} = -2.5 \qquad \text{Divide.}$$

Discovering Algebra Solutions Manual
©2007 Key Curriculum Press

b.

$$\frac{5(3-x)}{-2} = -17.5 \qquad \text{Original equation.}$$

$$-2\left[\frac{5(3-x)}{-2}\right] = -2(-17.5) \qquad \text{Multiply both sides by } -2.$$

$$5(3-x) = 35 \qquad \text{Multiply.}$$

$$15 - 5x = 35 \qquad \text{Use the distributive property.}$$

$$15 - 5x - 15 = 35 - 15 \qquad \text{Subtract 15.}$$

$$-5x = 20 \qquad \text{Subtract.}$$

$$\frac{-5x}{-5} = \frac{20}{-5} \qquad \text{Divide both sides by } -5.$$

$$x = -4 \qquad \text{Divide.}$$

c.

$$\frac{2}{x-1} = 3 \qquad \text{Original equation.}$$

$$\frac{x-1}{2} = \frac{1}{3} \qquad \text{Invert the proportion.}$$

$$x - 1 = \frac{2}{3} \qquad \text{Multiply both sides by 2.}$$

$$x = \frac{2}{3} + 1 \qquad \text{Add 1 to both sides of the equation.}$$

$$x = \frac{5}{3}, \text{ or } 1\frac{2}{3} \qquad \text{Add and reduce.}$$

16. a. $y = -25.9 - 2.5x$

   b. Slope: -2.5, y-intercept: -25.9

IMPROVING YOUR GEOMETRY SKILLS

Possible answers:

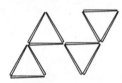 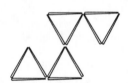

LESSON 7.4

EXERCISES

1. a. $3(3) + 2 = 11$, $Y_1(3) = 11$

   b. $3x + 2 = 2$, $x = 0$; $Y_1(0) = 2$

   c. $(5)^2 - 1 = 24$, $Y_2(5) = 24$

   d. $(-3)^2 - 1 = 8$, $Y_2(-3) = 8$

2. a. $-2(6) - 5 = -17$ **b.** $-2(0) - 5 = -5$

   c. $3.75(2.5)^2 = 23.4375$ **d.** $3.75(2.5)^{-2} = 0.6$

3. a. 0   **b.** 4   **c.** 2 and 5

   d. 0.5, 3, and 4.5

   e. Three. You can see this by drawing the horizontal line $y = 0.5$. This line crosses the graph three times.

   f. $x > 5$

   g. Domain: $-1 \le x \le 7$; range: $0 \le y \le 6$

4. a. Dependent variable (y): temperature (°F); independent variable (x): time (h)

   b. Domain: $0 \le x \le 24$; range: $5 \le y \le 35$

   c. $f(10)$ **d.** $f(x) = 10$

5. a. $f(x) = 7x + 5$ **b.** $f(x) = 5 + 7(x - 1)$

6. a. The level of the lake on the 60th day of the year

   b. At a certain time, the lake level was 3 in. below last year's mean.

   c. On certain days, the lake level was the same as it was on day 150.

7. a. Amount of medication in milligrams

   b. Time in hours

   c. $0 \le x \le 10$; all real numbers x

   d. $53 < y \le 500$, $y > 0$

   e. 500

   f. About 4 h

8. a. $f(x) = 650(1 - 0.085)^x$; domain: $x \ge 0$; range: $0 < y \le 650$

   b.

   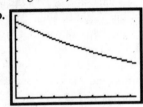

   $[0, 9.4, 1, 0, 700, 100]$

   c. The point of intersection is about $(7.8, 325)$.

   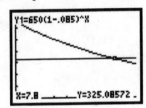

   d. After about 7.8 h, there are 325 bacteria present; the half-life is about 7.8 h.

9. a. $f(72) \approx 22.2°C$ **b.** $f(-10) \approx -23.3°C$

   c. $f(x) = 20$; $x = 68°F$ **d.** $f(x) = -5$; $x = 23°F$

10. FUN DAYS AHEAD

11. Answers will vary.

   a. Domain: all real numbers, lists of real numbers, square matrices of real numbers. Range: non-negative real numbers, lists of non-negative real numbers, square matrices of real numbers. The command is a function because the same input always results in the same output.

   b. Domain: all non-negative numbers or lists of non-negative numbers. Range: non-negative numbers or lists of non-negative numbers. The command is a function because the same input always results in the same output.

c. Domain: any size lists of real numbers. Range: all real numbers. The command is a function because the same input always results in the same output.

d. Two answers are possible. (1) This command does not take an input, but it gives a different output, such as 0.471359732, each time. It is not a function. (2) This command takes any real number, the seed, as the input. It gives a real-number output that depends on the seed. Domain: All real numbers. Range: All real numbers. The command always gives the same output for the same seed, so it is a function.

12. a. $f(x)$: The independent variable x is time in seconds, and the dependent variable y is height in meters.

$g(x)$: The independent variable x is time in seconds, and the dependent variable y is velocity in meters per second.

b. $f(x)$: The domain is $0 \leq x \leq 3.2$. The range is $0 \leq y \leq 50$.

$g(x)$: The domain is $0 \leq x \leq 3.2$. The range is $-31 \leq y \leq 0$.

c. Answers will vary. For the graph of $f(x)$, the ball is dropped from an initial height of 50 m. Its height decreases at a faster and faster rate until it hits the ground after about 3.2 s. For the graph of $g(x)$, the velocity starts at 0 m/s and decreases at a constant rate, becoming more and more negative.

d. In the 1st second, the ball falls about 5 m, from 50 m at $x = 0$ to about 45 m at $x = 1$.

e. In the 2nd second, the ball falls about 15 m, from about 45 m at $x = 1$ to about 30 m at $x = 2$.

f. The graph of $f(x)$ indicates that the ball hits the ground after about 3.2 s. The graph of $g(x)$ indicates that after 3.2 s, the velocity is about -31 m/s. So, the ball hits the ground at a speed of 31 m/s.

13. a. $\left(a^3\right)^{-3} = a^{3(-3)} = a^{-9} = \dfrac{1}{a^9}$

b. $\left(b^2\right)^5 = b^{2(5)} = b^{10}$

c. $\left(a^4 b^2\right)^3 = \left(a^4\right)^3 \cdot \left(b^2\right)^3 = a^{12}b^6$

d. $\left(c^2 d^3\right)^{-4} = \left(c^2\right)^{-4} \cdot \left(d^3\right)^{-4} = c^{-8} \cdot d^{-12} = \dfrac{1}{c^8 d^{12}}$

14. a. -1 **b.** $\dfrac{5}{11}$ **c.** 0

15. a. $x = -4$ **b.** $x = -0.75$

c. $x = 4$

LESSON 7.5

EXERCISES

1. a. 7   **b.** 0.5

c. $|-7 + 2| = |-5| = 5$ **d.** $|-7| + |2| = 7 + 2 = 9$

e. -5 **f.** -5

g. $|-4| \cdot |3| = 4 \cdot 3 = 12$ **h.** $\dfrac{|-6|}{|2|} = \dfrac{6}{2} = 3$

---

2. a. $|x| = 10$

There are two numbers, 10 and -10, that are 10 units from 0 on a number line, so $x = 10$ or $x = -10$.

b. $|x| > 4$

This inequality is satisfied by all x-values that are more than 4 units from 0 on a number line. These are all numbers to the right of 4 or to the left of -4, so $x > 4$ or $x < -4$.

3. a. $12 = 12$ **b.** $40 = 40$ **c.** $15 > 9$ **d.** $9 < 13$

e. $4 = 4$ **f.** $16 > \dfrac{1}{16}$

4. a. $3(5) - 5 = 10$ **b.** $3(-2.5) - 5 = -12.5$

c. $|-5 - 3| = |-8| = 8$ **d.** $|1 - 3| = |-2| = 2$

5. $|2.8| = 2.8, |-1.5| = 1.5$

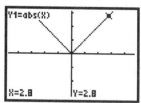

$[-4.7, 4.7, 1, -3.1, 3.1, 1]$

6.

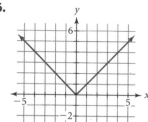

$y = |x|$, the absolute-value function.

7. Because $y = 2.85$, substitute 2.85 for y in the first equation. This gives $2.85 = |x|$, so $x = 2.85$ or $x = -2.85$. The solutions are $(2.85, 2.85)$ and $(-2.85, 2.85)$. You could also solve the equation by graphing both equations and finding the intersection points.

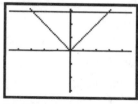

$[-4.7, 4.7, 1, -3.2, 3.2, 1]$

8. a. $x = -12$ or $x = 12$

b. $10 = |x| + 4$ Original equation.

$\quad 6 = |x|$ Subtract 4 from both sides.

$\quad x = -6$ or   Find the values with an absolute value

$\quad x = 6$ of 6.

Discovering Algebra Solutions Manual
©2007 Key Curriculum Press

c. $10 = 2|x| + 6$ Original equation.

$4 = 2|x|$ Subtract 6 from both sides.

$2 = |x|$ Divide both sides by 2.

$x = 2$ or $x = -2$ Find the values with an absolute value of 2.

d. $4 = 2(|x| + 2)$ Original equation.

$2 = |x| + 2$ Divide both sides by 2.

$0 = |x|$ Subtract 2 from both sides.

$x = 0$ Only 0 has an absolute value of 0.

9. The walker starts 5 m from the motion sensor and walks toward the motion sensor at a rate of 1 m/s for 4 s and then walks away from the motion sensor at the same rate for 4 s.

10. a. $Y_2 = 7$

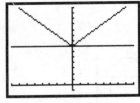

$[-8, 8, 1, -1, 14, 1]$

b. $Y_2 =$ any number less than 7; $Y_2 = 4$ is graphed below.

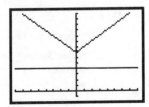

11. a. $g(x)$; $g(5) = |5| + 6 = 11$

b. $h(x)$; $h(1) = 18(1.5) = 27$

c. $g(x)$ or $h(x)$; $g(-2) = |-2| + 6 = 8$; $h(-2) = 18(1.5)^{-2} = 8$

d. $f(x)$; $f(3) = 7 + 4 \cdot 3 = 19$

12. a. Possible answer: The graphs of $y = 17$ and $y = |x - 4| + 3$ intersect twice, at $x = -10$ and $x = 18$.

b. $-10 \le x \le 18$. Possible answer: When $-10 \le x \le 18$, the graph of $y = |x - 4| + 3$ is at or below the graph of $y = 17$.

c. $x < -10$ or $x > 18$. Possible answer: When $x < -10$ or $x > 18$, the graph of $y = |x - 4| + 3$ is above the graph of $y = 17$.

13. Spider Lake: The mean weight is 1.5 lb. If you find the absolute value of the deviation, $|value - mean|$, for each data value, you get 0.3, 0.6, 0.7, 0.1, 1.2, 0.5, 1.1, 0.9. The mean of these deviations is 0.675.

Doll Lake: The mean weight is 1.575. If you find the absolute value of the deviation, $|value - mean|$, for each data value, you get 0.675, 0.475, 0.025, 0.325, 0.525, 0.175, 0.175, 0.625. The mean of these deviations is 0.375.

The mean of the absolute values of the deviations is greater for Spider Lake, indicating that the values vary more from the mean.

14. a. $|x + 1| = 7$ Original equation.

$x + 1 = 7$ or $x + 1 = -7$ $x + 1$ is equal to either 7 or -7.

$x = 6$ or $x = -8$ Subtract 1 from both sides of each equation.

b. $2|3x - 1| = 4$ Original equation.

$|3x - 1| = 2$ Divide both sides of the equation by 2.

$3x - 1 = 2$ or $3x - 1 = -2$ $3x - 1$ is equal to either 2 or -2.

$3x = 3$ or $3x = -1$ Add 1 to both sides of each equation.

$x = 1$ or $x = -\dfrac{1}{3}$ Divide both sides of each equation by 3.

c. $|2x - 4.2| - 3 = -3$ Original equation.

$|2x - 4.2| = 0$ Add 3 to both sides of the equation.

$2x - 4.2 = 0$ 0 is the only number with absolute value 0.

$2x = 4.2$ Add 4.2 to both sides of the equation.

$x = 2.1$ Divide both sides by 2.

d. $3|x + 2| = -6$ Original equation.

$|x + 2| = -2$ Divide both sides of the equation by 3.

The absolute value of a number is never negative, so the given equation has no solution.

15. a. $(-4.5, 1)$. Methods will vary. The elimination method is probably easiest because the coefficients of y are opposites, so adding the equations eliminates y.

b. $(3, -3)$. Methods will vary.

16. a. $-1\dfrac{2}{3} < x$, or $x > -1\dfrac{2}{3}$

b. $3(2 - x) + 4 \geq 13$ — Original equation.

$6 - 3x + 4 \geq 13$ — Apply the distributive property.

$10 - 3x \geq 13$ — Combine like terms.

$-3x \geq 3$ — Subtract 10 from both sides.

$x \leq -1$ — Divide both sides by -3 and reverse the inequality symbol.

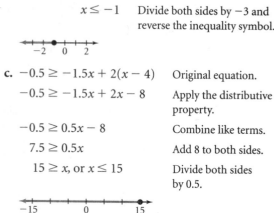
$-2 \quad 0 \quad 2$

c. $-0.5 \geq -1.5x + 2(x - 4)$ — Original equation.

$-0.5 \geq -1.5x + 2x - 8$ — Apply the distributive property.

$-0.5 \geq 0.5x - 8$ — Combine like terms.

$7.5 \geq 0.5x$ — Add 8 to both sides.

$15 \geq x$, or $x \leq 15$ — Divide both sides by 0.5.

$-15 \quad 0 \quad 15$

IMPROVING YOUR REASONING SKILLS

To square a positive integer that ends in 5, take the part of the number before the 5 and multiply it by one more than itself. Then put 25 on the end of that product. For example, to square 115, find $11 \cdot 12$, which is 132, and then append 25 to get 13,225. This procedure will always be successful.

To find the square root of 7225, find two consecutive positive integers whose product is 72. Then put a 5 after the smaller of the integers. Because $8 \cdot 9 = 72$, $\sqrt{7225} = 85$. This procedure will be successful whenever the number preceding the 25 is the product of two consecutive integers.

LESSON 7.6

EXERCISES

1.

Side (cm)	Perimeter (cm)	Area (cm²)
1	4	1
2	8	4
3	12	9
4	16	16
14	56	196
15	60	225
21	84	441
25.2	100.8	635.04
47	188	2209

2. a. $x = 6$ or $x = -6$

b. $x = 6$ or $x = -6$

c. $x = 3.8$ or $x = -3.8$

d. $x = 3.8$ or $x = -3.8$

3. a. $4.7 = |x| - 2.8$ — Original equation.

$7.5 = |x|$ — Add 2.8 to both sides.

$x = 7.5$ or $x = -7.5$ — Find the numbers with absolute value 7.5.

b. $-41 = x^2 - 28$ — Original equation.

$-13 = x^2$ — Add 28 to both sides.

The square of a number must be greater than or equal to 0, so this equation has no real solutions.

c. $11 = x^2 - 14$ — Original equation.

$25 = x^2$ — Add 14 to both sides.

$x = 5$ or $x = -5$ — Find two numbers whose square is 25.

4. a. $|x - 2| = 4$ — Original equation.

$x - 2 = 4$ or $x - 2 = -4$ — $x - 2$ is equal to either 4 or -4.

$x = 6$ or $x = -2$ — Add 2 to both sides of each equation.

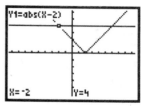
$[-9.4, 9.4, 1, -6.2, 6.2, 1]$

b. $(x - 2)^2 = 16$ — Original equation.

$\sqrt{(x - 2)^2} = \sqrt{16}$ — Take the square root of both sides.

$|x - 2| = 4$ — $\sqrt{x^2} = |x|$; see Exercise 7.

$x = 6$ or $x = -2$ — See 4a.

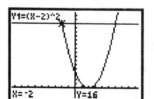
$[-9.4, 9.4, 1, -2.2, 18.6, 1]$

c. $|x + 3| = 7$ — Original equation.

$x + 3 = 7$ or $x + 3 = -7$ — $x + 3$ is equal to either 7 or -7.

$x = 4$ or $x = -10$ — Subtract 3 from both sides of each equation.

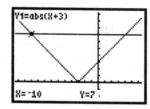
$[-12.4, 6.4, 1, -2.2, 10.2, 1]$

Discovering Algebra Solutions Manual
©2007 Key Curriculum Press

d.

$$(x + 3)^2 = 49 \qquad \text{Original equation.}$$

$$\sqrt{(x + 3)^2} = \sqrt{49} \qquad \begin{array}{l}\text{Take the square root}\\ \text{of both sides.}\end{array}$$

$$|x + 3| = 7 \qquad \begin{array}{l}\sqrt{x^2} = |x|; \text{ see}\\ \text{Exercise 7.}\end{array}$$

$$x = 4 \text{ or } x = -10 \qquad \text{See 4c.}$$

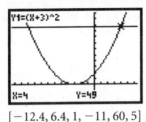

$[-12.4, 6.4, 1, -11, 60, 5]$

5. $-1 \le x \le 1$

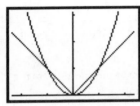

$[-2.35, 2.35, 1, 0, 3.1, 1]$

6. a. Because x^2 must be greater than or equal to 0, the equation $y = x^2$ has no solutions when $y < 0$.

b. Because 0 is the only number with one square root, the equation $y = x^2$ has only one solution when $y = 0$.

c. Because every positive number has two square roots, the equation $y = x^2$ has two solutions when $y > 0$.

7.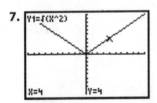

$[-9, 9.4, 1, -6.2, 6.2, 1]$

The equation $y = |x|$ or $f(x) = |x|$ produces the same graph as $f(x) = \sqrt{x^2}$.

8. Answers will vary. Possible answer: The rate of change from $x = 0$ to $x = 1$ is 1, but the rate of change from $x = 1$ to $x = 2$ is 3. Because the rate of change varies, the relationship is nonlinear.

9. a. $1 + 3 + 5 + 7 + 9 = 25$, or 5^2

b. $1 + 3 + 5 + 7 + 9 + \cdots + 29 = 225$, or 15^2

c. n^2

d. Each large square in the pattern is created by adding a border of small squares to two sides of the previous square. The number of small squares added at each stage is the next odd number. So, the number of small squares in each large square is 1, then $1 + 3$, then $1 + 3 + 5$, and so on. That is, the

number of squares in the nth large square is the sum of the first n odd integers. But, the number of small squares in each large square is also 1^2, then 2^2, then 3^2, and so on. So, the sum of the first n positive odd integers is n^2.

10. a. $y = 8 - 2x$ **b.** $y = x^2$

    c. $y = |x|$

11. a. There are sixteen 1-by-1 squares, nine 2-by-2 squares, four 3-by-3 squares, and one 4-by-4 square.

b. A 3-by-3 grid has 14 squares (nine 1-by-1 squares, four 2-by-2 squares, and one 3-by-3 square). A 2-by-2 grid has five squares (four 1-by-1 squares and one 2-by-2 square). A 1-by-1 grid has one square.

c. Answers will vary. Possible response: For an n-by-n grid, the number of 1-by-1 squares is n^2, the number of 2-by-2 squares is $(n - 1)^2$, the number of 3-by-3 squares is $(n - 2)^2$, and so on. So, a 5-by-5 grid would have $25 + 16 + 9 + 4 + 1$ or 55 squares.

12. Answers will vary. Possible answer: If x is a negative number, then x^2 is a negative times a negative, which is positive. If x is a positive number, then x^2 is a positive times a positive, which is also positive. If x is 0, then x^2 is 0 times 0, which is 0. So, x^2 must be greater than or equal to 0, no matter what x is.

13. a. To find the constant multiplier, divide the y-value for $x = 4$ by the y-value for $x = 3$. The result is $\frac{126.5625}{168.75}$, or 0.75. To find the starting value, you can start at 168.75, the y-value for $x = 3$, and divide by 0.75 three times. The result is 400. So, the equation is $y = 400(0.75)^x$.

b.

x	y
0	400
4	126.5625
3	168.75
1	300
≈ -3.19	1000

14. a. $48x^9$ **b.** $30x^8$ **c.** $24x^9$ **d.** $62.5x^{14}$

    e. $-2.5x^3$ **f.** $-48x^{11}$ **g.** $\dfrac{6y^6}{x^6}$ **h.** $375x^3y^6$

15.

$[-9.4, 9.4, 1, -6.2, 6.2, 1]$

Possible answer: The solution is 2.

IMPROVING YOUR VISUAL THINKING SKILLS

The numbers of cubes in the figures shown are $1^3 = 1$, $2^3 = 8$, and $3^3 = 27$. These are the volumes measured in cubic units. In general, if the side length of the cube is n, the volume is $n \cdot n \cdot n$, which is n^3 or "n cubed."

The last two questions lead to a profound result, so let students play with them. If the length of one edge is doubled, the volume is multiplied by 8, which is 2^3. If the length of an edge is tripled, the volume is multiplied by 27, which is 3^3. In general, if the length is multiplied by k, the volume is multiplied by k^3. In even more generality, if all lengths in an n-dimensional figure are multiplied by k, the "size" (length, or area, or volume, or the equivalent for n dimensions) is multiplied by k^n.

CHAPTER 7 Review

EXERCISES

1. a. $-2 \leq x \leq 4$ **b.** $1 \leq f(x) \leq 3$ **c.** 1
   d. -1 and 3

2. a. This table represents a function because each x-value corresponds to only one y-value.
   b. This table does not represent a function because the input $x = 3$ has two different output values, 5 and 7.
   c. This table represents a function because each x-value corresponds to only one y-value.

3. The graph shows that the object is moving at a constant velocity of 0.5 m/s, so the graph of the velocity is a horizontal line segment at 0.5 m/s.

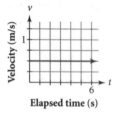

4. a. DESCARTES   **b.** HYPATIA
   c. EUCLID
   d. This code shifts forward 20 spaces, or back 6 spaces, in the alphabet.

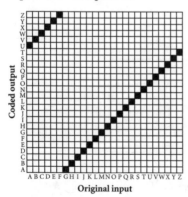

5. a. Possible answer: At the 20 s mark, each girl is moving at the same velocity. Bea's velocity increases steadily in a linear fashion. Caitlin's velocity increases slowly at first and then at a faster and faster rate. Abby's velocity increases very quickly at first and then at a slower and slower rate.
   b. No. Until the 20 s mark, Abby is moving faster than both Bea and Caitlin, so even when she slows down to their speed, she stays ahead.

6. a. $y = 4.25x + 1.00$
   b.

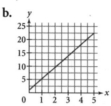

   c. It shifts the graph up 0.50 unit on the y-axis.
   d. $y = 4.25x + 1.50$

7. a. Answers will vary. The graph should pass the vertical line test. Sample graph:

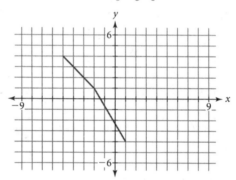

   b. Answers will vary. The graph will fail the vertical line test. Sample graph:

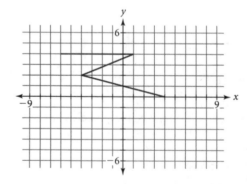

8.

A	B	C	D	E	F	G	H	I	J
1	2	3	4	5	6	7	8	9	10
2	4	6	8	10	12	14	16	18	20

K	L	M	N	O	P	Q	R
11	12	13	14	15	16	17	18
22	24	26	2	4	6	8	10

Discovering Algebra Solutions Manual
©2007 Key Curriculum Press

S	T	U	V	W	X	Y	Z
19	20	21	22	23	24	25	26
12	14	16	18	20	22	24	26

The code is a function because each input has only one output. The rule for decoding is not a function because each coded letter corresponds to two decoded letters. For example, the coded letter D corresponds to the decoded letters B and O.

9. a. $f(-3) = |-3| = 3$ **b.** $f(2) = |2| = 2$

  c. 10 and -10

10. a.

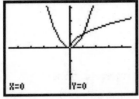

$[-4.7, 4.7, 1, -3.1, 3.1, 1]$

b. The graph of $y = \sqrt{x}$ looks like half of the graph of $y = x^2$ lying on its side.

c. The graph has one branch because the $\sqrt{\ }$ symbol indicates only the positive root.

d. This equation does not represent a function because every input but 0 has two outputs. For example, if $x = 4$, $y = 2$ or $y = -2$.

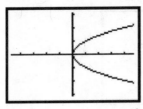

$[-4.7, 4.7, 1, -3.1, 3.1, 1]$

11. a. Let t be the number of T-shirts, and let s be the number of sweatshirts.

$$\begin{cases} t + s = 12 \\ 6t + 10s = 88 \end{cases}$$

b. 8 T-shirts and 4 sweatshirts

12. a. Praying Mantis Length

1	7
2	1 2 6 6
3	4
4	8
5	3 3 3 4 6 6
6	2
7	
8	2
9	4 8
10	
11	
12	1

Key

1	7 means 1.7 cm

b. 10.4 cm

c. Mean: approximately 5.4 cm; median: 5.3 cm; mode: 5.3. Choice and explanations will vary.

13. a. 21 [ENTER], Ans $-$ 4 [ENTER], [ENTER], ... ;
10th term $= -15$

b. -5 [ENTER], Ans $\cdot$ -3 [ENTER], [ENTER], ... ;
10th term $= 98,415$

c. 2 [ENTER], Ans $+$ 7 [ENTER], [ENTER], ... ;
10th term $= 65$

14. The systems of equations in 14a and 14b can also be solved by other methods.

a. $\begin{cases} y = 6x - 3 \\ y = 1.2x + 6 \end{cases}$

To solve this equation by substitution, substitute $6x - 3$ for y in the second equation, and solve for x.

$$6x - 3 = 1.2x + 6$$
$$6x - 3 - 1.2x = 1.2x + 6 - 1.2x$$
$$4.8x - 3 = 6$$
$$4.8x - 3 + 3 = 6 + 3$$
$$4.8x = 9$$
$$\frac{4.8x}{4.8} = \frac{9}{4.8}$$
$$x = 1.875$$

Now substitute 1.875 for x in the first original equation, and solve for y.

$$y = 6(1.875) - 3 = 8.25$$

Thus, the solution of the given system is $x = 1.875$, $y = 8.25$.

b. $\begin{cases} 3x - 1.5y = -12.3 \\ 2x - y = -8.2 \end{cases}$

To solve this system by elimination, multiply the first equation by 2 to obtain $6x - 3y = -24.6$, and multiply the second equation by -3 to obtain $-6x + 3y = 24.6$. Add these two new equations to obtain $0 = 0$, which indicates that the given system has infinitely many solutions. (The graphs of the two given equations are the same line, so any point on this line is a solution of the system.)

15. a. $y = 1.6x$, where x is a measurement in miles and y is a measurement in kilometers.

b. 400 km

c. 3.2 km

d. Approximately 168 m

16. Right triangle

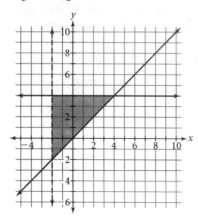

17. The equations in 17a–d can also be solved by other methods.

a. $-2(4 - d) + 3 = -13$ Original equation.

$-8 + 2d + 3 = -13$ Use the distributive property.

$-5 + 2d = -13$ Add.

$-5 + 2d + 5 = -13 + 5$ Add 5 to both sides.

$2d = -8$ Add.

$\dfrac{2d}{2} = \dfrac{-8}{2}$ Divide both sides by 2.

$d = -4$ Divide.

b. $42 - 7(d - 8) = 7$ Original equation.

$42 - 7d + 56 = 7$ Use the distributive property.

$98 - 7d = 7$ Add.

$98 - 7d - 98 = 7 - 98$ Subtract 98 from both sides.

$-7d = -91$ Subtract.

$\dfrac{-7d}{-7} = \dfrac{-91}{-7}$ Divide both sides by -7.

$d = 13$ Divide.

c. $0.5(d - 2) - 3 = -10$ Original equation.

$0.5d - 1 - 3 = -10$ Use the distributive property.

$0.5d - 4 = -10$ Subtract.

$0.5d - 4 + 4 = -10 + 4$ Add 4 to both sides.

$0.5d = -6$ Add.

$\dfrac{0.5d}{0.5} = \dfrac{-6}{0.5}$ Divide both sides by 0.5.

$d = -12$ Divide.

d. $3d - 5 + d = 0.5d + 2$ Original equation.

$4d - 5 = 0.5d + 2$ Combine like terms.

$4d - 5 + 5 = 0.5d + 2 + 5$ Add 5 to both sides.

$4d = 0.5d + 7$ Add.

$4d - 0.5d = 0.5d + 7 - 0.5d$ Subtract 0.5d from both sides.

$3.5d = 7$ Combine like terms.

$\dfrac{3.5d}{3.5} = \dfrac{7}{3.5}$ Divide both sides by 3.5.

$d = 2$ Divide.

18. a. Slope: $\frac{5}{2}$; y-intercept: $-\frac{11}{2}$

b. Slope: undefined; y-intercept: none

c. Slope: $-\frac{1}{2}$; y-intercept: $-\frac{5}{2}$

19. a. \$19,777   **b.** \$22,104

c. $y = 23{,}039(1 + 0.0225)^{-8}(1 + 0.035)^{-2}$; approximately \$18,000

20. Answers will vary depending on the method used. The following possible answers used the Q-point method and a decimal approximation of the slope.

a. $y = 96 - 5.7(x - 5)$

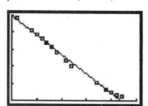

[0, 25, 5, 0, 125, 25]

b. $y = 124.5 - 5.7x$

c. Approximately 16 days

d. The y-intercept would become 200; $y = 200 - 5.7x$.

e. 86 g

21. a. Independent: number of licks; dependent: mass; decreasing, discrete

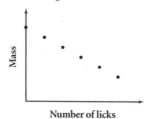

b. Independent: number of scoops; dependent: cost; increasing, discrete

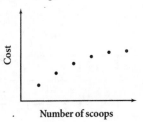

Number of scoops

c. Independent: amount of stretch; dependent: flying distance; increasing, continuous

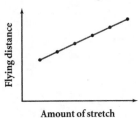

Amount of stretch

d. Independent: number of coins flipped; dependent: number of heads; increasing, discrete

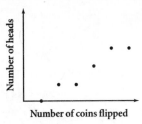

Number of coins flipped

TAKE ANOTHER LOOK

1. The inverse of the equation that converts temperatures from degrees Celsius to degrees Fahrenheit is a function. Encourage exploration of several functions, both algebraically and with graphs. A function has an inverse that's a function if its graph passes the horizontal line test: no horizontal line crosses the graph at more than one point. Equivalently, some students may say that the graph "doesn't turn around." That is, it's either always increasing or always decreasing. Students should also realize that the inverse of a constant function or a step function will not be a function.

Often a function is restricted to a domain over which it's just increasing or decreasing in order to have an inverse function. For example, when $y = x^2$ is restricted to the domain of positive values for x, it has the inverse function $y = \sqrt{x}$.

2. a. Mean ≈ 12.6; mean absolute deviation ≈ 4.1; the data values are generally spread within about 4.1 lb of 12.6 lb, so they are mostly between 8.5 and 16.7 lbs.

b. Standard deviation ≈ 5.3 lb; this is somewhat close to the mean absolute deviation.

c. Community's standard deviation ≈ 5.5 lb; the community's trash bags will have a mean of about 12.6 lb, and will mostly be spread within about 5.5 lb of the mean. That is, most will be between 7.1 lb and 18.1 lb.

CHAPTER 8

LESSON 8.1

EXERCISES

1. a. $(-2, 3), (4, 1), (2, -5)$

b. $(-5, 1), (3, 4), (6, -3), (-3, -5)$

2. a. A translation left 5 units

b. A translation right 1 unit and up 2 units

3. a. A translation up 4 units

b. The x-coordinates are unchanged.

c. The y-coordinates are increased by 4.

4. a.

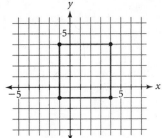

b. Translating the figure left 2 units decreases each x-coordinate by 2 (for example, $(1, 4)$ is translated to $(-1, 4)$). So, the image of the point (x, y) is $(x - 2, y)$.

5. a. The spider is translated right 10 units and down 8 units.

b. You need to add 10 to the original x-coordinates in list L_1 to get the image x-coordinates in list L_3. You also need to subtract 8 from the original y-coordinates in list L_2 to get the image y-coordinates in list L_4. So, $L_3 = L_1 + 10$ and $L_4 = L_2 - 8$.

c. If the lower right spider were the original, the translation would be left 10 units (instead of right 10 units) and up 8 units (instead of down 8 units). So, the operations in the definitions from 5b would change to the inverse operations: $L_3 = L_1 - 10, L_4 = L_2 + 8$.

6. a. Enter the x-coordinates into list L_1. Enter the first x-coordinate again at the end of the list. Enter the y-coordinates (in the same order as the corresponding x-coordinates) into list L_2. Enter the first y-coordinate again at the end of the list. So, $L_1 = \{2, 5, 1, 2\}$ and $L_2 = \{-1, 0, 2, -1\}$. Then make a connected plot.

b. **i.** A translation up 4 units

ii. A translation left 5 units

iii. A translation right 3 units and down 2 units

7. a. This is a translation up 3 units. The coordinates of the image are $(2, 4)$, $(4, 6)$, and $(3, 3)$.

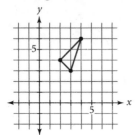

b. This is a translation left 2 units. The coordinates of the image are $(0, 1)$, $(2, 3)$, and $(1, 0)$.

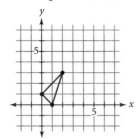

c. This is a translation right 3 units and down 1 unit. The coordinates of the image are $(5, 0)$, $(7, 2)$, and $(6, -1)$.

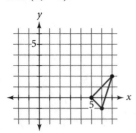

8. a. A translation right 12 units and up 7 units

b. $(x + 12, y + 7)$

c. She should move each point $\frac{1}{20}$ of the total horizontal distance and $\frac{1}{20}$ of the total vertical distance with each frame. So, if (x, y) is a point on the figure in one frame, its image in the next frame would be $\left(x + \frac{12}{20}, y + \frac{7}{20}\right)$, or $(x + 0.6, y + 0.35)$.

9. a. In the 10th new frame, the image of point (x, y) is $(x - 10(0.25), y + 10(0.05))$. So, the new coordinates are $(4.5, 1.5)$, $(4.5, 2.5)$, $(5.5, 1.5)$, $(5.5, 2.5)$.

b. In the 25th new frame, the image of point (x, y) is $(x - 25(0.25), y + 25(0.05))$. So, the new coordinates are $(0.75, 2.25)$, $(0.75, 3.25)$, $(1.75, 2.25)$, $(1.75, 3.25)$.

c. In the 40th new frame, the image of point (x, y) is $(x - 40(0.25), y + 40(0.05))$. So, the new coordinates are $(-3, 3)$, $(-3, 4)$, $(-2, 3)$, $(-2, 4)$.

10.

x	0	1	2	3	4	5	6
g(x)	3	2	1	0	1	2	3
h(x)	9	4	1	0	1	4	9

11. a. $f(x) = 2 + 3(5) = 2 + 15 = 17$

b. $2 + 3x = -10$

$3x = -12$

$x = -4$

c. $f(x + 2) = 2 + 3(x + 2) = 2 + 3x + 6 = 8 + 3x$

d. $f(2x - 1) = 2 + 3(2x - 1) = 2 + 6x - 3$
$= -1 + 6x$

12. Other methods may be used to solve the equations in this exercise.

a. $5 = -3 + 2x$ — Original equation.

$8 = 2x$ — Add 3 to both sides.

$4 = x$, or $x = 4$ — Divide both sides by 2.

b. $-4 = -8 + 3(x - 2)$ — Original equation.

$-4 = -8 + 3x - 6$ — Use the distributive property.

$-4 = -14 + 3x$ — Subtract.

$10 = 3x$ — Add 14 to both sides.

$\dfrac{10}{3} = x$ — Divide both sides by 3.

$x = \dfrac{10}{3}$, or $3.\bar{3}$

c. $7 + 2x = 3 + x$ — Original equation.

$7 + x = 3$ — Subtract x from both sides.

$x = -4$ — Subtract 7 from both sides.

13. a. $y = -2 + x$　　　**b.** $y = 1 - 0.5(x - 1)$

c. $y = |x|$　　　**d.** $y = 1.5^x$

LESSON 8.2

EXERCISES

1. a. $2|5 + 4| + 1 = 2(9) + 1 = 18 + 1 = 19$

b. $2|-6 + 4| + 1 = 2|-2| + 1 = 2(2) + 1$
$= 4 + 1 = 5$

c. $\left(2|-2 + 4| + 1\right) + 3 = 2(2) + 1 + 3$
$= 4 + 1 + 3 = 8$

d. $2|(x + 2) + 4| + 1 = 2|x + 6| + 1$

2. a. $L_3 = L_1 + 8$; $L_4 = L_2 - 4$

b. A translation right 8 units and down 4 units

3. a. $(1, -3)$　　　**b.** $(-5, -3)$

c. $(6, 4)$　　　**d.** $(-1, 0)$

4. a. A translation of $y = |x|$ right 1.5 units and down 2.5 units

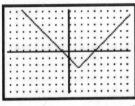

$[-9.4, 9.4, 1, -6.2, 6.2, 1]$

b. A translation of $y = x^2$ left 3 units

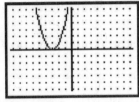

$[-9.4, 9.4, 1, -6.2, 6.2, 1]$

c. A translation of $y = |x|$ up 3.5 units

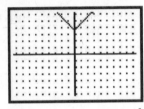

$[-9.4, 9.4, 1, -6.2, 6.2, 1]$

d. A translation of $y = 3^x$ left 1 unit and up 2 units

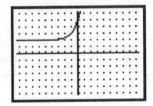

5. a. To translate down 2 units, replace y with $y - (-2)$ to get $y - (-2) = x^2$. Then, solve for y to get $y = x^2 - 2$.

b. To translate the graph right 5 units, replace x with $x - 5$ to get $y = 4^{x-5}$.

c.

$y = \lvert x \rvert$	Original function.
$y = \lvert x + 4 \rvert$	Replace x with $x - (-4)$ to translate the graph left 4 units.
$y - 1 = \lvert x + 4 \rvert$	Replace y with $y - 1$ to translate the graph up 1 unit.
$y = \lvert x + 4 \rvert + 1$	Solve for y.

The equation for the image is $y = \lvert x + 4 \rvert + 1$.

6. a. A translation of $y = x^2$ right 1 unit and down 3 units; $y = (x - 1)^2 - 3$

b. A translation of $y = |x|$ left 5 units and down 3 units; $y = \lvert x + 5 \rvert - 3$

c. A translation of $y = |x|$ right 6 units and up 4 units; $y = \lvert x - 6 \rvert + 4$

d. A translation of $y = x^2$ left 1 unit; $y = (x + 1)^2$

7. a. The input variable is time. The output variable is distance.

b. Time is in seconds, and distance is in meters.

c. Domain: $0 \le t \le 5$, where t is time in seconds; range: $1 \le d \le 4$, where d is distance in meters

d. Possible answer: Beth starts 3 m from her teacher and walks toward the teacher at 1 m/s for 2 s. When she turns in her test, she is 1 m from the teacher. Beth then turns and walks away from the teacher at 1 m/s for 3 s.

e. The graph is a translation of the graph of $d = |t|$ right 2 units and up 1 unit, so the function is $d = \lvert t - 2 \rvert + 1$.

8. a. A translation down 4 units

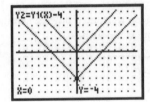

b. A translation right 4 units

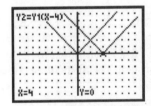

9. a. A translation right 3 units

b. A translation left 2 units

c. A translation down 2 units

d. A translation up 3 units

10. a. $y = a \cdot b^{x-10}$

b. Approximately 0.955 volt/s. The value of b is 0.955.

c. To find the value of a, let $x = 10$ in the equation $y = a \cdot b^{x-10}$: $6.579 = a \cdot 0.995^{10-10} = a \cdot 0.995^0 = a \cdot 1 = a$. Therefore, $a = 6.579$, and the equation is $y = 6.579(0.955)^{x-10}$.

d. When $x = 0$, $y = 6.579(0.955)^{0-10} = 6.579(0.955)^{-10} \approx 10.426$, so the voltage at time 0 is approximately 10.426 volts.

e. Solving $6.579(0.955)^{x-10} < 1$ graphically shows that the voltage drops below 1 approximately 51 s after the capacitor is connected to the load, and remains below 1 from then on.

11. a. Let x represent time in minutes, and let y represent temperature in degrees Celsius. The scatter plot suggests an exponential function.

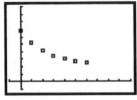

$[-1, 10, 1, -10, 100, 10]$

b. Ratios to the nearest thousandth: 0.765, 0.788, 0.829, 0.882, 0.900, 0.926. The ratios are not approximately constant, so they do not appear to support the idea that this is an exponential function.

c.

Time (min)	0	1	2	3	4	5	6
Temperature (°C)	47	31	20	13	9	6	4

The points have been translated down 21 units. The long-run value will now be 0°C.

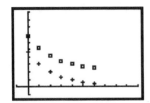

d. Ratios to the nearest thousandth: 0.660, 0.645, 0.650, 0.692, 0.667, 0.667. The ratios are approximately constant. The mean of the ratios is approximately 0.66.

e. The starting value, A, is 47, and the rate of decrease, r, is $1 - 0.66$, or 0.34. So, the equation is $y = 47(1 - 0.34)^x$.

f. A translation up 21 units

g. To model the original data, translate the function $y = 47(1 - 0.34)^x$ up 21 units. This gives the equation $y = 47(1 - 0.34)^x + 21$.

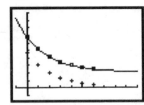

12. a. The year is the input variable, x, and population in billions is the output variable, y.

b. Sketches will vary. The graph should be an increasing exponential function passing through the point $(2004, 6.4)$.

c. $(2004, 6.4)$

d. If 6.4 billion were the population in year 0, the equation would be $y = 6.4(1 + 0.0114)^x$. However, 6.4 billion is the population in 2004, so the function needs to be translated right 2004 units. (This translates the point $(0, 6.4)$ to $(2004, 6.4)$.) Therefore, this situation can be modeled by the equation $y = 6.4(1.0114)^{x-2004}$. An appropriate window might be $[1995, 2015, 1, 5, 8, 1]$.

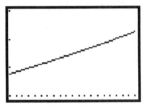

$[1995, 2015, 1, 5, 8, 1]$

e. 1995: 5.8 billion; 2015: 7.2 billion

13. a. The point $(0, 0)$ is translated to $(4, 8)$. So, $(4, 8)$ is one point on the new graph.

b. $y = b(x - 4) + 8$

c. The point $(0, 0)$ is translated to (H, V). So, (H, V) is one point on the new graph.

d. $y = b(x - H) + V$

14. a. 90.6%   **b.** Answers will vary.

c. $\dfrac{77 + 10}{85 + 10} = \dfrac{87}{95} \approx 0.916 \approx 91.6\%$

15. Other methods may be used to solve the systems in this exercise.

a. $\begin{cases} y = 5 + 2x \\ y = 8 - 2x \end{cases}$

To solve this system by substitution, substitute $5 + 2x$ for y in the second equation, and solve for x.

$5 + 2x = 8 - 2x$

$5 + 4x = 8$

$4x = 3$

$x = \dfrac{3}{4} = 0.75$

Substitute 0.75 in the first original equation, and solve for y:

$y = 5 + 2(0.75) = 5 + 1.5 = 6.5$

The given system has one solution, $(0.75, 6.5)$.

b. $\begin{cases} y = -2 + 3(x - 4) \\ y = 3 + 5(x - 2) \end{cases}$

Use the distributive property and combine like terms to rewrite each equation.

1st equation:

$y = -2 + 3(x - 4)$

$y = -2 + 3x - 12$

$y = 3x - 14$

Discovering Algebra Solutions Manual
©2007 Key Curriculum Press

2nd equation:

$y = 3 + 5(x - 2)$

$y = 3 + 5x - 10$

$y = 5x - 7$

To solve by substitution, substitute $5x - 7$ for y in the equation $y = 3x - 14$, and solve for x.

$5x - 7 = 3x - 14$

$2x - 7 = -14$

$2x = -7$

$x = \dfrac{-7}{2} = -3.5$

Finally, substitute -3.5 for x in the original equation $y = -2 + 3(x - 4)$ and solve for y.

$y = -2 + 3(-3.5 - 4)$

$y = -24.5$

The given system has one solution, $(-3.5, -24.5)$.

c. $\begin{cases} 2x + 7y = 13 \\ 5x - 14y = 1 \end{cases}$

To solve this system by elimination, multiply the first given equation by 2 to obtain $4x + 14y = 26$. Add this new equation to the second given equation to obtain $9x = 27$, and solve this equation to get $x = 3$. Next, substitute 3 for x in either of the given equations. Using the first equation gives $2(3) + 7y = 13$, which is equivalent to $7y = 7$, or $y = 1$.

The given system has one solution, $(3, 1)$.

IMPROVING YOUR VISUAL THINKING SKILLS

The vertical shift divided by the horizontal shift is the same as the slope of Jose's line, so the line was in effect shifted along itself to lie on top of itself. You might ask what shift would have taken Tammy's line to itself. Students may be surprised to discover that any translation by the same amount horizontally and vertically will leave Tammy's line unchanged. A translation horizontally H units and vertically V units will leave a line with the slope $\frac{V}{H}$ unchanged. Ask if this could happen to figures other than lines, to help students appreciate the importance of lines' constant slope.

LESSON 8.3

EXERCISES

1. a. $0.5(5 - 3)^2 - 3 = 0.5 \cdot 4 - 3 = -1$

   b. $0.5(-6 - 3)^2 - 3 = 0.5 \cdot 81 - 3 = 37.5$

   c. $4\left[0.5(2 - 3)^2 - 3\right] = 4(0.5 \cdot 1 - 3)$
   $= 4(-2.5) = -10$

   d. $0.5(-x - 3)^2 - 3$

   e. $-\left[0.5(x - 3)^2 - 3\right] = -0.5(x - 3)^2 + 3$

2. a. A translation of the graph of $y = x^2$ down 2 units; $y = x^2 - 2$

   b. A translation of the graph of $y = |x|$ right 3 units; $y = |x - 3|$

   c. A translation of the graph of $y = x^2$ left 2 units and down 1 unit; $y = (x + 2)^2 - 1$

   d. A translation of the graph of $y = |x|$ right 1 unit and up 1 unit; $y = |x - 1| + 1$

3. a. A reflection across the x-axis

   b. A translation right 6 units or a reflection across the y-axis

   c. A translation left 2 units

   d. A translation left 2 units and a reflection across the x-axis

4. a. Predictions will vary. This graph will be a reflection across the y-axis.

   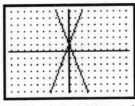

   $[-9.4, 9.4, 1, -6.2, 6.2, 1]$

   b. Predictions will vary. This graph will be a reflection across the x-axis.

   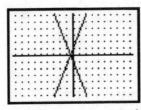

   $[-9.4, 9.4, 1, -6.2, 6.2, 1]$

5. a. A reflection across the x-axis

   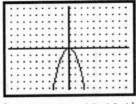

   $[-9.4, 9.4, 1, -6.2, 6.2, 1]$

   b. A translation left 3 units and a reflection across the x-axis

   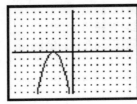

   $[-9.4, 9.4, 1, -6.2, 6.2, 1]$

c. A reflection across the *x*-axis followed by a translation up 3 units

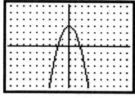

$[-9.4, 9.4, 1, -6.2, 6.2, 1]$

d. A reflection across the *y*-axis and a translation up 3 units (or just a translation up 3 units)

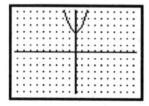

6. a. Possible answer: Enter the *x*-coordinates into list L₁. Enter the first *x*-coordinate again at the end of the list. Enter the *y*-coordinates (in the same order as the corresponding *x*-coordinates) into list L₂. Enter the first *y*-coordinate again at the end of the list. So, $L_1 = \{2, 7, 7, 2\}$ and $L_2 = \{2, 2, 4, 2\}$. Then make a connected plot of (L_1, L_2).

b. **i.** Let $L_3 = -L_1$ and $L_4 = L_2$, and make a connected plot of (L_3, L_4).

  ii. Let $L_3 = -L_1$ and $L_4 = -L_2$, and make a connected plot of (L_3, L_4).

  iii. Let $L_3 = L_1$ and $L_4 = -L_2$, and make a connected plot of (L_3, L_4).

  iv. Let $L_3 = L_1 + 2$ and $L_4 = -L_2$, and make a connected plot of (L_3, L_4).

7. a. A reflection across the *y*-axis

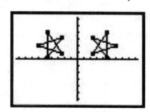

b. A reflection across the *x*-axis

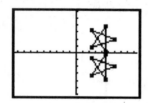

c. A translation left 8 units and a reflection across the *x*-axis

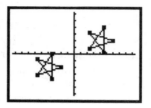

d. A translation right 2 units and down 4 units

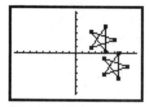

e. A reflection across the *x*- and *y*-axes

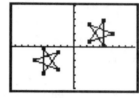

f. A reflection across the line $y = x$

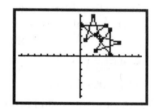

8. a. The graph looks like the graph of $y = |x|$ shifted right 4 units and up 1 unit, so the equation $y = |x - 4| + 1$ models the walk.

b. This graph shows Cheryl's walk.

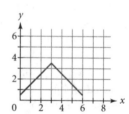

This is the graph of $y = |x|$ reflected across the *x*-axis and then shifted right 3 units and up 3.5 units. Its equation is $y = -|x - 3| + 3.5$.

c. Domain: $0 \leq x \leq 6$; range: $0.5 \leq y \leq 3.5$

9. To get to the star on the right, the star on the left is translated right 11 units and reflected across the *x*-axis. To accomplish this in 11 frames (with a top-to-bottom flip in each frame), each point must be translated right 1 unit and reflected across the *x*-axis in each frame. So, if a point has coordinates (x, y), the coordinates of its image in the next frame would be $(x + 1, -y)$.

Discovering Algebra Solutions Manual
©2007 Key Curriculum Press

10. a. A reflection across the x-axis followed by a translation right 3 units and up 6 units; $y = -(x - 3)^2 + 6$

 b. A reflection across the x-axis and a reflection across the y-axis, followed by a translation left 2 units and down 4 units; $y = -f(-(x + 2)) - 4$

11. a. **i.** The transformation is the same as a reflection across the x-axis followed by a translation down 4 units, so the equation is $y = -x^2 - 4$.

 ii. The transformation is the same as a reflection across the x-axis followed by a translation up 7 units, so the equation is $y = -|x| + 7$.

 iii. The transformation is the same as a reflection across the y-axis followed by a translation right 6 units, so the equation is $y = 2^{-(x-6)}$.

 iv. The transformation is the same as a reflection across the y-axis followed by a translation either down 16 units or left 8 units, or a reflection across the x-axis followed by a translation either down 8 units or left 4 units; the equation is equivalent to $y = -12 - 2x$.

 b. **i.** $y = -2$ **ii.** $y = 3.5$
 iii. $x = 3$ **iv.** $x = -4$ or $y = -4$

 c. If the line of reflection is $x = a$ or $y = b$, the amount of translation is twice a or b.

 d. A reflection across the horizontal line $y = b$ is the same as a reflection across the x-axis and a translation up or down $2b$ units, so the equation is $y = -f(x) + 2b$.

 e. A reflection across the vertical line $x = a$ is the same as a reflection across the y-axis and a translation right or left $2a$ units, so the equation is $y = f(-x + 2a)$.

12. a. There is a 12% decrease per minute $(1 - 0.12 = 0.88)$.

 b. As x gets larger and larger, y gets closer and closer to 0. So, the long-run value of y is 0 grams. This means that eventually all the reactant will be used.

 c. As x gets larger and larger, y gets closer and closer to 100. So, the long-run value of y is 100 grams. This means that eventually only 100 grams will remain, and this 100 grams will never be consumed.

 d. Both graphs are decreasing exponential graphs. The graph of $y = 500(0.88)^x$ shows a starting amount of 500 grams of reactant. The graph of $y = 500(0.88)^x + 100$ shows a starting amount of 600 grams of reactant. The second graph is a translation of the first graph up 100 units.

13. 47 tablespoons $\cdot \dfrac{1 \text{ cup}}{16 \text{ tablespoons}} \cdot \dfrac{1 \text{ quart}}{4 \text{ cups}} = \dfrac{47}{64}$ quart ≈ 0.734 quart

14. a. Possible answers using Q-points:
 $y = 36 + 3.6(x - 4)$ or $y = 72 + 3.6(x - 14)$

 b. Approximately 22 min

IMPROVING YOUR REASONING SKILLS

Mayan numbers converted to base 10 numbers:

9	13	17	0	3
2	6	10	14	18
1	5	7	11	15
4	8	12	16	19

LESSON 8.4

EXERCISES

1. This is the graph of $y = |x|$ shifted right 5 units, so the equation is $y = |x - 5|$.

2. a.

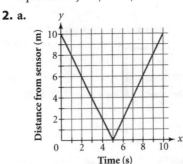

 b. Each point on the graph in 2a is twice the distance from the x-axis as the corresponding point on $y = |x - 5|$. So, the graph is a vertical stretch of $y = |x - 5|$ by a factor of 2. The equation is $y = 2|x - 5|$.

3. a. On the graph of $y = |x - 5|$ in Exercise 1, if you start at the vertex and move right 5 units, you must move up 5 units to reach a point on the graph. On this graph, if you move right 5 units from the vertex, you must move *down* 6 units to reach a point on the graph, so the graph of $y = |x - 5|$ is flipped over the x-axis and stretched by a factor of $\frac{6}{5}$, or 1.2. It is also translated up 6 units. The equation is $y = -1.2|x - 5| + 6$.

 b. Ted started at the motion sensor and walked away at 1.2 m/s for 5 s. When he was 6 m away, he turned and walked back toward the sensor at the same speed.

4. Answers will vary.

5. Answers will vary.

6. In a vertical stretch, all the y-coordinates are multiplied by a number. Because multiplying 0 by any number gives a result of 0, the point $(2, 0)$ will not be affected by a vertical stretch.

7. a. A vertical stretch of $y = x^2$ by a factor of 2

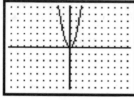

$[-9.4, 9.4, 1, -6.2, 6.2, 1]$

b. A vertical shrink of $y = |x|$ by a factor of 0.25, then a translation right 2 units and up 1 unit

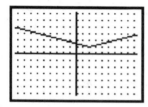

c. A reflection of $y = x^2$ across the x-axis, then a translation left 4 units and down 1 unit

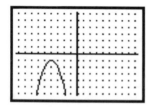

d. A vertical stretch of $y = |x|$ by a factor of 2 and a reflection across the x-axis, then a translation right 3 units and up 4 units

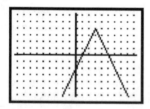

8. The absolute-value graph is stretched vertically by a factor of 3. Its vertex remains at $(0, 0)$.

9. (See table at bottom of page.)

10. a. A reflection across the x-axis and a translation left 3 units. The order of the transformations does not matter.

b. Possible answers: A vertical shrink by a factor of 0.5 followed by a translation right 2 units and up 1 unit, or, a translation right 2 units, followed by a vertical shrink by a factor of 0.5, followed by a translation up 1 unit.

11. a. A horizontal stretch by a factor of 3

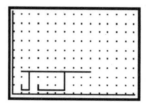

b. A horizontal stretch by a factor of 3 and a vertical stretch by a factor of 3

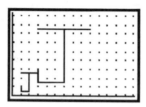

c. A horizontal shrink by a factor of 0.5 and a vertical shrink by a factor of 0.5

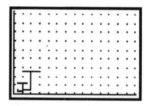

d. These transformations increase or decrease the overall size of the figure without changing its shape.

Lesson 8.4, Exercise 9.

Change	Equation	Transformation
Replace x with $x - 3$	$y = |x - 3|$	Translation right 3 units
Replace y with $y + 2$	$y = |x| - 2$	Translation down 2 units
Replace y with $-y$	$y = -|x|$	**Reflection across the x-axis**
Replace y with $y - 2$	$y = |x| + 2$	**Translation up 2 units**
Replace y with $\frac{y}{0.5}$	$y = 0.5|x|$	Vertical shrink by a factor of 0.5
Replace x with $x + 4$	$y = |x + 4|$	Translation left 4 units
Replace y with $\frac{y}{1.5}$	$y = 1.5|x|$	**Vertical stretch by a factor of 1.5**
Replace x with $x - 1$	$y = |x - 1|$	Translation right 1 unit
Replace y with $\frac{y}{3}$	$y = 3|x|$	**Vertical stretch by a factor of 3**

12. Predictions will vary.

a. A vertical shrink by a factor of 0.5 and a reflection across the *x*-axis

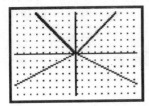

b. A vertical stretch by a factor of 2 and a translation right 4 units

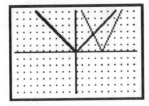

c. A vertical stretch by a factor of 3 and a reflection across the *x*-axis, then a translation left 2 units and up 4 units (*Note:* The stretch, the reflection, and the translation left can be performed in any order, but the translation up must be done *after* the reflection and the stretch.)

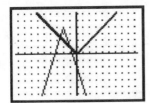

13. a. Answers will vary. The plot is shaped like an absolute-value function. Students can experiment with transformations of $y = |x|$ until they find a good fit. Possible answer: $f(x) = -25|x - 3.2| + 80$

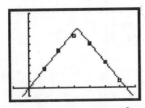

$[-1, 7, 1, -10, 100, 10]$

b. Answers will vary. Using the equation in 13a, $f(2.5) = 62.5$. This means that the depth of the snow after 2.5 months (mid-December) was about 62.5 cm.

c. Answers will vary. Using the equation in 13a, $x = 1.88$ or $x = 4.52$. This means that the depth of the snow was 47 cm after 1.88 months (end of November) and after 4.52 months (mid-February).

d. Answers will vary. Using the answer in 13a, the snow was deepest after 3.2 months (early January). At that time, it was 80 cm deep.

14. The tree should move left 1 unit in each frame, and it should be shrunk vertically by a factor of 0.8. So, each move must transform the point (x, y) into the point $(x - 1, 0.8y)$.

15. a. Yes; when you substitute 1 for *x*, you get $y = a \cdot 1^2 = a$.

b. Yes; when you substitute 1 for *x*, you get $y = a \cdot |1| = a$.

c. No; unless $f(1) = 1$, *a* will not be the same as the *y*-value. For example, if $f(1) = 3$, then $y = a \cdot f(1) = a \cdot 3$. In this case, $a = \frac{y}{3}$.

16. a. $\frac{1}{2^9}$ **b.** 5^{10} **c.** $2^{12} \cdot 3^6$ **d.** $\frac{1}{3^8 \cdot x^{12}}$

17. a. *x* represents actual temperature, and *y* represents the wind chill temperature.

b. Solve the equation $-15 = -29 + 1.4x$. The solution is $x = 10$, so if the wind chill temperature is $-15°F$ with a wind speed of 40 miles per hour, the actual temperature is approximately $10°F$.

18. a. $\dfrac{1}{x + 3} = \dfrac{1}{2x}$

$$\frac{x + 3}{1} = \frac{2x}{1}$$

$$x + 3 = 2x$$

$$3 = x$$

b.
$$\frac{20}{x} = \frac{15}{x - 4}$$

$$\frac{x}{20} = \frac{x - 4}{15}$$

$$60\left(\frac{x}{20}\right) = 60\left(\frac{x - 4}{15}\right)$$

$$3x = 4(x - 4)$$

$$3x = 4x - 16$$

$$x = 16$$

c.
$$\frac{5}{2x} + \frac{1}{2} = \frac{9}{4}$$

$$\frac{5}{2x} = \frac{9}{4} - \frac{1}{2}$$

$$\frac{5}{2x} = \frac{9}{4} - \frac{2}{4}$$

$$\frac{5}{2x} = \frac{7}{4}$$

$$\frac{2x}{5} = \frac{4}{7}$$

$$35\left(\frac{2x}{5}\right) = 35\left(\frac{4}{7}\right)$$

$$7(2x) = 5(4)$$

$$14x = 20$$

$$x = \frac{10}{7} \approx 1.43$$

d. $-95 = \dfrac{5}{x-10} - 100$

$$5 = \dfrac{5}{x-10}$$

$$\dfrac{1}{5} = \dfrac{x-10}{5}$$

$$1 = x - 10$$

$$11 = x$$

IMPROVING YOUR REASONING SKILLS

Possible equations for the horizontal stretch include $y = \left(\dfrac{x}{2}\right)^2$ and $y = (0.5x)^2$. Because these equations are equivalent to $y = 0.25x^2$, the horizontal stretch can also be considered a vertical shrink by a factor of 0.25. Just as a vertical dilation of $f(x)$ by a factor of a is given by $\dfrac{y}{a} = f(x)$, a horizontal stretch or shrink by a factor of b can be represented generically by $y = f\left(\dfrac{x}{b}\right)$. You may want to ask why the variable x is divided by the factor b. For a point (x, y) on the transformed equation, the point $\left(\dfrac{x}{b}, y\right)$ satisfies the original equation, so the new graph has the equation $y = f\left(\dfrac{x}{b}\right)$.

LESSON 8.5

Activity Day: There are no answers for this lesson.

LESSON 8.6

EXERCISES

1. a. Possible answer: A reflection of the graph of $y = x^2$ across the x-axis, then a translation up 2 units; $y = -x^2 + 2$

   b. A vertical shrink of the graph of $y = |x|$ by a factor of $\dfrac{1}{3}$ and a translation right 2 units; $y = \dfrac{1}{3}|x - 2|$

   c. Possible answer: A vertical shrink of the graph of $y = x^2$ by a factor of 0.5, then a translation right 1 unit and down 1 unit (*Note:* The translation right can be done before the shrink, but the translation down must be done *after* the shrink.); $y = 0.5(x - 1)^2 - 1$

   d. Possible answer: A vertical stretch of the graph of $y = |x|$ by a factor of 2 and a reflection across the x-axis, then a translation left 2 units and up 3 units (*Note:* The stretch, the reflection, and the translation left can be done in any order, but the translation up must be done *after* the reflection and the stretch.); $y = -2|x + 2| + 3$

2. Each y-value in the table is twice the corresponding y-value for $y = \dfrac{1}{x}$, so the equation is $y = \dfrac{2}{x}$.

3. The graph of $y = \dfrac{1}{x}$ contains the point $(-1, -1)$. The corresponding point on this graph is $(-1, 5)$. So, the graph is a vertical stretch of $y = \dfrac{1}{x}$ by a factor of 5 and a reflection across the x-axis. The equation is $y = -\dfrac{5}{x}$.

4. The blue curve is $g(x) = \dfrac{8}{x}$ and the red curve is $f(x) = \dfrac{4}{x}$. Explanations will vary. Possible explanation: The red curve is closer to the origin, and $f(x) = \dfrac{4}{x}$ indicates less vertical stretch. Or, $f(1) = 4$, which is a point on the red curve, whereas $g(1) = 8$.

5. a. A vertical stretch by a factor of 4; domain: $x \neq 0$

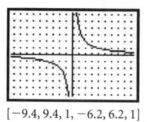

$[-9.4, 9.4, 1, -6.2, 6.2, 1]$

   b. A translation right 5 units and down 2 units; domain: $x \neq 5$

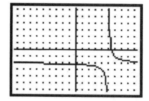

   c. A vertical shrink by a factor of 0.5, then a translation up 3 units; domain: $x \neq 0$

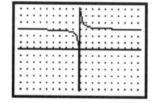

   d. A vertical stretch by a factor of 3, a reflection across the x-axis, and a translation left 3 units; domain: $x \neq -3$

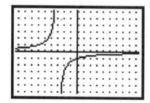

6. If the expressions were equivalent, the two graphs would be the same. The graph shows that they are not. You can cancel only *factors*, and $3x + 7$ and $x + 7$ don't have any factors in common.

7. a. This is a graph of $y = \dfrac{1}{x}$ shifted right 3 units, so the equation is $y = \dfrac{1}{x - 3}$.

   b. This is a graph of $y = \dfrac{1}{x}$ shifted left 2 units, so the equation is $y = \dfrac{1}{x + 2}$.

   c. This is a graph of $y = \dfrac{1}{x}$ shifted right 1 unit and up 1 unit, so the equation is $y = \dfrac{1}{x - 1} + 1$.

   d. This is a graph of $y = \dfrac{1}{x}$ shifted right 1 unit and down 2 units, so the equation is $y = \dfrac{1}{x - 1} - 2$.

8. a. $y = -f(x)$ or $y = -\frac{1}{x}$

b. $y = f(-x)$ or $y = \frac{1}{-x}$ (See sketch above.)

c. The reflections produce the same graph because $\frac{1}{-x} = -\frac{1}{x}$.

9. Because 5% of the 0.5 liter of solution is salt, the solution contains 0.05(0.5), or 0.025 liter of salt. So, if x is the amount of water added in liters, and y is the concentration of salt, then the equation is $y = \frac{0.025}{0.5 + x}$. To find the amount of water that should be added to create a 1% solution, solve $\frac{0.025}{0.5 + x} = 0.01$. The solution is $x = 2$, so 2 liters need to be added.

10. a. $700

b.

Additional businesses	0	5	10	15	20
Cost per business ($)	700.00	350.00	233.33	175.00	140.00

c. $y = \frac{3500}{5 + x}$, where x is the number of additional businesses that have signed up and y is the cost per business

d. $150 = \frac{3500}{5 + x}$; $x = 18.\overline{3}$; 19 additional businesses

11. a. $\frac{120x^4}{24x^5} = \frac{2 \cdot 2 \cdot 2 \cdot 3 \cdot 5 \cdot x \cdot x \cdot x \cdot x}{2 \cdot 2 \cdot 2 \cdot 3 \cdot x \cdot x \cdot x \cdot x \cdot x} = \frac{5}{x}$, where $x \neq 0$

This expression can also be simplified by using the division property of exponents:

$\frac{120x^4}{24x^5} = \frac{2 \cdot 2 \cdot 2 \cdot 3 \cdot 5 \cdot x^4}{2 \cdot 2 \cdot 2 \cdot 3 \cdot x^5} = 5x^{4-5} = 5x^{-1} = \frac{5}{x}$, where $x \neq 0$.

b. $\frac{(5x^3)(16x^2)}{80x^3} = \frac{80x^5}{80x^3} = x^{5-3} = x^2$, where $x \neq 0$

c. $\frac{28x^2(x - 5)}{7(x - 5)^2} = \frac{28x^2(x - 5)}{7(x - 5)(x - 5)} = \frac{4x^2}{x - 5}$, where $x \neq 5$

d. $\frac{4 + 20x}{20x} = \frac{4(1 + 5x)}{4(5x)} = \frac{1 + 5x}{5x}$, where $x \neq 0$

e. $\frac{5x - 15x^4}{5x} = \frac{5x(1 - 3x^3)}{5x} = 1 - 3x^3$, where $x \neq 0$

12. a. $\frac{6x}{5} - \frac{x}{5} = \frac{6x - x}{5} = \frac{5x}{5} = x$

Because there are no variables in the denominators of the original fractions, there are no restrictions on the variable.

b. $\frac{5}{12x} + \frac{1}{6x} = \frac{5}{12x} + \frac{1}{6x} \cdot \frac{2}{2}$ — Least common denominator is $12x$; write both fractions with this denominator.

$= \frac{5}{12x} + \frac{2}{12x}$ — Multiply.

$= \frac{7}{12x}$, where $x \neq 0$ — Combine the fractions. State restrictions on the variable.

c. $\frac{5}{2x} - \frac{5}{3} = \frac{5}{2x} \cdot \frac{3}{3} - \frac{5}{3} \cdot \frac{2x}{2x}$ — Least common denominator is $6x$; write both fractions with this denominator.

$= \frac{15}{6x} - \frac{10x}{6x}$ — Multiply.

$= \frac{15 - 10x}{6x}$, where $x \neq 0$ — Combine the fractions. State restrictions on the variable.

d. $\frac{5}{x - 5} + \frac{2}{x + 2}$ — Least common denominator is $(x - 5)(x + 2)$; write both fractions with this denominator.

$= \frac{5}{x - 5} \cdot \frac{x + 2}{x + 2} + \frac{2}{x + 2} \cdot \frac{x - 5}{x - 5}$

$= \frac{5(x + 2)}{(x - 5)(x + 2)} + \frac{2(x - 5)}{(x + 2)(x - 5)}$ — Multiply.

$= \frac{5x + 10}{(x - 5)(x + 2)} + \frac{2x - 10}{(x - 5)(x + 2)}$ — Use the distributive property.

$= \frac{7x}{(x - 5)(x + 2)}$, where $x \neq 5$ and $x \neq -2$ — Combine the fractions. State restrictions on the variable.

13. a. $\frac{4x^3}{24x^6} \cdot \frac{12x^4}{15x}$ — Factor and multiply numerators and denominators.

$= \frac{2 \cdot 2 \cdot x^3 \cdot 2 \cdot 2 \cdot 3 \cdot x^4}{2 \cdot 2 \cdot 2 \cdot 3 \cdot x^6 \cdot 3 \cdot 5 \cdot x}$

$= \frac{2x^7}{15x^7}$ — Eliminate common factors; use the multiplication property of exponents.

$= \frac{2}{15}$, where $x \neq 0$ — Write the expression in lowest terms. State restrictions on the variable.

b. $\dfrac{3(x-6)}{18} \cdot \dfrac{4(x+6)}{8(x-6)}$ Factor and multiply numerators and denominators.

$= \dfrac{3 \cdot (x-6) \cdot 2 \cdot 2 \cdot (x+6)}{2 \cdot 3 \cdot 3 \cdot 2 \cdot 2 \cdot 2 \cdot (x-6)}$

$= \dfrac{x+6}{12}$, where $x \neq 6$ Write expression in lowest terms. State restrictions on the variable.

c. $\dfrac{4xy^3}{(2x)^3} \div \dfrac{2y^2}{1} = \dfrac{4xy^3}{(2x)^3} \cdot \dfrac{1}{2y^2}$ Rewrite the division as multiplication by a reciprocal.

$= \dfrac{4xy^3}{8x^3} \cdot \dfrac{1}{2y^2}$ Power property of exponents: $(ab)^n = a^n b^n$

$= \dfrac{4xy^3}{16x^3 y^2}$ Multiply numerators and denominators.

$= \dfrac{y}{4x^2}$, where $x \neq 0$ and $y \neq 0$ Write the expression in lowest terms. State restrictions on the variable.

d. $\dfrac{3(x+4)}{5x} \cdot \dfrac{20x^2}{6x^2+24x}$ Factor the denominator.

$= \dfrac{3(x+4)}{5x} \cdot \dfrac{20x^2}{6x(x+4)}$

$= \dfrac{60x^2(x+4)}{30x^2(x+4)}$ Multiply numerators; multiply denominators.

$= 2$, where $x \neq 0$ and $x \neq -4$ Write the expression in lowest terms. State restrictions on the variable.

14. a. $4 - 2x > 8$ Original inequality.

$4 - 2x - 4 > 8 - 4$ Subtract 4 from both sides.

$-2x > 4$ Evaluate.

$\dfrac{-2x}{-2} < \dfrac{4}{-2}$ Divide both sides by -2, and reverse the inequality symbol.

$x < -2$ Divide.

b. $-8 + 3(x-2) \geq -20$ Original inequality.

$-8 + 3x - 6 \geq -20$ Use the distributive property.

$3x - 14 \geq -20$ Evaluate.

$3x - 14 + 14 \geq -20 + 14$ Add 14 to both sides.

$3x \geq -6$ Evaluate.

$\dfrac{3x}{3} \geq \dfrac{-6}{3}$ Divide both sides by 3.

$x \geq -2$ Divide.

c. $7 + 2x \leq 3 + 3x$ Original inequality.

$7 + 2x - 3x \leq 3 + 3x - 3x$ Subtract $3x$ from both sides.

$7 - x \leq 3$ Combine like terms.

$7 - x - 7 \leq 3 - 7$ Subtract 7 from both sides.

$-x \leq -4$ Evaluate.

$\dfrac{-x}{-1} \geq \dfrac{-4}{-1}$ Divide both sides by -1, and reverse the inequality symbol.

$x \geq 4$ Divide.

15. Vertex: $(3, 1)$; point to the left: $(2, 3)$; point to the right: $(4, 3)$. To create the graph of $y = 2(x-3)^2 + 1$, the graph of $y = x^2$ is translated right 3 units and up 1 unit, so the image of the vertex $(0, 0)$ is $(3, 1)$. To find the point to the left, substitute 2 for x. To find the point to the right, substitute 4 for x.

16. a. $[A] + [B] = \begin{bmatrix} 39 & 34 \\ 17 & 24 \\ 11 & 13 \end{bmatrix}$. These are the total numbers of items sold for each category of baked goods, in dozens, for the last two years.

b. $[C] \cdot [B] = \begin{bmatrix} 20.50 & 24.10 \\ 90.25 & 102.75 \end{bmatrix}$. The first row gives the total expenses, in dollars, for the fall and spring bake sales this year, and the second row gives the total income from the fall and spring bake sales this year.

17. a. i

b. ii

c. iv

d. Answers will vary as students create a scenario for graph iii. Sample answer: Jack walks steadily from the tower to the creek (or the cabin) and back to the tower.

IMPROVING YOUR VISUAL THINKING SKILLS

Fabric A has a 123123 . . . pattern. You can interpret the pattern as a series of translations of (123) along the length of the fabric. The repeating unit must be as wide as the distance from stripe 1 to the next stripe 1. There are infinitely many units because you could measure from the edge of stripe 2 to the edge of the next stripe 2, or from the middle of stripe 3 to the middle of the next stripe 3, and so on.

Fabric B has a 123212321 . . . pattern. You can interpret the pattern as a series of translations (1232) along the length of the fabric, or as a series of reflections across stripe 1 or stripe 3. The repeating unit will depend on the transformation chosen, but there will still be infinitely many units.

Fabric C has a 1232112321 . . . pattern of vertical stripes and it has a 2121 . . . pattern of horizontal stripes. You can interpret the pattern as generated by a horizontal translation; you can also interpret the pattern as a reflection across horizontal stripes 1 or 2.

Fabric D has the same pattern along its length and across its width as Fabric A. You can interpret the pattern as a lengthwise or widthwise translation similar to Fabric A. There is no reflection.

Fabric D would result in the most expensive shirt. It's not possible to cut symmetrical pieces like sleeves or shirt fronts from a folded piece of fabric. Hence, there would be more fabric waste as pieces are individually positioned, and more time would be involved.

LESSON 8.7

EXERCISES

1. a. $(-2, 2), (1, 2), (-2, 6)$

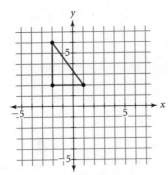

b. To shift down 3 units, you must add -3 to each y-coordinate, so you would need to add the matrix $\begin{bmatrix} 0 & 0 & 0 \\ -3 & -3 & -3 \end{bmatrix}$.

c. $\begin{bmatrix} -2 & 1 & -2 \\ 2 & 2 & 6 \end{bmatrix} + \begin{bmatrix} 0 & 0 & 0 \\ -3 & -3 & -3 \end{bmatrix}$

$= \begin{bmatrix} -2 & 1 & -2 \\ -1 & -1 & 3 \end{bmatrix}$

2. a. $\begin{bmatrix} -4 & -2 & -2 \\ 3 & 5 & 1 \end{bmatrix}$ (The order of the columns may vary.)

b. $\begin{bmatrix} -4 & -2 & -2 \\ 3 & 5 & 1 \end{bmatrix} + \begin{bmatrix} 9 & 9 & 9 \\ 0 & 0 & 0 \end{bmatrix} = \begin{bmatrix} 5 & 7 & 7 \\ 3 & 5 & 1 \end{bmatrix}$

c. $\begin{bmatrix} -4 & -2 & -2 \\ 3 & 5 & 1 \end{bmatrix} + \begin{bmatrix} -4 & -4 & -4 \\ -4 & -4 & -4 \end{bmatrix}$

$= \begin{bmatrix} -8 & -6 & -6 \\ -1 & 1 & -3 \end{bmatrix}$

3. a. $[6 \quad 15]$ **b.** $\begin{bmatrix} 6 \\ 15 \end{bmatrix}$

c. $[4 \cdot 2 + 7 \cdot 8] = [64]$

d. $\begin{bmatrix} 8 & 32 \\ 14 & 56 \end{bmatrix}$

4. a. $\begin{bmatrix} -1 & 0 \\ 0 & 1 \end{bmatrix}$ **b.** $\begin{bmatrix} 1 & -0 \\ 0 & 1 \end{bmatrix}$

5. a. A rectangle

b. Possible answer: For the x-coordinate, multiply row 1 of the transformation matrix by column 2 of the quadrilateral matrix: $[1 \quad 0] \cdot \begin{bmatrix} 2 \\ -1 \end{bmatrix} = 2$. This result goes in row 1, column 2, of the image matrix. For the y-coordinate, multiply row 2 of the transformation matrix by column 2 of the quadrilateral matrix: $[0 \quad 2] \cdot \begin{bmatrix} 2 \\ -1 \end{bmatrix} = -2$. This result goes in row 2, column 2, of the image matrix.

c. $\begin{bmatrix} -1 & 2 & 1 & -2 \\ 4 & -2 & -4 & 2 \end{bmatrix}$

d. A parallelogram

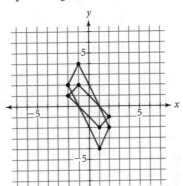

6. a. $[S] = \begin{bmatrix} 0 & 1 & 1 & 0 \\ 0 & 0 & 1 & 1 \end{bmatrix}$ (The order of the columns may vary.)

b. **i.** This matrix operation multiplies each y-coordinate by 3, resulting in a vertical stretch by a factor of 3.

  ii. This matrix operation multiplies each y-coordinate by -3, resulting in a vertical stretch by a factor of 3 and a reflection across the x-axis.

  iii. This matrix operation multiplies each x-coordinate by 4 and each y-coordinate by 2, resulting in a horizontal stretch by a factor of 4 and a vertical stretch by a factor of 2.

  iv. This matrix operation adds 4 to each x-coordinate and 2 to each y-coordinate, resulting in a translation right 4 units and up 2 units.

7. a. $[Q] = \begin{bmatrix} 2 & 3 & 6 & 7 \\ 2 & 4 & 5 & 1 \end{bmatrix}$ (The order of the columns may vary.)

b. $\begin{bmatrix} 1 & 0 \\ 0 & 0.5 \end{bmatrix} \cdot [Q] = \begin{bmatrix} 2 & 3 & 6 & 7 \\ 1 & 2 & 2.5 & 0.5 \end{bmatrix}$

c. $\begin{bmatrix} 0.5 & 0 \\ 0 & 0.5 \end{bmatrix} \cdot [Q] = \begin{bmatrix} 1 & 1.5 & 3 & 3.5 \\ 1 & 2 & 2.5 & 0.5 \end{bmatrix}$

d. $\begin{bmatrix} -1 & 0 \\ 0 & -1 \end{bmatrix}$; $\begin{bmatrix} -1 & 0 \\ 0 & -1 \end{bmatrix} \cdot [Q]$

$= \begin{bmatrix} -2 & -3 & -6 & -7 \\ -2 & -4 & -5 & -1 \end{bmatrix}$, which is a reflection

across both the *x*- and *y*-axes. Multiplying by just

$\begin{bmatrix} 1 & 0 \\ 0 & -1 \end{bmatrix}$ results in a reflection across the *x*-axis,

and multiplying by just $\begin{bmatrix} -1 & 0 \\ 0 & 1 \end{bmatrix}$ results in a

reflection across the *y*-axis.

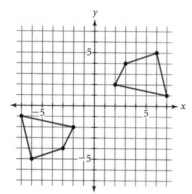

e. $\begin{bmatrix} -2 & -4 & -5 & -1 \\ 2 & 3 & 6 & 7 \end{bmatrix}$; a quarter-turn

counterclockwise

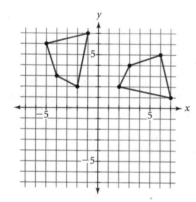

8. a. $y = x^2$

b. $[P] = \begin{bmatrix} -2 & -1 & 0 & 1 & 2 \\ 4 & 1 & 0 & 1 & 4 \end{bmatrix}$

c. $\begin{bmatrix} 1 & 2 & 3 & 4 & 5 \\ 6 & 3 & 2 & 3 & 6 \end{bmatrix}$. The matrix operation

represents a translation right 3 units and
up 2 units, so the equation is $y = (x - 3)^2 + 2$.

d. $\begin{bmatrix} 2 & 1 & 0 & -1 & -2 \\ 4 & 1 & 0 & 1 & 4 \end{bmatrix}$. The matrix operation

represents a reflection across the *y*-axis, so the
equation is $y = (-x)^2$, or $y = x^2$, because the graph
is symmetric across the *y*-axis.

9. a. Answers will vary. Sample answer:

$[R] = \begin{bmatrix} 0 & 3 & 4 \\ 0 & 2 & 0 \end{bmatrix}$

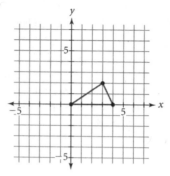

b. Answers will vary. Sample answer based on
polygon in 9a:

$\begin{bmatrix} 0.5 & -0.866 \\ 0.866 & 0.5 \end{bmatrix} \cdot \begin{bmatrix} 0 & 3 & 4 \\ 0 & 2 & 0 \end{bmatrix}$

$= \begin{bmatrix} 0 & -0.232 & 2 \\ 0 & 3.598 & 3.464 \end{bmatrix}$

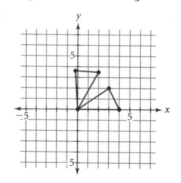

c. A rotation 60° counterclockwise about the origin,
or the point $(0, 0)$

d. $\begin{bmatrix} -0.5 & -0.866 \\ 0.866 & -0.5 \end{bmatrix}$. Sample answer based on the
polygon in 9a:

$\begin{bmatrix} -0.5 & -0.866 \\ 0.866 & -0.5 \end{bmatrix} \cdot \begin{bmatrix} 0 & 3 & 4 \\ 0 & 2 & 0 \end{bmatrix}$

$= \begin{bmatrix} 0 & -3.232 & -2 \\ 0 & 1.598 & 3.464 \end{bmatrix}$; a rotation 120°

counterclockwise about the origin.

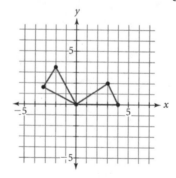

Discovering Algebra Solutions Manual
©2007 Key Curriculum Press

e. Possible answer: Multiply $\begin{bmatrix} 0.5 & -0.866 \\ 0.866 & 0.5 \end{bmatrix}$ by itself three times ($3 \cdot 60° = 180°$). Then, multiply the result by $[R]$.

f. Possible answer: Multiply $\begin{bmatrix} 0.5 & -0.866 \\ 0.866 & 0.5 \end{bmatrix}$ by itself six times ($6 \cdot 60° = 360°$). Then, multiply the result by $[R]$. Or just multiply $[R]$ by $\begin{bmatrix} 1 & 0 \\ 0 & 1 \end{bmatrix}$.

10. a.

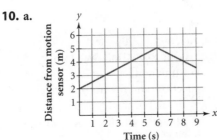

b. $y = 5 - 0.5|x - 6|$

11. a. Five-number summary (in millions): 127, 141, 171.5, 293, 1299

b.   Most Populated Countries, 2004

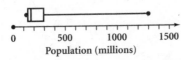

c. Yes; China and India are outliers

12. $x = 0$ or $x = 6$

Equation: $4(x - 3)^2 + 1 = 37$		
Description	Undo	Result
Pick x.		0, 6
$-(3)$	$+(3)$	± 3
$(\ )^2$	$\pm\sqrt{\ }$	9
$\cdot(4)$	$/(4)$	36
$+(1)$	$-(1)$	37

CHAPTER 8 Review

EXERCISES

1. a. A translation left 2 units and up 1 unit

b. $(x - 2, y + 1)$

2. a. i. A vertical shrink by a factor of 0.5 and a translation left 6 units

    ii. Possible answers: A reflection across the x-axis, then a translation up 2 units; or a translation down 2 units, then a reflection across the x-axis.

    iii. Possible answer: A horizontal stretch by a factor of 2 and a reflection across the y-axis, then a translation right 5 units and down 3 units

(*Note:* The stretch, the reflection, and the translation down can be done in any order, but the translation right must be done *after* the stretch and the reflection.) Another answer: A translation left 3 units and down 3 units, followed by a reflection across the y-axis, a horizontal stretch by a factor of 2, then a translation left 1 unit.

b. i. $L_3 = L_1 - 6$; $L_4 = 0.5 \cdot L_2$

    ii. Possible answer: $L_3 = L_1$; $L_4 = -L_2 + 2$

    iii. Possible answer: $L_3 = -2 \cdot L_1 + 5$; $L_4 = L_2 - 3$

3. Answers will vary. For these possible answers, list L_3 and list L_4 are used for the x- and y-coordinates, respectively, of the image.

a. Let $L_3 = L_1$ and $L_4 = -L_2$, and make a connected plot of (L_3, L_4).

b. Let $L_3 = -L_1$ and $L_4 = L_2$, and make a connected plot of (L_3, L_4).

c. Let $L_3 = L_1 + 3$ and $L_4 = -L_2$, and make a connected plot of (L_3, L_4).

4. a. A vertical stretch of the graph of $y = |x|$ by a factor of 2, then a translation up 1 unit

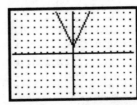

$[-9.4, 9.4, 1, -6.2, 6.2, 1]$

b. A reflection of the graph of $y = |x|$ across the x-axis, then a translation left 2 units and up 2 units (*Note:* The translation left can be done before the reflection, but the translation up must be done *after* the reflection.)

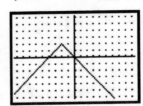

c. A vertical shrink of the graph of $y = x^2$ by a factor of 0.5 and a reflection across the y-axis, then a translation down 1 unit (or, because the graph is symmetric across the y-axis, just a vertical shrink by a factor of 0.5, then a translation down 1 unit)

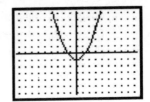

d. A reflection of the graph of $y = x^2$ across the x-axis, then a translation right 2 units and up 1 unit (*Note:* The translation right can be done before the reflection, but the translation up must be done *after* the reflection.)

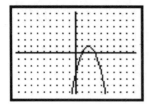

5. The graph of $g(x)$ is the image of the graph of $f(x)$ after a translation right 1 unit and up 2 units, so its equation is $g(x) = f(x - 1) + 2$.

6. a. $y = -|x| + 3$ **b.** $y = (x + 4)^2 - 2$

  c. $y = 0.5x^2 - 5$ **d.** $y = -2|x - 3| + 1$

7. a.

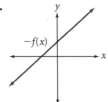

  b. Answers will vary. A correct equation will have a negative slope and a negative y-intercept. Possible answer: $Y_1 = -x - 2$; $Y_2 = -Y_1$ reflects the graph across the x-axis (because $-Y_1 = -(-x - 2) = x + 2$). This supports the answer to 7a.

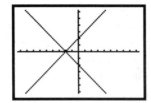

8. a. A translation right 3 units; asymptotes: $x = 3$, $y = 0$

  b. A vertical stretch by a factor of 3 and a translation left 2 units; asymptotes: $x = -2$, $y = 0$

  c. A translation right 5 units and down 2 units; asymptotes: $x = 5$, $y = -2$

9. a. $\frac{90}{16}$, or 5.625 lumens

  b. Solve $20 = \frac{90}{d^2}$.

$$20 = \frac{90}{d^2} \qquad \text{Original equation.}$$
$$20d^2 = 90 \qquad \text{Multiply both sides by } d^2.$$
$$d^2 = 4.5 \qquad \text{Divide both sides by 20.}$$
$$d \approx 2.12 \text{ or } -2.12$$

  Only the positive solution, 2.12, makes sense in this situation. The distance from the bulb is about 2.12 m.

10. a. A translation of $y = \frac{1}{x}$ right 3 units and down 2 units; $y = \frac{1}{x - 3} - 2$

  b. A translation of $y = 2^x$ right 4 units and down 2 units; $y = 2^{x-4} - 2$

  c. A reflection of $y = 2^x$ across the x-axis and across the y-axis, followed by a translation up 3 units (*Note:* The reflection across the y-axis can be done at any time, but the translation up must be done after the reflection across the x-axis.); $y = -2^{-x} + 3$

  d. A vertical stretch of $y = \frac{1}{x}$ by a factor of 4 and a reflection across the x-axis, followed by a translation up 1 unit and left 2 units (Note: The stretch, the reflection, and the translation left can be done in any order, but the translation up must be done *after* the stretch and the reflection.); $y = -\frac{4}{x + 2} + 1$

11. a. $\dfrac{x}{2x - 3} - \dfrac{2x + 3}{8x - 12}$ Factor the second denominator.

$= \dfrac{x}{2x - 3} - \dfrac{2x + 3}{4(2x - 3)}$

$= \dfrac{x}{2x - 3} \cdot \dfrac{4}{4} - \dfrac{2x + 3}{4(2x - 3)}$ Least common denominator is $4(2x - 3)$; write both fractions with this denominator.

$= \dfrac{4x}{4(2x - 3)} - \dfrac{2x + 3}{4(2x - 3)}$ Multiply.

$= \dfrac{4x - (2x + 3)}{4(2x - 3)}$ Combine fractions.

$= \dfrac{4x - 2x - 3}{4(2x - 3)}$ Use the distributive property.

$= \dfrac{2x - 3}{4(2x - 3)}$ Combine like terms.

$= \dfrac{1(2x - 3)}{4(2x - 3)}$ Show the factor of 1 in the numerator.

$= \dfrac{1}{4}$, where $x \neq \dfrac{3}{2}$ Write the expression in lowest terms. State restrictions on the variable.

  b. $\dfrac{42x^2}{x - 3} \div \dfrac{3}{2x - 6}$ Rewrite the division as multiplication by a reciprocal.

$= \dfrac{42x^2}{x - 3} \cdot \dfrac{2x - 6}{3}$

$= \dfrac{42x^2}{x - 3} \cdot \dfrac{2(x - 3)}{3}$ Factor the second numerator.

$= \dfrac{84x^2(x - 3)}{3(x - 3)}$ Multiply the numerators and denominators.

$= 28x^2$, where $x \neq 3$ Write the expression in lowest terms. State restrictions on the variable.

12. a. $[A] = \begin{bmatrix} -1 & 1 & 1 & -1 \\ 1 & 1 & -1 & -1 \end{bmatrix}$ (The order of the columns may vary.)

b. i. Nothing; the image is identical to the original square.

ii. A reflection across the x-axis and across the y-axis, or a rotation of 180°; because of symmetry, the square will still look the same.

iii. A vertical stretch by a factor of 3

iv. A translation right 1 unit and up 1 unit

TAKE ANOTHER LOOK

The equation of the line of reflection is $y = x$. Students should find that the coordinates of each point are interchanged after the reflection. That is, the image of a point (x, y) is (y, x). For example, the image of $(2, 4)$ is $(4, 2)$. An example of a function whose inverse is also a function is $y = 2x$. An example of a function whose inverse is not a function is $y = x^2$.

CHAPTER 9

LESSON 9.1

EXERCISES

1. a. $x^2 + 3x - 7 = 11$

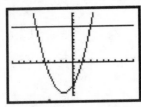

$[-10, 10, 1, -10, 15, 1]$

$x = -6$ or $x = 3$

b. $-x^2 + x + 4 = 7$

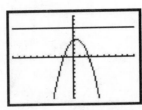

$[-10, 10, 1, -10, 10, 1]$

There are no real solutions.

c. $x^2 - 6x + 14 = 5$

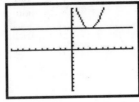

$[-10, 10, 1, -10, 10, 1]$

$x = 3$

d. $-3x^2 - 5x - 2 = -5$

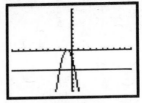

$[-10, 10, 1, -10, 10, 1]$

$x \approx -2.14$ or $x \approx 0.47$

2. a. Real, rational

b. Real, rational, integer

c. Real, irrational

d. Real, rational, integer, whole number, natural number

3. a.

$x^2 = 18$	Original equation.
$\sqrt{x^2} = \sqrt{18}$	Take the square root to undo the squaring.
$\|x\| = \sqrt{18}$	Definition of absolute value.
$x = \pm\sqrt{18}$	Use $\pm$ to undo the absolute value.

b.

$x^2 + 3 = 52$	Original equation.
$x^2 = 49$	Subtract 3 to undo the addition.
$\sqrt{x^2} = \sqrt{49}$	Take the square root to undo the squaring.
$\|x\| = \sqrt{49}$	Definition of absolute value.
$x = \pm7$	Use $\pm$ to undo the absolute value.

c.

$(x - 2)^2 = 25$	Original equation.
$\sqrt{(x-2)^2} = \sqrt{25}$	Take the square root to undo the squaring.
$\|x - 2\| = \sqrt{25}$	Definition of absolute value.
$x - 2 = \pm5$	Use $\pm$ to undo the absolute value.
$x = 5 + 2$ or $x = -5 + 2$	Add 2 to undo the subtraction.
$x = 7$ or $x = -3$	Evaluate.

d. $2(x + 1)^2 - 4 = 10$ Original equation.

    $2(x + 1)^2 = 14$ Add 4 to undo the subtraction.

    $(x + 1)^2 = 7$ Divide by 2 to undo the multiplication.

    $\sqrt{(x + 1)^2} = \sqrt{7}$ Take the square root to undo the squaring.

    $|x + 1| = \sqrt{7}$ Definition of absolute value.

    $x + 1 = \pm\sqrt{7}$ Use $\pm$ to undo the absolute value.

    $x = -1 \pm \sqrt{7}$ Subtract 1 to undo the addition.

4. Sample answers:

a.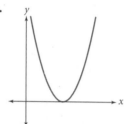

b.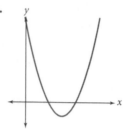

c.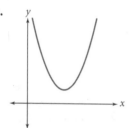

d.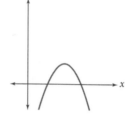

5. a. $h(0) = -4.9(0)^2 + 147 = 147$. This means that the ball was released from a height of 147 m.

b. $-4.9t^2 + 147 = 20$ Original equation.

    $-4.9t^2 = -127$ Subtract 147 from both sides.

    $t^2 \approx 25.92$ Divide both sides by -4.9.

    $t \approx \pm 5.09$ Take the square root of both sides.

To find the solution graphically, graph $y = -4.9t^2 + 147$ and $y = 20$, and find the intersection points. The graph shows two solution points: $(5.09, 20)$ and $(-5.09, 20)$.

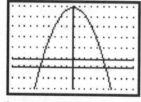

$[-10, 10, 1, -50, 150, 25]$

c. No, only the solution $(5.09, 20)$ makes sense because the time t must be positive.

d. The graph shows that the height is less than 20 m when $t > 5.09$ s. (*Note*: $h(t)$ is also less than 20 when $t < -5.09$, but negative time values do not make sense in this situation.)

e. The ball hits the ground when $t \approx 5.48$ s because the positive x-intercept is near the point $(5.48, 0)$. (You could also find this answer by solving $-4.9t^2 + 147 = 0$ symbolically.)

6. a. Because the rocket is fired from the ground, the height is 0 m when $t = 0$, so the graph goes through $(0, 0)$. The height is 108 m when $t = 4.70$, so the graph goes through $(4.70, 108)$. Because the rocket hits the ground at 9.40 s, the height is 0 when $t = 9.40$, so the graph goes through $(9.40, 0)$.

b. Sample answer: $[-1, 10, 1, -10, 120, 10]$

c. The vertex is the highest point of the graph. The problem states that the rocket is at its highest point, 108 m, after 4.70 s. So, the vertex is $(4.7, 108)$.

d. The equation must be in the form $h(t) = a(t - 4.7)^2 + 108$. Because $(0, 0)$ is on the graph, substitute it into the equation and solve for a:

$$0 = a(0 - 4.7)^2 + 108$$

$$0 = 22.09a + 108$$

$$-108 = 22.09a$$

$$-4.9 \approx a$$

So, the equation is $h(t) = -4.9(x - 4.7)^2 + 108$.

e. $h(3) = -4.9(3 - 4.7)^2 + 108$
$= -4.9(-1.7)^2 + 108 \approx 94$. The height at 3 s is about 94 m.

f. Solve $-4.9(t - 4.7)^2 + 108 = 47$.

  $-4.9(t - 4.7)^2 + 108 = 47$ Original equation.

    $-4.9(t - 4.7)^2 = -61$ Subtract 108 from both sides.

    $(t - 4.7)^2 = \dfrac{61}{4.9}$ Divide both sides by -4.9.

    $t - 4.7 = \pm\sqrt{\dfrac{61}{4.9}}$ Take the square root of both sides.

    $t = 4.7 \pm\sqrt{\dfrac{61}{4.9}}$ Add 4.7 to both sides.

    $t \approx 1.17$ or   Evaluate.

    $t \approx 8.23$

At about 1.17 s and 8.23 s, the rocket will be 47 m above the ground.

Discovering Algebra Solutions Manual
©2007 Key Curriculum Press

7. a. $p(2) = -0.23(2 - 3.4)^2 + 4.2 \approx 3.75$. After the ball has gone 2 m horizontally, it will be approximately 3.75 m above the ground.

b. Solve $-0.23(x - 3.4)^2 + 4.2 = 2$.

$-0.23(x - 3.4)^2 + 4.2 = 2$	Original equation.
$-0.23(x - 3.4)^2 = -2.2$	Subtract 4.2 from both sides.
$(x - 3.4)^2 = \dfrac{2.2}{0.23}$	Divide both sides by -0.23.
$x - 3.4 = \pm\sqrt{\dfrac{2.2}{0.23}}$	Take the square root of both sides.
$x = 3.4 \pm \sqrt{\dfrac{2.2}{0.23}}$	Add 3.4 to both sides
$x \approx 0.31$ or	Evaluate.
$x \approx 6.49$	

The ball will be 2 m above the ground when it has gone 0.31 m horizontally and again when it has gone 6.49 m horizontally. Exact solutions to the equation are $3.4 \pm \sqrt{\dfrac{220}{23}}$.

c. When the ball is released, the horizontal distance x is 0, so find $p(x)$ when $x = 0$: $p(0) = -0.23(0 - 3.4)^2 + 4.2 = 1.5412$. So, the ball's height is 1.5412 m when it is released.

d. When the ball hits the ground, $p(x) = 0$, so solve $-0.23(x - 3.4)^2 + 4.2 = 0$.

$-0.23(x - 3.4)^2 + 4.2 = 0$	Original equation.
$-0.23(x - 3.4)^2 = -4.2$	Subtract 4.2 from both sides.
$(x - 3.4)^2 = \dfrac{4.2}{0.23}$	Divide both sides by -0.23.
$x - 3.4 = \pm\sqrt{\dfrac{4.2}{0.23}}$	Take the square root of both sides.
$x = 3.4 \pm \sqrt{\dfrac{4.2}{0.23}}$	Add 3.4 to both sides.
$x \approx -0.87$ or	Evaluate.
$x \approx 7.67$	

Only the positive solution makes sense in this situation. The ball hits the ground when it has traveled about 7.67 m horizontally. The exact solutions to the equation are $3.4 \pm \sqrt{\dfrac{420}{23}}$.

8. a. The graph shows that only one solution exists at the intersection of $y = 4$ and $y = -2(x - 3)^2 + 4$. Tracing the graph shows the intersection point is $(3, 4)$, so the solution is $x = 3$.

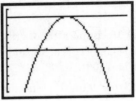

$[0, 6, 1, -5, 5, 1]$

b. The table shows the solution is $x = 3$.

X	Y1	Y2
0	-14	4
1	-4	4
2	2	4
3	4	4
4	2	4
5	-4	4
6	-14	4

X=3

c.

$4 = -2(x - 3)^2 + 4$	Original equation.
$0 = -2(x - 3)^2$	Subtract 4 from both sides.
$0 = (x - 3)^2$	Divide both sides by -2.
$0 = x - 3$	Take the square root of both sides.
$3 = x$	Add 3 to both sides.

9. a. The x-intercepts indicate when the projectile is at ground level.

b. 2.63 s and 7.58 s

c. Find the average of 2.63 s and 7.58 s, which is 5.105; $h(5.105) \approx 30.051$.

d. The projectile is 30.051 m above the ground, its maximum height, after 5.105 s.

e. $h(3.2) = 12.324$ m. This is the height at 3.2 s.

f. Answers will vary. The horizontal line $y = 12.5$ intersects the parabola twice—when $x \approx 3.2$ s and when $x \approx 7.0$ s.

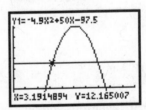

$[0, 10, 1, -5, 35, 5]$

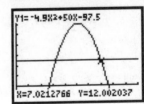

10. a. $y = -16(x - 3)^2 + 20$

  i. A vertical stretch of 16 units, a reflection across the x-axis, a horizontal translation right 3 units, and a vertical translation up 20 units

  ii. (3, 20)

  iii. -16 or $\frac{1}{2}(-32)$ ft/s^2 is the effect of gravity, the maximum height occurs at 3 s, and the maximum height is 20 ft.

 b. **i.** A vertical stretch of 4.9 units, a reflection over the x-axis, a horizontal translation right 4.2 units, and a vertical translation up 12 units

  ii. (4.2, 12)

  iii. -4.9 or $\frac{1}{2}(-9.8)$ m/s^2 is the effect of gravity, the maximum height occurs at 4.2 s, and the maximum height is 12 m.

11. $-3x + 4 > 16$ The given inequality.

  $-3x > 12$ Subtract 4 from both sides.

  $x < -4$ Divide both sides by -3 and reverse inequality symbol.

12. The slope of the line is $\frac{1-6}{6-0} = \frac{-5}{6}$ and the y-intercept is 6, so the equation for the line is $y = 6 - \frac{5}{6}x$. Because the line is solid and the area above it is shaded, the inequality is $y \geq 6 - \frac{5}{6}x$.

LESSON 9.2

EXERCISES

1. The average of the x-intercepts 3 and -2 is $\frac{3 + (-2)}{2} = \frac{1}{2}$ or 0.5, so the equation of the axis of symmetry is $x = 0.5$, and the vertex has an x-coordinate of 0.5.

2. Substitute 0.5 for x to obtain $y = 0.4(0.5)^2 - 0.4(0.5) - 2.4 = -2.5$.

3.
$$0 = (x + 1.5)^2 - 7.25$$
$$7.25 = (x + 1.5)^2$$
$$\pm\sqrt{7.25} = x + 1.5$$
$$-1.5 \pm \sqrt{7.25} = x$$
$$x \approx 1.193 \text{ or}$$
$$x \approx -4.193$$

The solutions match the approximations in Examples A and B.

4. a. $x \approx -2.732, 0.732$ **b.** $x \approx -1.869, 0.535$

5. a. $(x + 3)^2 = 7$
$$(x + 3) = \pm\sqrt{7}$$
$$x = -3 \pm \sqrt{7}$$
$$x \approx -5.646 \text{ or } x \approx -0.354$$

b. $(x - 2)^2 - 8 = 13$
$$(x - 2)^2 = 21$$
$$x - 2 = \pm\sqrt{21}$$
$$x = 2 \pm \sqrt{21}$$
$$x \approx -2.583 \text{ or } x \approx 6.583$$

6. Answers will vary. The solutions, -5.646 and -0.354, are the x-intercepts of the intersection points of the graphs.

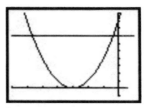

$[-7, 1, 1, -1, 10, 1]$

7. a. The ball is on the ground when $h = 0$. So, to find the times when the ball is on the ground, solve $-16t^2 + 48t = 0$. The solutions are $t = 0$ and $t = 3$, so the ball is on the ground at 0 s and at 3 s.

 b. The ball is at its highest point at $t = 1.5$ s, halfway through its flight.

 c. $h = 36$ when $t = 1.5$, so the ball goes 36 ft high.

 d. Domain: $0 \leq t \leq 3$; range: $0 \leq h \leq 36$

8. a. The ball hits the ground between 3.67 s when the height is still positive and 3.68 s when the height is negative.

 b. Starting the table at 3.67 and setting ΔTbl equal to 0.001 gives the answer 3.676 s.

 c. According to the table, the maximum height occurs between 1.81 and 1.82 s after Taylor hits the ball. Zooming in on a calculator table, the ball is at its highest point at about 1.813 s. At this time, it is 55.5625 ft high.

9. a. Possible answer: The ball is thrown from an initial height of about 8 m. It reaches a maximum height of about 25 m in 2 s and hits the ground at about 4.3 s.

 b. Possible answer: The ball is thrown upward with a velocity of 20 m/s and slows down at a constant rate. At 2 s, it is not moving. Then it starts falling. It is moving downward at a speed of 22 m/s when it hits the ground.

 c. When the velocity is negative, the ball is falling.

 d. This is when the ball is at its maximum height and, at that instant, not moving. Its velocity is zero.

 e. From the second graph, the velocity is 15 m/s when $t = \frac{1}{2}$ s and -15 m/s when $t = 3\frac{1}{2}$ s. From the first graph, you can see that these are the two times when the ball is about 13 m high.

f. The domain for both graphs is $0 \le t \le 4.3$. The range for the height graph is $0 \le h(t) \le 26$. The range for the velocity graph is $-23 \le v(t) \le 20$.

10. a. Bo's ball reaches its highest point 0.5(3.4) s, or 1.7 s after it is hit. Gale's ball reaches its highest point 0.5(4.7) s, or 2.35 s after it is hit.

b. You can't tell whose ball goes farther or higher. Gale's ball is in the air longer, but we don't know whether this is because she hit it farther or because she hit it higher.

11. a.

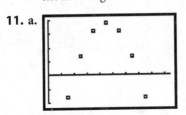

$[0, 9.4, 1, -10, 20, 5]$

b. $x = 4.5$

c. $(4.5, 19)$

d. Figure out how the graph of $y = x^2$ is transformed to get this graph. The graph of $y = x^2$ increases by 1 as you move left or right 1 unit from the vertex. This graph decreases by 3 as you move left or right 1 unit from the vertex. So, the graph of $y = x^2$ is reflected over the x-axis and stretched vertically by a factor of 3. The vertex of $y = x^2$ is $(0, 0)$ and the vertex of this graph is $(4.5, 19)$, so $y = x^2$ is also translated right 4.5 units and up 19 units. The equation for this graph must be $y = -3(x - 4.5)^2 + 19$.

12. $y = a(x - h)^2 + k$

Because the vertex is $(2, 67)$, substitute 2 for h and 67 for k.

$y = a(x - 2)^2 + 67$

Because $(0, 3)$ is on the graph, substitute 0 for x and 3 for y, and solve for a.

$3 = a(0 - 2)^2 + 67$

$3 = 4a + 67$

$-64 = 4a$

$a = -16$

Therefore, the particular equation is $y = -16(x - 2)^2 + 67$.

13. a. $y = 2 + \frac{1}{3}x$ **b.** $y = 3.5 - \frac{1}{4}x$

IMPROVING YOUR VISUAL THINKING SKILLS

A plane perpendicular to the axis will form a circle. To form an ellipse, the plane should be tilted, but not to the extent that it becomes parallel to the edge, when it forms a parabola. Any greater tilt of the plane, including parallel to

the cone's axis, will intersect both pieces of the cone and form a hyperbola.

Circular section

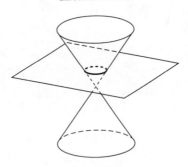

Elliptical section

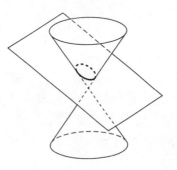

Hyperbolic section

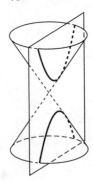

A plane through the cone's vertex might intersect the cone in a point, a single line (if the plane is tangent to the cone), or a pair of lines (if the plane contains the axis). These figures are called *degenerate conics*.

LESSON 9.3

EXERCISES

1. a. Yes; three terms (trinomial)

b. Yes; two terms (binomial)

c. No. The first term has a negative exponent.

d. No. The expression is equivalent to $3x^{-2} - 5x + 2$, which has a negative exponent.

e. Yes; one term (monomial)

f. Yes; three terms (trinomial)

g. Yes; two terms (binomial)

h. Not a polynomial as written, but it is equivalent to $3x - 6$, which is a polynomial with two terms (binomial).

2. a. This diagram shows that $(x + 5)^2 = x^2 + 5x + 5x + 25 = x^2 + 10x + 25$.

	x	5
x	x^2	$5x$
5	$5x$	25

b. This diagram shows that
$(x - 7)^2 = x^2 - 7x - 7x + 49 = x^2 - 14x + 49.$

	x	-7
x	x^2	$-7x$
-7	$-7x$	49

c. First, expand $(x - 2)^2$. The diagram shows that
$(x - 2)^2 = x^2 - 4x + 4$. Then, multiply by 3:
$3(x - 2)^2 = 3(x^2 - 4x + 4) = 3x^2 - 12x + 12.$

	x	-2
x	x^2	$-2x$
-2	$-2x$	4

3. a.

	x	2
x	x^2	$2x$
2	$2x$	4

$(x + 2)^2 = x^2 + 4x + 4$

b.

	x	12
x	x^2	$12x$
12	$12x$	144

$(x + 12)^2 = x^2 + 24x + 144$

c.

	x	-7
x	x^2	$-7x$
-7	$-7x$	49

$(x - 7)^2 = x^2 - 14x + 49$

4. a. $y = (x + 5)^2 + 4$
$= x^2 + 10x + 25 + 4$
$= x^2 + 10x + 29$

b. $y = 2(x - 7)^2 - 8$
$= 2(x^2 - 14x + 49) - 8$
$= 2x^2 - 28x + 98 - 8$
$= 2x^2 - 28x + 90$

c. $y = -3(x + 4)^2 + 1$
$= -3(x^2 + 8x + 16) + 1$
$= -3x^2 - 24x - 48 + 1$
$= -3x^2 - 24x - 47$

d. $y = 0.5(x - 3)^2 - 4.5$
$= 0.5(x^2 - 6x + 9) - 4.5$
$= 0.5x^2 - 3x + 4.5 - 4.5$
$= 0.5x^2 - 3x$

5. a.

	x	2
x	x^2	$2x$
4	$4x$	8

$(x + 2)(x + 4) = x^2 + 6x + 8$

b.

	x	3
x	x^2	$3x$
5	$5x$	15

$(x + 3)(x + 5) = x^2 + 8x + 15$

c.

	x	2
x	x^2	$2x$
-5	$-5x$	-10

$(x + 2)(x - 5) = x^2 - 3x - 10$

d.

	x
x	x^2
-3	$-3x$

$x(x - 3) = x^2 - 3x$

e.

	x	2
$2x$	$2x^2$	$4x$
5	$5x$	10

$(x + 2)(2x + 5) = 2x^2 + 9x + 10$

f.

	$3x$	-1
$2x$	$6x^2$	$-2x$
3	$9x$	-3

$(3x - 1)(2x + 3) = 6x^2 + 7x - 3$

6. a. The coordinates of the vertex are $(2, 3)$.

b. $y = (x - 2)^2 + 3$

c. $y = (x - 2)^2 + 3$
$= x^2 - 4x + 4 + 3$
$= x^2 - 4x + 7$

7. No. Possible explanation: By squaring the values inside the parentheses, Heather is accounting for only two of the four rectangles in a squaring diagram. She needs to add the two rectangles that sum to the middle term.

Discovering Algebra Solutions Manual
©2007 Key Curriculum Press

8. a. 70 m

b. To find the speed, solve $50 = 0.0056x^2 + 0.14x$ by tracing a graph or zooming in on a table. The speed is about 83 km/h.

9. a. The vertex is at $(0.4, 2.5)$, so the ball reaches a maximum height of 2.5 m.

b. $h(t) = -4.9(t - 0.4)^2 + 2.5$
$= -4.9(t^2 - 0.8t + 0.16) + 2.5$
$= -4.9t^2 + 3.92t - 0.784 + 2.5$
$= -4.9t^2 + 3.92t + 1.716$

c. The pitcher released the ball at a height of 1.716 m.

d. Domain: $0 \le t \le 1.1$; range: $0 \le h \le 2.5$

10. a. Yes

b. No. The right side should be $2x^2 - 18.8x + 46.98$.

c. No. The right side should be $-3.5x^2 - 11.2x - 11$.

d. Yes

11. a. Meaningful domain: $0 \le x \le 6.5$; meaningful range: $0 \le y \le 897.81$. The maximum value is 897.8125, but because it represents money, \$897.81 is a meaningful upper boundary for the range.

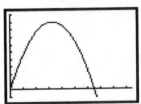

$[0, 9.4, 1, -100, 1000, 100]$

b. Answers will vary. Possible answer: Average the two x-intercepts to find the x-coordinate of the vertex. Then substitute this value into the equation to find the y-coordinate of the vertex. The vertex is $(3.25, 897.8125)$.

c. A price of \$3.25 gives the maximum income, \$897.81.

d. If the price of a yo-yo is \$0 or \$6.50, there will be no income.

e. If $x = 5$, then $y = -85(5)^2 + 552.5(5) = 637.5$. This means that if the Warehouse charges \$5 per yo-yo, the income will be \$637.50.

12. a.

	x	y	3
x	x^2	xy	$3x$
y	xy	y^2	$3y$
3	$3x$	$3y$	9

$x^2 + y^2 + 2xy + 6x + 6y + 9$

b.

	$2x$	$-y$	5
$2x$	$4x^2$	$-2xy$	$10x$
$-y$	$-2xy$	y^2	$-5y$
5	$10x$	$-5y$	25

$4x^2 + y^2 - 4xy + 20x - 10y + 25$

13. $y = x^2 + 8x + 16$. Answers will vary.

14. No, it doesn't pass a vertical line test.

15. The message is POLYNOMIALS.

a. 16; P **b.** 15; O **c.** 12; L **d.** 25; Y
e. 14; N **f.** 15; O **g.** 13; M **h.** 9; I
i. 1; A **j.** 12; L **k.** 19; S

16. a. Possible answer: $[0, 400, 50, -20, 100, 10]$

b. Use a graphing calculator to find the approximate value of the positive x-intercept of the parabola. The x-intercept is approximately 340, and negative values of x are not meaningful in this application, so the domain $0 \le x \le 340$ makes sense.

c. Use a graphing calculator to find the maximum point on the graph, which is the vertex of the parabola. The maximum height of the ball is the y-coordinate of the vertex, which is approximately 70.3. Negative values of y are not meaningful in this context, so the range $0 \le y \le 70.3$ makes sense.

LESSON 9.4

EXERCISES

1. a. $x + 4 = 0$ or $x + 3.5 = 0$, so $x = -4$ or $x = -3.5$.

b. $x - 2 = 0$ or $x - 6 = 0$, so $x = 2$ or $x = 6$.

c. $x + 3 = 0$ or $x - 7 = 0$ or $x + 8 = 0$, so $x = -3$ or $x = 7$ or $x = -8$.

d. $x = 0$ or $x - 9 = 0$ or $x + 3 = 0$, so $x = 0$ or $x = 9$ or $x = -3$.

2. a.

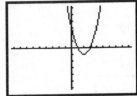

$[-9.4, 9.4, 1, -6.2, 6.2, 1]$

The x-intercepts are 1 and 3, so the factored form is $y = (x - 3)(x - 1)$.

b.

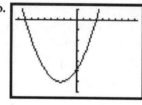

$[-9.4, 9.4, 1, -35, 5, 5]$

$y = (x + 8)(x - 3)$

c.

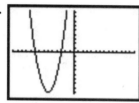

$[-14.1, 14.1, 1, -9.3, 9.3, 1]$

$y = (x + 3)(x + 9)$

d.

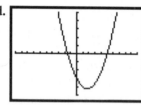

$[-20, 20, 2, -50, 50, 10]$

$y = (x - 10)(x + 3)$

3. a. The x-intercepts are 7 and -2.

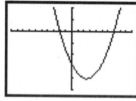

$[-10, 10, 1, -25, 10, 5]$

b. The x-intercepts are -1 and -8.

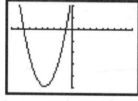

$[-10, 10, 1, -25, 10, 5]$

c. The x-intercepts are 11 and -7.

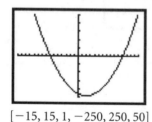

$[-15, 15, 1, -250, 250, 50]$

d. The x-intercepts are -5 and 9.

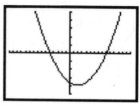

$[-15, 15, 1, -25, 25, 5]$

4. a. $y = (x - 2.5)(x + 1)$

   b. $y = (x + 4)(x + 4)$ or $y = (x + 4)^2$

   c. $y = (x + 2)(x - 2)$

   d. $y = (x - r_1)(x - r_2)$

5. a. The graph has two x-intercepts, -1 and 3.

   b. The x-coordinate of the vertex is 1, the average of the x-intercepts. To find the y-coordinate, substitute 1 for x in the equation, $y = (1 + 1)(1 - 3) = 2(-2) = -4$. So, the vertex is $(1, -4)$.

   c. $y = (x - 1)^2 - 4$; a translation of $y = x^2$ right 1 unit and down 4 units

6. a. Yes

   b. No; change to $(x - 6)(x - 5)$.

   c. Yes

   d. No; change to $4(x + 1)^2$.

   e. Yes

   f. No; change to $(x + 6)(x - 6)$.

7. a.

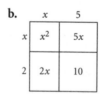

$x^2 + 7x + 6 = (x + 6)(x + 1)$

   b.

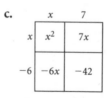

$x^2 + 7x + 10 = (x + 5)(x + 2)$

   c.

	x	7
x	x^2	$7x$
-6	$-6x$	-42

$x^2 + x - 42 = (x + 7)(x - 6)$

Discovering Algebra Solutions Manual
©2007 Key Curriculum Press

d.

	x	-6
x	x^2	$-6x$
3	$3x$	-18

$$x^2 - 3x - 18 = (x - 6)(x + 3)$$

e.

	x	-4
x	x^2	$-4x$
-6	$-6x$	24

$$x^2 - 10x + 24 = (x - 4)(x - 6)$$

f.

	x	12
x	x^2	$12x$
-4	$-4x$	-48

$$x^2 + 8x - 48 = (x + 12)(x - 4)$$

8. a. *(See table at bottom of page.)*

   b. The sum of the roots needs to be -2, and the product needs to be -8. The numbers 2 and -4 satisfy this requirement.

9. a. Answers may vary. Most students will answer $y = (x - 3)(x - 7)$, but any equation of the form $y = a(x - 3)(x - 7)$ is correct.

   b. Answers depend on the equation in 8a. The equation $y = (x - 3)(x - 7)$ has vertex $(5, -4)$.

   c. Answers depend on the equation in 8a, but for any correct equation, the x-intercepts are 3 and 7, and the x-coordinate of the vertex is 5. Answer based on equation in 8a: $y = -(x - 3)(x - 7)$; x-intercepts: $x = 3$ and $x = 7$; vertex: $(5, 4)$.

   d. Answers depend on the equation in 8a, but for any correct equation, the x-intercepts are 3 and 7, and the x-coordinate of the vertex is 5. Answer based on equation in 8a: $y = 2(x - 3)(x - 7)$; x-intercepts: $x = 3$ and $x = 7$; vertex: $(5, -8)$.

   e. Possible answer: There are infinitely many quadratic equations with x-intercepts 3 and 7. Each is created by substituting a different value of a into $y = a(x - 3)(x - 7)$. Hence, all are vertical stretches or shrinks and/or reflections of

$y = (x - 3)(x - 7)$ across the x-axis. The x-coordinate of the vertex is always 5, but the y-coordinate depends on the value of a.

10. The equation must be in the form $y = a(x + 3)(x - 9)$. To find the value of a, substitute the coordinates of the vertex $(3, -9)$ into the equation:

$$-9 = a(3 + 3)(3 - 9)$$

$$-9 = a \cdot 6(-6)$$

$$-9 = -36a$$

$$0.25 = a$$

The equation is $y = 0.25(x + 3)(x - 9)$.

11. a. If the width is 30 ft, the length is $200 - 2(30)$, or 140 ft. The area is then $30 \cdot 140$, or 4200 ft^2.

   b. $l = 200 - 2w$

   c. $A = w \cdot l = w(200 - 2w)$. If the width is 30 feet, then $A = 30(200 - 2 \cdot 30) = 30(140) = 4200$, which matches the answer from 11a.

   d. Solve $w(200 - 2w) = 0$. The solutions are $w = 0$ and $w = 100$, so widths of 0 ft and 100 ft give an area of 0.

   e. The maximum area corresponds to the vertex of the graph of $A = w(200 - 2w)$ which is $(50, 5000)$. So, a width of 50 ft gives the maximum area, 5000 ft^2.

12. a. x-intercepts: $x = 3$ and $x = -3$

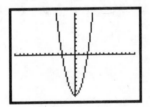

$$[-14.1, 14.1, 1, -9.3, 9.3, 1]$$

   b. $y = (x - 3)(x + 3)$

   c. The x-intercepts are the positive and negative square roots of the number subtracted from x^2.

   d. **i.** $y = (x + 7)(x - 7)$
      ii. $y = (4 + x)(4 - x)$
      iii. $y = (x + \sqrt{47})(x - \sqrt{47})$
      iv. $y = (x + \sqrt{28})(x - \sqrt{28})$

Lesson 9.4, Exercise 8. a.

Factored form	Roots	Sum of roots	Product of roots	General form
$y = (x + 3)(x - 4)$	-3 and 4	$-3 + 4 = 1$	$(-3)(4) = -12$	$y = x^2 - 1x - 12$
$y = (x - 5)(x + 2)$	5 and -2	$5 - 2 = 3$	$5(-2) = -10$	$y = x^2 - 3x - 10$
$y = (x + 2)(x + 3)$	-2 and -3	-5	6	$y = x^2 + 5x + 6$
$y = (x - 5)(x + 5)$	-5 and 5	0	-25	$y = x^2 - 25$

e. $a^2 - b^2 = (a + b)(a - b)$

f. There are no x-intercepts. The graph is above the x-axis.

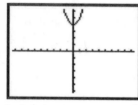

$[-9.4, 9.4, 1, -6.2, 6.2, 1]$

g. Because there are no x-intercepts, there are no roots, so there is no factored form of the equation.

13. Answers will vary. Possible answer: Derek is correct because substituting 4 or -4 for x gives $0 = 16 + 16$, or 32, not 0; the roots should satisfy the equation.

14. a. $\dfrac{(x-2)(x+2)}{(x+2)(x+3)} = \dfrac{x-2}{x+3}$, where $x \neq -2$ and $x \neq -3$

b. $\dfrac{x^2 + 3x + 2}{(x-4)(x+2)} = \dfrac{(x+2)(x+1)}{(x-4)(x+2)} = \dfrac{x+1}{x-4}$, where $x \neq 4$ and $x \neq -2$

c. $\dfrac{x^2 - 3x - 10}{x^2 - 5x} = \dfrac{(x-5)(x+2)}{x(x-5)} = \dfrac{x+2}{x}$, where $x \neq 0$ and $x \neq 5$

d. $\dfrac{x^2 + 2x - 3}{x^2 + 5x + 6} = \dfrac{(x+3)(x-1)}{(x+3)(x+2)} = \dfrac{x-1}{x+2}$, where $x \neq -3$ and $x \neq -2$

e. $\dfrac{x^2 + x - 6}{x^2 + 6x + 9} = \dfrac{(x+3)(x-2)}{(x+3)(x+3)} = \dfrac{x-2}{x+3}$, where $x \neq -3$

15. a.

	x	-21
x	x^2	$-21x$
2	$2x$	-42

$(x - 21)(x + 2) = x^2 - 21x + 2x - 42$ Use rectangle diagram.

$= x^2 - 19x - 42$ Combine like terms.

b.

	$3x$	1
x	$3x^2$	x
4	$12x$	4

$(3x + 1)(x + 4) = 3x^2 + x + 12x + 4$ Use rectangle diagram.

$= 3x^2 + 13x + 4$ Combine like terms.

c. First, multiply the binomials.

	$2x$	-3
x	$2x^2$	$-3x$
2	$4x$	-6

$2(2x - 3)(x + 2) = 2(2x^2 - 3x + 4x - 6)$ Use rectangle diagram.

$= 2(2x^2 + x - 6)$ Combine like terms.

$= 4x^2 + 2x - 12$ Use the distributive property.

16. a. Possible answer: $s = -14.5(w - 8.6)^2 + 827$. The vertex is between 8 and 9 weeks, but closer to 9, because the s-value at 9 is higher. So, try 8.6 as the w-value of the vertex. The s-value will be slightly higher than 821 and 825, so try 827. Then, use guess-and-check to find a value of a that fits the data well.

b. One approach is to use a calculator to find the greater x-intercept of the parabola, which is about 16.2. Therefore, if the pattern continues, people will stop buying the game in week 16 or 17. Another approach is to look at a calculator table for this equation and observe that the value of y goes from positive to negative between x-values 16 and 17.

c. Add the numbers of games sold shown on the table in the exercise to get 5664 games sold during the first 10 weeks. Then, add the numbers for weeks 11–16 obtained from a calculator table for the equation to get 2618 or 2619 additional games sold during those weeks. This gives a total of approximately 8282 or 8283 games sold when people stop buying the game.

d. If 2619 games are needed for weeks 11 onward, and there are 1000 games left in the stockroom at the start of week 11, Edward should buy $2619 - 1000 = 1619$ additional games.

LESSON 9.5

Activity Day: There are no answers for this lesson.

LESSON 9.6

EXERCISES

1. a. $2(x + 3)^2 - 4 = 0$ Original equation.

$2(x + 3)^2 = 4$ Add 4 to both sides.

$(x + 3)^2 = 2$ Divide both sides by 2.

$x + 3 = \pm\sqrt{2}$ Take the square root of both sides.

$x = -3 \pm \sqrt{2}$ Add -3 to both sides.

b. $x = 5 \pm \sqrt{2}$

c. $x = -8 \pm \sqrt{\dfrac{7}{3}}$

d. $x = -6 \pm \sqrt{\dfrac{7}{5}}$

2. a. $x - 5 = 0$ or $x + 3 = 0$, so $x = 5$ or $x = -3$.

b. $2x + 6 = 0$ or $x - 7 = 0$, so $x = -3$ or $x = 7$.

c. $3x + 4 = 0$ or $x + 1 = 0$, so $x = -\frac{4}{3}$ or $x = -1$.

d. $x = 0$ or $x + 6 = 0$ or $x + 9 = 0$, so $x = 0$ or $x = -6$ or $x = -9$.

3. To find the number that must be added, square half the coefficient of x.

a. $\left(\dfrac{18}{2}\right)^2 = 81;\ x^2 + 18x + 81 = (x + 9)^2$

b. $\left(\dfrac{-10}{2}\right)^2 = 25;\ x^2 - 10x + 25 = (x - 5)^2$

c. $\left(\dfrac{3}{2}\right)^2 = \dfrac{9}{4};\ x^2 + 3x + \dfrac{9}{4} = \left(x + \dfrac{3}{2}\right)^2$

d. $\left(\dfrac{-1}{2}\right)^2 = \dfrac{1}{4};\ x^2 - x + \dfrac{1}{4} = \left(x - \dfrac{1}{2}\right)^2$

e. $\left(\dfrac{1}{2} \cdot \dfrac{2}{3}\right)^2 = \dfrac{1}{9};\ x^2 + \dfrac{2}{3}x + \dfrac{1}{9} = \left(x + \dfrac{1}{3}\right)^2$

f. $\left(\dfrac{-1.4}{2}\right)^2 = 0.49;\ x^2 - 1.4x + 0.49 = (x - 0.7)^2$

4. a.

$x^2 - 4x - 8 = 0$	Original equation.
$x^2 - 4x = 8$	Add 8 to both sides.
$x^2 - 4x + 4 = 12$	Add 4 to both sides to complete the square.
$(x - 2)^2 = 12$	Write the perfect square trinomial as a squared binomial.
$x - 2 = \pm\sqrt{12}$	Take the square root of both sides.
$x = 2 \pm \sqrt{12}$	Add 2 to both sides.

b.

$x^2 + 2x - 1 = -5$	Original equation.
$x^2 + 2x = -4$	Add 1 to both sides.
$x^2 + 2x + 1 = -3$	Add 1 to both sides to complete the square.
$(x + 1)^2 = -3$	Write the perfect square trinomial as a squared binomial.
$x + 1 = \pm\sqrt{-3}$	Take the square root of both sides.
$x = -1 \pm \sqrt{-3}$	Add −1 to both sides.

The number under the square root sign is negative, so there are no real solutions.

c.

$x^2 + 10x - 9 = 0$	Original equation.
$x^2 + 10x = 9$	Add 9 to both sides.
$x^2 + 10x + 25 = 34$	Add 25 to both sides to complete the square.
$(x + 5)^2 = 34$	Write the perfect square trinomial as a squared binomial.
$x + 5 = \pm\sqrt{34}$	Take the square root of both sides.
$x = -5 \pm \sqrt{34}$	Add −5 to both sides.

d.

$5x^2 + 10x - 7 = 28$	Original equation.
$5x^2 + 10x = 35$	Add 7 to both sides.
$x^2 + 2x = 7$	Divide both sides by 5.
$x^2 + 2x + 1 = 8$	Add 1 to both sides to complete the square.
$(x + 1)^2 = 8$	Write the perfect square trinomial as a squared binomial.
$x + 1 = \pm\sqrt{8}$	Take the square root of both sides.
$x = -1 \pm \sqrt{8}$	Add −1 to both sides.

5. a. $y = a(x - 2)^2 - 31.5$

b. Solve the equation $0 = a(5 - 2)^2 - 31.5$; $a = 3.5$.

c. $y = 3.5(x - 2)^2 - 31.5$

d. The equation is of the form $y = a(x - 2)^2 + 32$. To find the value of a, substitute 5 for x and 14 for y to get $14 = a(5 - 2)^2 + 32$ and then solve for a. The value of a is -2, so the equation is $y = -2(x - 2)^2 + 32$.

6. a. Let w represent the width in meters. Then the length is $w + 4$, so the area equation is $w(w + 4) = 12$.

b.

$$w^2 + 4w = 12$$
$$w^2 + 4w + 4 = 12 + 4$$
$$(w + 2)^2 = 16$$
$$w + 2 = \pm 4$$
$$w = -2 \pm 4$$
$$w = -6 \text{ or } 2$$

c. The width cannot be negative, so it must be 2 m. The length is 4 m more than the width, so the length is 6 m.

7. a.

$y = x^2 + 6x + 10$	Original equation.
$y = x^2 + 6x + 9 - 9 + 10$	Add 0 in the form $9 - 9$ to complete the square for $x^2 + 6x$.
$y = (x + 3)^2 + 1$	Write the perfect square trinomial $x^2 + 6x + 9$ as a binomial squared.

b. $(-3, 1)$. The equations are equivalent, so their graphs are the same.

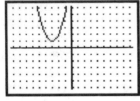

$[-9.4, 9.4, 1, -6.2, 6.2, 1]$

c. $x^2 + 6x + 10 = 0$

$$x^2 + 6x = -10$$

$$x^2 + 6x + 9 = -10 + 9$$

$$(x + 3)^2 = -1$$

$$x + 3 = \pm\sqrt{-1}$$

$$x = -3 \pm \sqrt{-1}$$

There are no real roots because the graph doesn't cross the x-axis.

8. a. The vertex is the highest point on the graph. Because the equation is in vertex form, you can see that the vertex is (2.2, 26.9). This means 2.2 s after it is kicked, the ball reaches a maximum height of 26.9 yd (80.7 ft).

b. $t = 2.2 \pm \sqrt{-26.9 \cdot \frac{3}{-16}}$, $t \approx -0.046$ or $t \approx 4.446$. The hang time is 4.446 s.

c. The initial height of the ball is the y-intercept of the graph. From the general form of the equation, $y = -\frac{16}{3}t^2 + 23.4\overline{6}t + 1.08\overline{6}$, you can see that the y-intercept is $1.08\overline{6}$, so the football is about 1 yd high when the punter kicks it.

d. The y-coordinate of the vertex is the maximum height of the ball, and the x-coordinate of the vertex is the time when the ball reaches this height. The y-intercept is the height of the ball when the punter kicks it. The positive x-intercept is the hang time. The other x-intercept has no real-world meaning.

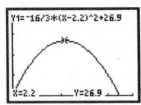

$[0, 5, 1, 0, 40, 10]$

9. a. $p = 2,500 - 5x$, where p represents the price in dollars per ticket and x represents the number of people in the group.

b. The cost for a group package is the number of people, x, times the cost per ticket, $2,500 - 5x$. If C represents the total cost of the group package, then $C = x(2,500 - 5x)$.

c.

$C = x(2,500 - 5x)$	Original equation.
$C = 2,500x - 5x^2$	Apply the distributive property.
$C = -5x^2 + 2,500x$	Apply the commutative property.
$C = -5(x^2 - 500x)$	Factor -5 from the coefficients.
$C = -5\left(x^2 - 500x + 62,500 - 62,500\right)$	Add zero in the form $62,500 - 62,500$.
$C = -5\left(x^2 - 500x + 62,500\right) - 5(-62,500)$	Rewrite to get a perfect square trinomial.
$C = -5(x - 250)^2 + 312,500$	Express the trinomial as a squared binomial.

d. When $x = 20$, $C = 20(2,500 - 100) = 48,000$. So, the cost for 20 people is $48,000.

e.

$x(2,500 - 5x) = 200,000$	Original equation.
$2,500x - 5x^2 = 200,000$	Distribute x.
$500x - x^2 = 40,000$	Divide both sides by 5.
$x^2 - 500x = -40,000$	Multiply both sides by -1.
$x^2 - 500x + 250^2 = 250^2 - 40,000$	Complete the square on the left side.
$(x - 250)^2 = 22,500$	Write the left side as a binomial squared.
$x - 250 = \pm 150$	Take the square root of both sides.
$x = 250 \pm 150$	Add 250 to both sides.
$x = 100$ or $x = 400$	Evaluate.

f. To earn a profit, the cruise company should allow only between 100 and 400 people.

10. a. $P(10) = 0.9$. This means that when there are 10 bears in the park, the population grows at a rate of 0.9 bear per year.

b. $P(b) = 0$ when $b = 0$ or 100. When there are no bears, the population does not grow. When there are 100 bears, the population does not grow.

c. The vertex lies halfway between the roots, 0 and 100, so the population is growing fastest when there are 50 bears.

d. Because the population does not grow when there are 100 bears, this value must be the maximum population.

e. It means that if bears were brought to the region to make a total of 120, the population would shrink, due to overpopulation.

11. a. $2x^3 + 5x^2 + 4x + 1$ **b.** $6x^3 - 11x^2 - 18x + 20$

12. a. $2x^2 + 4x + 2$ **b.** $3x^2 + 4x - 9$

   c. $-2x^2 - 2x$ **d.** $-3x^2 - 1$

13. a. $x^2 - 4x = 0$

$$x(x - 4) = 0$$
$$x = 0 \text{ or } x - 4 = 0$$
$$x = 0 \text{ or } x = 4$$

Verification by substitution:

$x = 0$:
$$0^2 - 4(0) \stackrel{?}{=} 0$$
$$0 = 0$$

$x = 4$:
$$4^2 - 4(4) \stackrel{?}{=} 0$$
$$16 - 16 \stackrel{?}{=} 0$$
$$0 = 0$$

(The solutions for the equations in the remaining parts of this exercise can be verified similarly.)

b. $x^2 + 2x - 3 = 0$
$$(x - 1)(x + 3) = 0$$
$$x - 1 = 0 \text{ or } x + 3 = 0$$
$$x = 1 \text{ or } x = -3$$

c. $x^2 - 3x = 4$
$$x^2 - 3x - 4 = 0$$
$$(x - 4)(x + 1) = 0$$
$$x - 4 = 0 \text{ or } x + 1 = 0$$
$$x = 4 \text{ or } x = -1$$

d. $2x^2 - 11x + 15 = 0$
$$(x - 3)(2x - 5) = 0$$
$$x - 3 = 0 \text{ or } 2x - 5 = 0$$
$$x = 3 \text{ or } 2x = 5$$
$$x = 3 \text{ or } x = \frac{5}{2}$$

e. $5x^2 - 13x + 8 = 0$
$$(x - 1)(5x - 8) = 0$$
$$x - 1 = 0 \text{ or } 5x - 8 = 0$$
$$x = 1 \text{ or } 5x = 8$$
$$x = 1 \text{ or } x = \frac{8}{5}$$

f. $3x^2 - 8 = -5x$
$$3x^2 + 5x - 8 = 0$$
$$(x - 1)(3x + 8) = 0$$
$$x - 1 = 0 \text{ or } 3x + 8 = 0$$
$$x = 1 \text{ or } 3x = -8$$
$$x = 1 \text{ or } x = -\frac{8}{3}$$

LESSON 9.7

EXERCISES

1. a. $5^2 - 4(3)(2) = 25 - 24 = 1$

   b. $(-3)^2 - 4(1)(-3) = 9 - (-12) = 9 + 12 = 21$

   c. $(-6)^2 - 4(-2)(-3) = 36 - 24 = 12$

   d. $9^2 - 4(9)(0) = 81 - 0 = 81$

2. a. $a = 2, b = 3, c = -7$

   b. $x^2 + 6x + 11 = 0; a = 1, b = 6, c = 11$

   c. $a = -3, b = -4, c = 12$

   d. $-4.9x^2 + 47x + 18 = 0; a = -4.9, b = 47, c = 18$

   e. $-16x^2 + 28x - 47 = 0; a = -16, b = 28, c = -47$

   f. $5x^2 - 6x - 7 = 0; a = 5, b = -6, c = -7$

3. a. $x = \frac{3 \pm \sqrt{(-3)^2 - 4(2)(4)}}{2(2)} = \frac{3 \pm \sqrt{-23}}{4}$.
There are no real solutions.

   b. First, rewrite in general form: $-2x^2 + 7x - 3 = 0$. Then, use the quadratic formula.

$$x = \frac{-7 \pm \sqrt{(7)^2 - 4(-2)(-3)}}{2(-2)}$$

$$= \frac{-7 \pm \sqrt{25}}{-4} = \frac{-7 \pm 5}{-4}; x = \frac{1}{2} \text{ or } x = 3$$

   c. This equation is most readily solved by completing the square.

$$x^2 - 6x - 8 = 0$$
$$x^2 - 6x = 8$$
$$x^2 - 6x + 9 = 17$$
$$(x - 3)^2 = 17$$
$$x - 3 = \pm\sqrt{17}$$
$$x = 3 \pm \sqrt{17}$$

   d. First, subtract 5 from both sides of the equation to rewrite it in general form. Then, use the quadratic formula.

$$x = \frac{-2 \pm \sqrt{(2)^2 - 4(3)(-6)}}{2(3)}; x = \frac{-2 \pm \sqrt{76}}{6}$$

$$= \frac{-2 \pm 2\sqrt{19}}{6} = \frac{-1 \pm \sqrt{19}}{3}$$

4. a. None; the graph does not cross the x-axis.

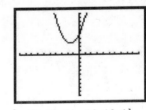

$[-10, 10, 1, -10, 10, 1]$

b. To use the quadratic formula, $a = 1$, $b = 3$, and $c = 5$.

$$x = \frac{-3 \pm \sqrt{(3)^2 - 4(1)(5)}}{2(1)}$$

$$= \frac{-3 \pm \sqrt{9 - 20}}{2} = \frac{-3 \pm \sqrt{-11}}{2}$$

There are no real square roots of negative numbers, so the equation has no real roots.

c. If the discriminant, $b^2 - 4ac$, is negative, there are no real roots. If it is positive or zero, there are real roots.

5. a. $-4.9t^2 + 6.2t + 1.9 = 0$;

$$t = \frac{-6.2 \pm \sqrt{(6.2)^2 - 4(-4.9)(1.9)}}{2(-4.9)}; t \approx -0.255 \text{ s}$$

or $t \approx 1.52$ s. The ball hits the ground after 1.52 s.

b. $-4.9t^2 + 6.2t + 1.9 = 3$. Rewrite the equation in the general form $-4.9t^2 + 6.2t - 1.1 = 0$, and then use the quadratic formula:

$$t = \frac{-6.2 \pm \sqrt{(6.2)^2 - 4(-4.9)(-1.1)}}{2(-4.9)}. \text{ The ball is}$$

3 m above ground when $t \approx 0.21$ s and when $t \approx 1.05$ s.

c. $-4.9t^2 + 6.2t + 1.9 = 4$. Rewrite the equation in the general form $-4.9t^2 + 6.2t - 2.1 = 0$, and then use the quadratic formula:

$$t = \frac{-6.2 \pm \sqrt{(6.2)^2 - 4(-4.9)(-2.1)}}{2(-4.9)};$$

$$t = \frac{-6.2 \pm \sqrt{-2.72}}{-9.8}. \text{ This equation has no real}$$

solutions, so the ball is never 4 m high.

6. Answers may vary. Sample answers:

a. The expression is the quadratic formula with $a = 1$, $b = -14$, and $c = 49$, so the quadratic equation in general form is $x^2 - 14x + 49 = 0$. The expression is equal to 7.

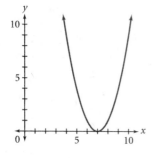

b. The expression is the quadratic formula with $a = 2$, $b = -3$, and $c = 2$, so the quadratic equation in general form is $2x^2 - 3x + 2 = 0$. This expression is not equal to a real number because the number under the square root sign is negative. There are no x-intercepts.

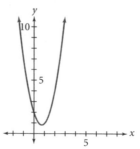

c. The expression is the quadratic formula with $a = 2$, $b = -3$, and $c = -2$, so the quadratic equation in general form is $2x^2 - 3x - 2 = 0$. The expression is equal to -0.5 and 2.

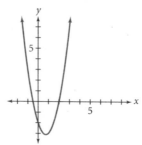

7. Find $b^2 - 4ac$ for each equation. If $b^2 - 4ac$ is negative, there are no x-intercepts (so the equation matches graph i). If it is zero, there is one x-intercept (so the equation matches graph iii). If it is positive, there are two x-intercepts (so the equation matches graph ii).

a. i   **b.** iii   **c.** ii

8. The average is the sum of the roots divided by 2. The sum is

$$\frac{-b + \sqrt{b^2 - 4ac}}{2a} + \frac{-b - \sqrt{b^2 - 4ac}}{2a}$$

$$= \frac{-b + (-b) + \sqrt{b^2 - 4ac} - \sqrt{b^2 - 4ac}}{2a}$$

$$= -\frac{2b}{2a} = -\frac{b}{a}$$

Dividing the result by 2 gives $\frac{-b}{2a}$. This is the x-coordinate of the vertex of the parabola.

9. To find how long the stone is in the air, you need to find the t-value when $h = 0$. So, you need to solve $-4.9t^2 + 17t + 2.2 = 0$. This equation is in general form with $a = -4.9$, $b = 17$, and $c = 2.2$. Substituting these values into the quadratic formula gives $t = \dfrac{-17 \pm \sqrt{17^2 - 4(-4.9)(2.2)}}{2(-4.9)}$. Evaluating this expression gives $t \approx -0.125$ or $t \approx 3.59$. The positive solution of 3.59 s makes sense in this situation. So, the stone is in the air about 3.59 s.

10. a.

Increase (x) (m)	Width (m)	Length (m)	Area (m²)	Perimeter (m)
0	4	7	28	22
0.5	4.5	6.5	29.25	22
1.0	5	6	30	22
1.5	5.5	5.5	30.25	22
2.0	6	5	30	22

b. The perimeter does not change.

c. The area increases and then decreases.

d. $A = (4 + x)(7 - x)$, where x represents the amount of change.

e. The largest area occurs at the vertex of the parabola. The x-coordinate of the vertex is 1.5, the average of the x-intercepts -4 and 7. So, the largest rectangle has a width of $4 + 1.5$ or 5.5 in. and a length of $7 - 1.5$ or 5.5 in. This rectangle is a square.

11. The graphs of these two equations are a parabola and a line, so they might have 0, 1, or 2 points of intersection. To find the intersection points algebraically, form the following system of equations, and then solve the system by substitution.

$$\begin{cases} y = x^2 + 4x + 2 \\ y = 0.5x + 4 \end{cases}$$

First, substitute $0.5x + 4$ for y in the first equation, and solve for x.

$0.5x + 4 = x^2 + 4x + 2$

$0 = x^2 + 3.5x - 2$	Subtract $0.5x + 4$ from both sides of the equation.
$0 = 2x^2 + 7x - 4$	Multiply both sides by 2.
$0 = (2x - 1)(x + 4)$	Factor.
$2x - 1 = 0$ or $x + 4 = 0$	Apply the zero product property.
$x = 0.5$ or $x = -4$	Solve each linear equation.

Now, substitute each value of x separately into either equation of the system to find the corresponding value of y.

Substituting 0.5 for x in the equation $y = 0.5x + 4$ gives $y = 0.5(0.5) + 4 = 0.25 + 4 = 4.25$.

Substituting -4 for x in the equation $y = 0.5x + 4$ gives $y = 0.5(-4) + 4 = -2 + 4 = 2$.

Therefore, the graphs have two intersection points, $(0.5, 4.25)$ and $(-4, 2)$.

12. a. $\dfrac{x^2 - 5x + 6}{x - 3} = \dfrac{(x - 3)(x - 2)}{x - 3} = x - 2$, where $x \neq 3$

b. $\dfrac{x^2 + 7x + 6}{x + 1} = \dfrac{(x + 1)(x + 6)}{x + 1} = x + 6$, where $x \neq -1$

c. $\dfrac{2x^2 - x - 1}{2x + 1} = \dfrac{(2x + 1)(x - 1)}{2x + 1} = x - 1$, where $x \neq -\dfrac{1}{2}$

d. $\dfrac{x^2 - 2x - 15}{x^2 - 3x - 10} = \dfrac{(x - 5)(x + 3)}{(x - 5)(x + 2)} = \dfrac{x + 3}{x + 2}$, where $x \neq 5$ and $x \neq -2$

e. $\dfrac{x^2 + 10x + 24}{x^2 + 2x - 24} = \dfrac{(x + 6)(x + 4)}{(x + 6)(x - 4)} = \dfrac{x + 4}{x - 4}$, where $x \neq -6$ and $x \neq 4$

13. a.

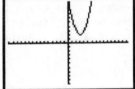

$[-15, 15, 1, -10, 10, 1]$

b.

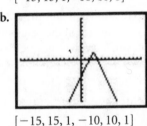

$[-15, 15, 1, -10, 10, 1]$

IMPROVING YOUR REASONING SKILLS

The square root recursive routine works for $x > -1$ to avoid square roots of negative numbers. The reciprocal recursive routine works if $x \neq -1$ or $x \neq 0$ to avoid division by zero. The radical form answers are $x = \dfrac{1 \pm \sqrt{5}}{2}$ (or $x \approx 1.618033989$ and $x \approx -0.6180339887$). A sample recursive routine is 0 ENTER; 1/(Ans − 1) ENTER, ENTER, ...

LESSON 9.8

EXERCISES

1. a. Perfect square; $47^2 = 2{,}209$

b. Perfect cube; $18^3 = 5{,}832$

c. Neither

d. Perfect square; $101^2 = 10{,}201$

2. a.

$(2x)^3 = 5{,}832$	The volume equals the side length cubed.
$2x = 18$	Take the cube root of both sides.
$x = 9$	Divide both sides by 2.

b. $(3.5x)^3 = 21,952$ The volume equals the side length cubed.

$3.5x = 28$ Take the cube root of both sides.

$x = 8$ Divide both sides by 3.5.

c. $2(2.3x)^3 = 3,309$ The volume of each half equals the side length cubed.

$(2.3x)^3 = 1654.5$ Divide by 2.

$2.3x \approx 11.827$ Take the cube root of both sides.

$x \approx 5.142$ Divide both sides by 2.3.

3. a. $4x(x + 3)$ **b.** $2x(3x - 2)$

c. $7x(2x^3 + x - 3)$ **d.** $3x^2(4x^3 + 2x + 1)$

4. a. Quadratic function   **b.** Linear function

c. Exponential function   **d.** Cubic function

5. a. The graph has x-intercepts at -4, -2, and 1, so its equation includes the factors $(x + 4)$, $(x + 2)$, and $(x - 1)$. If you graph $y = (x + 4)(x + 2)(x - 1)$, you'll see that the x-value -3 corresponds to the y-value 4. You want the x-value -3 to correspond to the y-value 2, so you need to vertically shrink the graph of $y = (x + 4)(x + 2)(x - 1)$ by a factor of 0.5. The equation is $y = 0.5(x + 4)(x + 2)(x - 1)$.

b. The graph has x-intercepts at -2 and 1. Because the graph does not cross the x-axis at $x = 1$, 1 is a double root. So, the equation contains the factors $(x + 2)$ and $(x - 1)^2$. If you graph the equation $y = (x + 2)(x - 1)^2$, you'll see that the graph needs to be reflected over the x-axis to match the given graph. The equation is $y = -(x + 2)(x - 1)^2$.

6. a. Answers will vary. Three possibilities are $0^2 = 0^3 = 0$, $1^2 = 1^3 = 1$, and $8^2 = 4^3 = 64$.

b. Possible answer: Start with any integer, a, and raise it to the 6th power. The result is both a perfect square and a perfect cube. (Because $a^6 = (a^3)^2 = (a^2)^3$, the square root of a^6 is a^3 and the cube root of a^6 is a^2. For example, $4^6 = 4,096$ is both a perfect square and a perfect cube. The square root of 4,096 is 64, which is 4^3, and the cube root of 4,096 is 16, which is 4^2.) Or enter $Y_1 = x^3$, $Y_2 = x^2$, and $Y_3 = x^6$ into your calculator and look at the table for integer X-values. Each value in the Y_3 column will be both a perfect square and a perfect cube. The square root of a Y_3-value will be the corresponding Y_1-value, and the cube root will be the corresponding Y_2-value.

7. a. If the width is w, the length is $w + 6$ and the height is $w - 2$, so the volume is given by the equation $V = w(w + 6)(w - 2)$.

b. Three solutions to the equation $47 = w(w + 6)(w - 2)$ are shown on the graph. However, only one solution is a positive value. A table gives the answer: $w \approx 3.4$. Widths greater than about 3.4 cm give volumes greater than 47 cm³.

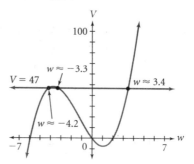

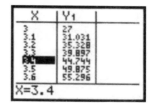

8. a. True. This can be determined by making a graph or a table.

b. False. This can be determined from a graph or table or by substituting 2 for x in the equation.

c. True. This can be determined by making a graph or a table.

d. True. This can be determined from a graph or table or by checking to see if the values satisfy the equation.

9. a. Use a rectangle diagram or the distributive property to multiply one pair of factors. This gives $(x + 1)(x^2 + 5x + 6)$ or $(x^2 + 3x + 2)(x + 3)$. Then, use another rectangle diagram or the distributive property to multiply the two expressions. The result is $x^3 + 6x^2 + 11x + 6$.

b. Multiply the first two factors to get $(x^2 - 4)(x - 3)$. Then, multiply again to get $x^3 - 3x^2 - 4x + 12$.

10. a. 50 cm   **b.** 70 cm

c. $10 \cdot 50 \cdot 70 = 35,000$ cm³

d. The width is 45 cm, and the length is 65 cm. The volume is $15 \cdot 45 \cdot 65 = 43,875$ cm³.

e. $w = \dfrac{120 - 2x}{2} = 60 - x$

f. $l = \dfrac{160 - 2x}{2} = 80 - x$

g. $V = x\left(\dfrac{120 - 2x}{2}\right)\left(\dfrac{160 - 2x}{2}\right) = x(60 - x)(80 - x)$

h. The roots are $x = 0$ cm, $x = 60$ cm, and $x = 80$ cm. These x-values make boxes with no volume.

Discovering Algebra Solutions Manual
©2007 Key Curriculum Press

i. Graph $Y_1 = x(60 - x)(80 - x)$ and $Y_2 = 48{,}488$ with a window of $[0, 60, 10, 0, 50000, 10000]$ to see that there are two solutions around $x = 23$. Use the table ($\text{TblStart} = 20$, $\Delta\text{Tbl} = 1$) to see one solution at 22 cm and another between 23 and 24 cm. For the solution with height 22 cm, the width is $60 - 22 = 38$ cm and the length is $80 - 22 = 58$ cm. Continue to zoom in on the table or the graph to approximate the other solution at $x \approx 23.265$ cm. For this solution, the height is approximately 23.265 cm, the width is approximately $60 - 23.265 = 36.735$ cm, and the length is approximately $80 - 23.265 = 56.735$ cm.

11. a.

	$3x$	-4
x^2	$3x^2$	$-4x^2$
$4x$	$12x^2$	$-16x$
5	$15x$	-20

$(3x - 4)(x^2 + 4x + 5)$ Use rectangle
$= 3x^3 - 4x^2 + 12x^2 - 16x + 15x - 20$ diagram.
$= 3x^3 + 8x^2 - x - 20$ Combine like terms.

The missing expression is $3x^3 + 8x^2 - x - 20$.

b.

	$3x$	5
$2x$	$6x^2$	$10x$
-4	$-12x$	-20

The missing expression is $2x - 4$.

c.

	x	-5
$2x$	$2x^2$	$-10x$
3	$3x$	-15

The missing expression is $2x + 3$.

d.

	x	5
$2x^2$	$2x^3$	$10x^2$
$4x$	$4x^2$	$20x$
-3	$-3x$	-15

The missing expression is $2x^2 + 4x - 3$.

12. a. $11x^3 + 2x^2 + 2x + 12$

   b. $5x^3 - 2x^2 - 12x - 12$

   c. $-6x^2 - 13x + 20$

   d. $-16x^4 + 34x^3 - 28x^2 - 131x + 99$

13. a. $\dfrac{x + 4}{x + 2} \cdot \dfrac{x^2 + 4x + 4}{x^2 - 16}$ Factor the numerator and denominator.

$= \dfrac{x + 4}{x + 2} \cdot \dfrac{(x + 2)(x + 2)}{(x + 4)(x - 4)}$

$= \dfrac{(x + 4)(x + 2)(x + 2)}{(x + 2)(x - 4)(x + 4)}$ Multiply numerators; multiply denominators.

$= \dfrac{x + 2}{x - 4}$, where $x \neq -2$,   Write the expression in
$x \neq 4$, and $x \neq -4$ lowest terms. State restrictions on the variable.

b. $\dfrac{x^2 + 2x}{x^2 - 4} \div \dfrac{x^2}{x^2 - 6x + 8}$ Rewrite the division as
$= \dfrac{x^2 + 2x}{x^2 - 4} \cdot \dfrac{x^2 - 6x + 8}{x^2}$ multiplication by the reciprocal.

$= \dfrac{x(x + 2)}{(x - 2)(x + 2)} \cdot \dfrac{(x - 2)(x - 4)}{x^2}$ Factor the numerators and denominators.

$= \dfrac{x - 4}{x}$, where $x \neq 0$, $x \neq 2$,   Write the expression in
$x \neq -2$, and $x \neq 4$ lowest terms. State restrictions on the variable.

c. $\dfrac{x}{x^2 + 6x + 9} + \dfrac{1}{x + 3}$ Factor the denominator of the first
$= \dfrac{x}{(x + 3)(x + 3)} + \dfrac{1}{x + 3}$ expression.

$= \dfrac{x}{(x + 3)(x + 3)} + \dfrac{1}{x + 3} \cdot \dfrac{x + 3}{x + 3}$ Write both expressions with the same denominator.

$= \dfrac{x + 1(x + 3)}{(x + 3)(x + 3)}$ Combine the expressions.

$= \dfrac{x + x + 3}{(x + 3)(x + 3)}$ Use the distributive property.

$= \dfrac{2x + 3}{(x + 3)^2}$, where $x \neq -3$ Combine like terms; rewrite the denominator. State restrictions on the variable.

d. $\dfrac{x-1}{x^2-1} - \dfrac{4}{x+1}$

 $= \dfrac{x-1}{(x-1)(x+1)} - \dfrac{4}{x+1}$ Factor denominator in the first expression.

 $= \dfrac{x-1}{(x+1)(x-1)} - \dfrac{4}{x+1} \cdot \dfrac{x-1}{x-1}$ Write both expressions with the same denominator.

 $= \dfrac{(x-1) - 4(x-1)}{(x+1)(x-1)}$ Combine the expressions.

 $= \dfrac{x-1-4x+4}{(x+1)(x-1)}$ Use the distributive property.

 $= \dfrac{-3x+3}{(x+1)(x-1)}$ Combine like terms.

 $= \dfrac{-3(x-1)}{(x+1)(x-1)}$ Factor the numerator.

 $= \dfrac{-3}{x+1}$, where $x \neq 1$ and $x \neq -1$ Write the expression in lowest terms. State restrictions on the variable.

14. a. Answers will vary

 b. Japan is the country with the largest increase ($16.48), and Mexico is the country with the least increase (−$0.13).

 c.

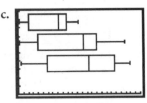

 $[0, 25, 1, 0, 10, 1]$

 Top box is 1980, middle is 1990, lowest is 2000.

 Possible answer: There is a much larger range in the data for 2000 than for 1980. It appears that compensation changed more between 1980 and 1990 than between 1990 and 2000. Overall, the lowest compensation has not changed much, but the top end has moved considerably. The median has moved upward as well.

CHAPTER 9 Review

EXERCISES

1. a. False. The right side should be $(x-3)(x+8)$.

 b. False. The right side should be $2x^2 - 4x + 5$.

 c. False. The right side should be $x^2 + 6x + 9$.

 d. True

2. A reflection across the x-axis and a vertical stretch by a factor of 2, followed by a translation left 5 units and up 4 units

3. a. $y = -(x-2)^2 + 3$; vertex form

 b. $y = 0.5(x-2)(x+3)$; factored form

4. a. $y = -3(x-1.5)^2 + 18.75$.

 b. $y = -1.6(x-5)^2 + 30$.

5. a. $2w + 9 = 0$ or $w - 3 = 0$, so $w = -4.5$ or $w = 3$.

 b. $2x + 5 = 0$ or $x - 7 = 0$, so $x = -2.5$ or $x = 7$.

6. a. $y = (x-1)^2 - 4$

 b. Answers will vary. Possible answers:
 $y = (x + 1.5)\left(x - \frac{1}{3}\right)$, $y = (2x + 3)(3x - 1)$.

7. a. $x^2 + 6x - 9 = 13$

  $x^2 + 6x = 22$

  $x^2 + 6x + 9 = 22 + 9$

  $(x + 3)^2 = 31$

  $x + 3 = \pm\sqrt{31}$

  $x = -3 \pm \sqrt{31}$

 b. $3x^2 - 24x + 27 = 0$

  $3x^2 - 24x = -27$

  $x^2 - 8x = -9$

  $x^2 - 8x + 16 = -9 + 16$

  $(x - 4)^2 = 7$

  $x - 4 = \pm\sqrt{7}$

  $x = 4 \pm \sqrt{7}$

8. a. $x = \dfrac{13 \pm \sqrt{(-13)^2 - 4(5)(18)}}{2(5)} = \dfrac{13 \pm \sqrt{-191}}{10}$.
 There are no real number solutions.

 b. $x = \dfrac{-7 \pm \sqrt{7^2 - 4(-3)(9)}}{2(-3)} = \dfrac{-7 \pm \sqrt{157}}{-6}$

9. a. $f(60) = 0.0015(60)(150 - 60)$, or 8.1. When there are 60 fish in the tank, the population is growing at a rate of about 8 fish per week.

 b. $f(x) = 0$ for $x = 0$ and $x = 150$. When there are no fish or 150 fish, the population does not grow.

 c. The maximum growth rate corresponds to the vertex. The x-coordinate of the vertex is 75, the number halfway between the x-intercepts. There are 75 fish when the population is growing fastest.

 d. The population no longer grows once there are 150 fish, so this is the maximum number of fish the tank has to support.

 e.

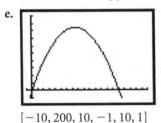

 $[-10, 200, 10, -1, 10, 1]$

Discovering Algebra Solutions Manual
©2007 Key Curriculum Press

10. The roots are at 0 and 1.6 seconds, so start with the equation $y = x(x - 1.6)$. Then reflect the graph across the x-axis. When $x = 0.5$, $y = 0.55$, but you need the value of y to be 8.8. So, apply a vertical stretch with a factor of $\frac{8.8}{0.55}$, or 16. The final equation is $y = -16x(x - 1.6)$.

11. a. The graph has no x-intercepts if $c > 9$. Possible solution methods: Find the c-values for which the discriminant is less than 0. To do this, solve the inequality $(-6)^2 - 4(1)c < 0$. The solution is $c > 9$. You can also find the answer by translating the graph of $y = x^2 - 6x$ vertically to see that for $c > 9$, the graph of $y = x^2 - 6x + c$ does not cross the x-axis.

b. The graph has one x-intercept if $c = 9$. Possible solution method: If the graph has one x-intercept, then the equation has a double root. So, $x^2 - 6x + c$ must be a perfect square trinomial. Completing the square gives the perfect square trinomial $x^2 - 6x + 9$, so $c = 9$.

c. The graph has two x-intercepts if $c < 9$. Possible solution methods: Find the c-values for which the discriminant is greater than 0. To do this, solve the inequality $(-6)^2 - 4(1)c > 0$. The solution is $c < 9$. You can also find the answer by translating the graph of $y = x^2 - 6x$ vertically to see that for $c < 9$, the graph of $y = x^2 - 6x + c$ crosses the x-axis twice.

12. a. $x = -5 + \sqrt{31}$ and $x = -5 - \sqrt{31}$

b. $x = 1$ and $x = \frac{5}{3}$

13. a. $x = -2, -1, 1,$ and 3;
$y = 2(x - 3)(x + 2)(x + 1)(x - 1)$

b. $x = -2$ (double root) and 3;
$y = -3(x + 2)^2(x - 3)$

14. a.

$\times$	x	3
x	x^2	$3x$
4	$4x$	12

$(x + 3)(x + 4)$

b.

$\times$	x	-7
x	x^2	$-7x$
-7	$-7x$	49

$(x - 7)^2$

c.

$\times$	x	-4
x	x^2	$-4x$
7	$7x$	-28

$(x + 7)(x - 4)$

d.

$\times$	x	-9
x	x^2	$-9x$
9	$9x$	-81

$(x - 9)(x + 9)$

TAKE ANOTHER LOOK

1. $i = \sqrt{-1}$

$i^2 = -1$

$i^3 = (-1)i = -i$

$i^4 = 1$

$i^5 = i$

This pattern repeats every four powers.

$i^{10} = i^8 \cdot i^2 = -1$

$i^{25} = i^{24} \cdot i = i$

$i^{100} = 1$

2. Answers will vary; here is one possibility for a Venn diagram of complex numbers and other number sets.

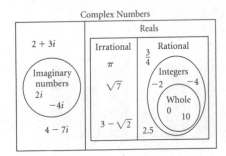

Complex Numbers

CHAPTER 10

LESSON 10.1

EXERCISES

1. To find the number of people with type O blood, find 43% of 75,000. Use a similar method to find the number of people with blood of each of the other types. Type AB = 3,750; type B = 9,000; type A = 30,000; type O = 32,250.

2. a. From the circle graph, the chance that a person has type A blood is 40%.

b. From the circle graph, the chance that a person has type O blood is 43%.

c. From the circle graph, the chance that a person has type AB blood is 5%, so the chance that a person does *not* have type AB blood is $100\% - 5\% = 95\%$.

3. c; the total of the values in $2c$ is 120. The values 12, 18, 24, 30, and 36 make up 10%, 15%, 20%, 25%, and 30% of this total, respectively. These percents match those in the graph.

4. No, the total height of all the bars must be 100%.

5.

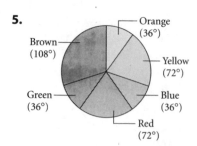

Orange (36°)
Brown (108°)
Yellow (72°)
Green (36°)
Blue (36°)
Red (72°)

6. a. There are a total of 58 candies. Convert each number to a percentage of the total. For example, to find the percentage for orange, solve this proportion $\frac{11}{58} = \frac{P}{100}$. Then, create a bar graph in which the vertical axis shows percentages.

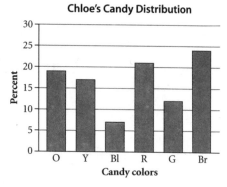

Chloe's Candy Distribution

Percent / Candy colors
O Y Bl R G Br

b.

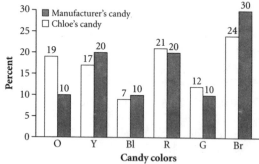

Comparing Chloe's Candy with the Manufacturer's

Manufacturer's candy
Chloe's candy

19 10 17 20 7 10 21 20 12 10 24 30

Percent / Candy colors
O Y Bl R G Br

Answers will vary. Chloe's bag of candy had the same dominant color as the graph from the manufacturer, and her least frequent color was one of the least manufactured. But the distributions are not very close.

7. a. 9th: 27%; 10th: 26%; 11th: 25%; 12th: 22%.

b. 9th: 189; 10th: 172; 11th: 170; 12th: 147. The total population before semester break was 676. After semester break, it is 678. So, the population has increased by 2 students. This is a 0.3% increase.

c.

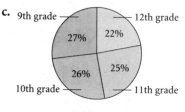

9th grade 27% — 12th grade 22%
10th grade 26% — 11th grade 25%

9th grade 28% — 12th grade 22%
10th grade 25% — 11th grade 25%

The ninth grade increased to 28% and the tenth grade decreased to 25%.

8. a. iii; in the circle graph, the A and D sections should be the largest, with D slightly larger than A. The B section should be about $\frac{2}{3}$ the size of the C section.

b. i; the D section should be the largest, then C, then A. The B section should be about half the size of A.

c. iv; the C section should be the largest, then A, then D. B should be much smaller than the other sections.

d. ii; the A section should be the largest, then D, then C, then B. B should be about half the size of D.

9. The chance that a randomly thrown dart will land in the circle is the ratio of the area of the circle to the area of the square.

Circle: radius = 4 in.; $A = \pi r^2 = 16\pi$ in.^{2}

Square: side = 8 in. (equal to diameter of circle); $A = s^2 = 64$ in.^{2}

Thus, the chance that a dart will land in the circle is $\frac{16\pi \text{ in.}^2}{64 \text{ in.}^2} = \frac{\pi}{4} \approx 79\%$.

10. Because the x-intercepts are -1 and 2.5, the parabola can be described by an equation of the form $y = a(x + 1)(x - 2.5)$. To find the value of a, use the y-intercept, $(0, -5)$. Substitute 0 for x and -5 for y into the equation:

$$-5 = a(0 + 1)(0 - 2.5)$$
$$-5 = a(1)(-2.5)$$
$$-5 = a(-2.5)$$
$$a = 2$$

Thus, the factored form of the equation of the parabola is $y = 2(x + 1)(x - 2.5)$. To rewrite this equation in general form, multiply:

$$y = 2(x^2 - 1.5x - 2.5)$$
$$y = 2x^2 - 3x - 5$$

11. a. If p is the pulses per second, then $\frac{p}{40} = \frac{4.5}{1}$. The anemometer should be giving off 180 pulses per second.

b. If s is the wind speed, then $\frac{84}{s} = \frac{4.5}{1}$. The wind speed is $18.\overline{6}$ m/s.

12. a.

Fastest-Growing Counties between 2000 and 2001

County	Change from 2000 to 2001	Percent growth
Douglas County, CO	23,987	13.6
Loudoun County, VA	21,304	12.6
Forsyth County, GA	11,889	12.1
Rockwall County, TX	4,903	11.4
Williamson County, TX	28,100	11.2

(U.S. Census Bureau, *www.census.gov*)

Douglas County had the largest percent growth.

b. Los Angeles County grew by 118,156, a change of 1.2%.

c. Los Angeles County grew by over 4.9 times more people than did Douglas County, but it increased by only 1.2% rather than 13.6%. The population growth of L.A. County was more manageable from the point of view of the stress on the infrastructure, such as roads, schools, and utilities.

LESSON 10.2

EXERCISES

1. a. Heads, tails   **b.** 1, 2, 3, 4, 5, 6

   c. 2, 3, 4, 5, 6, 7, 8, 9, 10, 11, 12

   d. A, B, C, D, E

2. a. The probability of selecting a particular type of candle is $\frac{\text{number of candles of that type}}{\text{total number of candles}}$. For example, the probability of selecting a vanilla candle, $P(V)$, is $\frac{4}{20}$, or 0.20. Here are the probabilities for selecting each of the other types: $P(O) = 0.10$; $P(S) = 0.30$; $P(C) = 0.25$; $P(W) = 0.15$.

   b. $P(S \text{ or } C)$

   $= \frac{\text{number of strawberry} + \text{number of cinnamon}}{\text{total number of candles}}$

   $= \frac{6+5}{20} = \frac{11}{20} = 0.55$

   c. $P(W \text{ or } S \text{ or } V) = \frac{3+6+4}{20} = \frac{13}{20} = 0.65$

   d. $P(C) = 0.25$. All probabilities would be the same as for the original pack because the ratios wouldn't change.

3. a. $\frac{\text{number in shaded area}}{\text{number in circle}} = \frac{27}{100} = 0.27$

   b. $P(\text{landing in shaded area}) = 0.25$ because the shaded area makes up $\frac{1}{4}$ of the circle.

4. There are 16 possible ways the four coins could land: HHHH, HTHH, HHTH, HHHT, HTTH, HHTT, HTHT, HTTT, TTTT, THTT, TTHT, TTTH, THHT, TTHH, THTH, THHH. Because TTTT and HHHH are 2 of the 16 outcomes, the probability of getting four heads or four tails is $\frac{2}{16}$, or $\frac{1}{8}$.

5. Answers will vary. The probability for 5f is 0 or very nearly 0; the probability for 5g is 1.

6. The area of the rectangle is $77 \cdot 63$, or 4851. Because 136 of the 350 beans are in the shaded region, the ratio of the shaded area to the total area should be about $\frac{136}{350}$. Solving the proportion $\frac{a}{4851} = \frac{136}{350}$ gives a shaded area of about 1885, or approximately 1900.

7. a. Finding and counting a litter is a trial; the outcomes are 1 cub, 2 cubs, 3 cubs, and 4 cubs.

   b. No. If the outcomes were equally likely, then the number of litters of each size would be about the same, with about 9 litters of each size.

   c. $\frac{\text{litters with three cubs}}{\text{total number of litters}} = \frac{22}{35} \approx 0.63$

8. a.

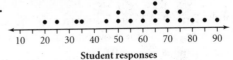

Student responses

   b. $\frac{\text{number of responses of 75\% or greater}}{\text{number of responses}} = \frac{5}{20} = \frac{1}{4}$

   c. $\frac{3}{4}$ (15 out of 20) of responses are 50% or greater. So, you could expect that $\frac{3}{4}$ of the 4500 students, or 3375 students, would give estimates of 50% or greater.

9. a. $\frac{1}{8}$

   b. $\frac{1}{2} + \frac{1}{4} = \frac{3}{4}$

   c. $\frac{1}{4}$

   (The result of the previous contestant's spin does not affect the current contestant's spin.)

10. a. 1 to 12 is red, 13 to 30 is orange, 31 to 45 is yellow, 46 to 63 is green, 64 to 75 is light blue, and 76 to 100 is dark blue.

   b. Answers will vary. For some calculators, a routine that works is randInt(1,100,50).

   c. Answers will vary. Sorting the list in ascending order is suggested.

   d. Answers will vary.

11. Outcomes: Cup lands on its bottom, cup lands on its top, cup lands on its side. Answers will vary, but the outcomes are probably not equally likely. To test the conjecture, flip or toss a cup many times, record the results, and calculate the experimental probability of each outcome.

12. Answers will vary. Possible answer:
$(-4, 1), (-1, 3), (4, 3), (1, 1)$.

13. The hitter had 8 official at bats (the two walks and the sacrifice bunt do not count). Let h represent the number of hits he got. Because his batting average did not change, $\frac{h}{8} = 0.375$. Multiplying both sides by 8 gives $h = 3$. So, he got 3 hits.

LESSON 10.3

EXERCISES

1. Theoretical probability: $\frac{74}{180} \approx 0.411$; experimental probability: $\frac{15}{50} = 0.30$. Possible answers: There are many possible reasons why the experimental probabilities are different from the theoretical probability. Perhaps the method of selecting students was not random. For example, the results could be only from students who were participating in after-school activities or only from students in a particular class. Perhaps the question was worded in such a way that students were biased in their response or reluctant to answer honestly.

2. a. Of the estimated 3500 rainbow trout in the lake, 100 are tagged. So the probability of catching a tagged trout is $\frac{100}{3500}$, or 0.0286.

b. You have to assume that the population is 3500, it remains stable (no fish die and no new fish hatch), and the fish are well mixed.

c. Of the 100 trout she caught, 3 were tagged. So the experimental probability of catching a tagged trout is $\frac{3}{100}$, or 0.03.

3. a. $\frac{15}{250} = 0.06$ **b.** $\frac{235}{250} = 0.94$ **c.** $\frac{15}{250} = 0.06$

4. Of the 126 squares, 32 are shaded. So, if points are plotted randomly, the ratio of points in the shaded region to total points should be about $\frac{32}{126}$. To find the number of points you would need to plot to get 25 points in the shaded region, you could solve the proportion $\frac{32}{126} = \frac{25}{t}$. The result is $t \approx 98$, so you would need to plot about 98 points.

5. a. H, H, T, H, H, T

b. Find the cumulative sum of list L1.

```
2randInt(0,1,100
)-1→L1
{1 -1 1 1 -1 -1…
cumSum(L1)
{1 0 1 2 1 0 -1…
```

c. Even after many steps, you may still be close to 0.

6. a. Answers will vary.

b. Answers will vary. Experiments using a tack with a 9 mm diameter head and a 6 mm point gave an

experimental probability of "point up" of about 0.55.

c. In one actual experiment, there was no change between a hard surface and a soft one.

7. One possible routine is randInt(1,6). Assign students, in order, to groups 1 to 6; skip a number when that group is full.

8. a. $2\,|2x - 5| + 4 = 7$ Original equation.

$2\,|2x - 5| = 3$ Subtract 4 from both sides.

$|2x - 5| = 1.5$ Divide both sides by 2.

$2x - 5 = \pm 1.5$ Definition of absolute value.

$2x = 6.5$ or $2x = 3.5$ Add 5 to both sides of each equation.

$x = 3.25$ or $x = 1.75$ Divide by 2.

b. $-0.5(x - 2)^2 + 7 = 4$ Original equation.

$-0.5(x - 2)^2 = -3$ Subtract 7 from both sides.

$(x - 2)^2 = 6$ Divide both sides by -0.5.

$x - 2 = \pm\sqrt{6}$ Take the square root of each side.

$x = 2 \pm \sqrt{6}$ Add 2 to both sides.

$x \approx 4.45$ or
$x \approx -0.45$

c. Graphical solution: Graph the absolute-value function $y = 2\,|2x - 5| + 4$ and the constant function $y = 7$ on the same calculator screen. When $1.75 \le x \le 3.25$, the graph of the absolute-value function $y = 2\,|2x - 5| + 4$ is at or below the graph of the line $y = 7$, so the solution of the inequality is $1.75 \le x \le 3.25$, or $x \ge 1.75$ and $x \le 3.25$.

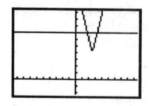

$[-9.4, 9.4, 1, -2.2, 10.2, 1]$

d. $-0.5(x - 2)^2 + 7 < 4$

Graph the quadratic function $y = -0.5(x - 2)^2 + 7$ and the constant function $y = 4$ on the same calculator screen.

When $x > 2 + \sqrt{6} \approx 4.45$ or $x < 2 - \sqrt{6} \approx$ -0.45, the parabola is below the horizontal line, so the solution is $x > 2 + \sqrt{6}$ or $x < 2 - \sqrt{6}$.

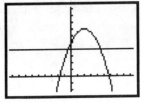

$[-9.4, 9.4, 1, -2.2, 10.2, 1]$

9. Solve the proportion $\frac{60}{t} = \frac{22}{84}$. There are about 229 chipmunks in the campground.

10. a. 64   **b.** $\frac{1}{36}$ **c.** $\frac{9}{16}$

    d. 3^3 **e.** $\left(\frac{1}{5}\right)^3$ **f.** $\left(\frac{2}{9}\right)^2$ or $\frac{2^2}{3^4}$

11. Answers will vary. You could cover the rectangle with beans. Then, find the number of beans needed to cover the shaded region. Solve the proportion:

$$\frac{\text{number of beans in shaded region}}{\text{total number of beans}}$$
$$= \frac{\text{area of shaded region}}{150,000}$$

LESSON 10.4

EXERCISES

1. Your choice is a combination because the order of the three side dishes doesn't matter, and all three side dishes must be different.

2. a. Each committee is a combination. No student can be chosen more than once, and the order in which the students are chosen does not matter.

    b. Each ice cream cone is a permutation. Each scoop must be a different flavor, and the order in which the scoops are placed in the cone matters.

    c. Each ice cream cone is a combination. Each scoop must be a different flavor, and the order in which the scoops are placed in the cone does not matter.

    d. Neither combination nor permutation, because the same flavor of ice cream can be repeated.

3. a. $_5P_3 = 5 \cdot 4 \cdot 3 = 60$

    b. $_5C_3 = \frac{_5P_3}{_3P_3} = \frac{60}{6} = 10$

    c. $_5P_4 = 5 \cdot 4 \cdot 3 \cdot 2 = 120$

    d. $_5C_4 = \frac{_5P_4}{_4P_4} = \frac{120}{24} = 5$

4. a.

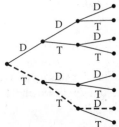

    b. The dashed branches show the path TTD.

    c. This situation involves neither permutations nor combinations because repetition of the objects is allowed. (The same team can win more than one game.)

    d. $\frac{1}{8}$, or 0.125

    e. $\frac{1}{4}$, or 0.25

5. a. Possible answer: I own eight pairs of shoes and am deciding which two pairs to take. I will wear one pair and pack the other. There are 56 ways to do this.

    b. Possible answer: I have 12 pairs of socks and am deciding which 4 pairs to take. It doesn't matter in what order I wear them. There are 495 ways to do this.

    c. Possible answer: I have six pairs of pants and am deciding which two to take. I can wear them in either order. There are 15 ways to do this.

6. a. The number of ways to arrange six books on a shelf is $_6P_6 = 720$.

    b. If the position of one book is fixed, the number of arrangements is the number of ways to arrange the other five books, which is $_5P_5 = 120$.

    c. Because 120 of the 720 arrangements have *The Chamber of Secrets* as the rightmost book, the probability is $\frac{120}{720} = \frac{1}{6} \approx 0.167$.

    d. The probability of one particular arrangement is $\frac{1}{720} \approx 0.001$.

    e. There are $720 - 1 = 719$ arrangements in which the books are *not* in the exact order in which they were published, so the probability is $\frac{719}{720} \approx 0.999$.

7. The answer to Exercise 6e can be found by subtracting the answer to 6d from 1. (Or, the answers to 6d and 6e sum to 1.) The probabilities of complementary outcomes always sum to 1.

8. a. The number of possible different arrangements is $5 \cdot 4 \cdot 3 \cdot 2 \cdot 1 = 120$.

    b. If Jon must be first, the number of arrangements is the number of ways to seat the other four students, which is $4 \cdot 3 \cdot 2 \cdot 1 = 24$.

    c. The order in which the students are seated matters, so the seating arrangements are permutations.

9. a. $8! = 8 \cdot 7 \cdot 6 \cdot 5 \cdot 4 \cdot 3 \cdot 2 \cdot 1 = 40{,}320$

  b. $10! = 3{,}628{,}800$

  c. $_nP_n = n!$

10. a. Because the prizes are different, this involves permutations. The number of ways in which the three prizes can be assigned is $_{150}P_3 = 3{,}307{,}800$.

  b. Because the prizes are the same, this involves combinations. The number of ways in which the three prizes can be assigned is $_{150}C_3 = 551{,}300$.

11. $_6C_2 = {_6C_4} = 15$. Possible answer: Every time you select a group of four students from six students, you are also selecting a group of two students who are left out.

12. a. $_{20}C_6 = 38{,}760$

  b. The number of groups including both Noah and Rita is the number of ways of choosing the other 4 group members from the 18 other students, which is $_{18}C_4 = 3{,}060$.

  c. $\dfrac{3{,}060}{38{,}760} \approx 0.08$

13. a. $\dfrac{18}{100}$, or 0.18

  b. $\dfrac{1}{6}$, or about 0.17

  c. $15 + 18 + 18 = 51$, so the probability is $\dfrac{51}{100}$, or 0.51.

  d. $\dfrac{1}{6} + \dfrac{1}{6} + \dfrac{1}{6} = \dfrac{1}{2} = 0.5$

  e. Yes, the results are close. The die is probably fair.

14. a. To subtract one polynomial from another, distribute the subtraction through the parentheses and then combine like terms.

$$\left(x^2 + 5x - 4\right) - \left(3x^3 - 2x^2 + 6\right)$$
$$= x^2 + 5x - 4 - 3x^3 + 2x^2 - 6$$
$$= -3x^3 + x^2 + 2x^2 + 5x - 4 - 6$$
$$= -3x^3 + 3x^2 + 5x - 10$$

  b. Use a rectangle diagram to multiply the binomials.

	x	7
x^4	x^5	$7x^4$
$-4x$	$-4x^2$	$-28x$

$$(x + 7)\left(x^4 - 4x\right) = x^5 + 7x^4 - 4x^2 - 28x$$

  c. First, apply the distributive property to remove parentheses; then, combine like terms.

$$3x + 7(x + y) - 4y(x - 8)$$
$$= 3x + 7x + 7y - 4yx + 32y$$
$$= 10x + 39y - 4xy$$

15. a. The figure is a triangle.

$$A = \tfrac{1}{2}bh = \tfrac{1}{2} \cdot 10 \cdot 4 = 20 \text{ square units}$$

  b. The figure is a parallelogram.

$$A = bh = 9 \cdot 3.5 = 31.5 \text{ square units}$$

  c. This is a composite figure. It can be broken down into a rectangle, a square, and a right triangle.

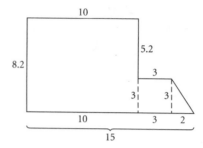

Area of composite figure = area of rectangle + area of square + area of triangle = $10 \cdot 8.2 + 3 \cdot 3 + \tfrac{1}{2} \cdot 2 \cdot 3 = 82 + 9 + 3 = 94$ square units

16. a. $\begin{cases} y = 0 \\ y = 2 + 3x \end{cases}$

To solve this system by the substitution method, substitute 0 for y in the second equation and solve for x.

$$0 = 2 + 3x$$
$$-2 = 3x$$
$$x = -\dfrac{2}{3}$$

The solution is $x = -\dfrac{2}{3}, y = 0$.

  b. $\begin{cases} y = 0.25x - 0.25 \\ y = 0.75 + x \end{cases}$

To solve this system by the substitution method, substitute $0.75 + x$ for y in the first equation and solve for x.

$$0.75 + x = 0.25x - 0.25$$
$$x = 0.25x - 1$$
$$0.75x = -1$$
$$x = \dfrac{-1}{0.75} = -\dfrac{4}{3}, \text{ or } -1.\overline{3}$$

Now substitute $-\tfrac{4}{3}$ for x in the second equation of the original system and solve for y.

$$y = 0.75 + \left(-\dfrac{4}{3}\right) = \dfrac{3}{4} + \left(-\dfrac{4}{3}\right) = -\dfrac{7}{12},$$
or $-0.58\overline{3}$

The solution is $x = -\tfrac{4}{3}, y = -\tfrac{7}{12}$, or $x = -1.\overline{3}$, $y = -0.58\overline{3}$.

  c. $\begin{cases} 2y = x - 2 \\ 3y = x - 3 \end{cases}$

To solve this system by the substitution method, solve the first equation for x to obtain $x = 2y + 2$, substitute $2y + 2$ for x in the second original equation, and solve for y.

$$3y = 2y + 2 - 3$$
$$y = -1$$

Discovering Algebra Solutions Manual
©2007 Key Curriculum Press

Now substitute -1 for y in the original first equation $2y = x - 2$ and solve for x.

$$2(-1) = x - 2$$
$$-2 + 2 = x$$
$$x = 0$$

The solution is $x = 0, y = -1$.

17. $\frac{6}{16}$, or $\frac{3}{8}$

LESSON 10.5

EXERCISES

1. a. From the tree diagram, $P(M_1 \text{ and } M_2) = \frac{1}{4} \cdot \frac{1}{2} = \frac{1}{8}$.

b. This is the probability that she makes the second shot if she misses the first shot.

2. a. At each branch point, the sum of the probabilities of the two options must be 1. Therefore, $a = 1 - 0.7 = 0.3, b = 1 - 0.8 = 0.2$, and $c = 1 - 0.3 = 0.7$. Then, by the multiplication rule, $d = (0.7)(0.8) = 0.56, e = (0.7)(0.2) = 0.14$, $f = (0.3)(0.7) = 0.21$, and $g = (0.3)(0.3) = 0.09$.

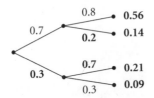

b. $0.56 + 0.14 + 0.21 + 0.09 = 1$. The sum of the probabilities of all the outcomes should be 1, because the probability that one of the outcomes happens is 100%, or 1.

3.

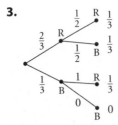

4.

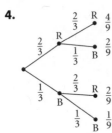

5. a. Independent

b. Dependent

c. Independent

6. $a = 1 - 0.75 = 0.25; b = 1 - 0.8 = 0.2;$
$c = (0.75)(0.8) = 0.2; d = (0.25)(0.2) = 0.05;$
$e = \frac{0.5625}{0.75} = 0.75; f = 1 - 0.75 = 0.25;$
$g = (0.75)(0.25) = 0.1875$

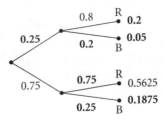

7.

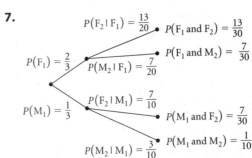

8. Because "another student" means "a different student," these events are dependent. The first student selected has an impact on the probabilities for the second choice. This is an example of choosing an item without replacement, because the same person can't be selected twice.

9. a. The two spins are independent events, so $P(\text{Blue}_2 \mid \text{Red}_1) = P(\text{Blue}_2) = \frac{1}{4}$.

b. $P(\text{Blue}_2 \mid \text{Blue}_1) = P(\text{Blue}_2) = \frac{1}{4}$.

c. $P(\text{Blue}_1) \cdot P(\text{Blue}_2 \mid \text{Blue}_1) = P(\text{Blue}_1) \cdot P(\text{Blue}_2)$
$= \frac{1}{4} \cdot \frac{1}{4} = \frac{1}{16}$

10. a. The number of different arrangements is $_7P_7 = 7! = 5040$.

b. The probability that any particular ingredient is first is $\frac{1}{7}$, so the probability that onions come first is $\frac{1}{7}$.

c. Because there are 5040 possible orders, the probability of one specific order is $\frac{1}{5040}$.

d. This is the complementary event to the event in 7c, so the probability is $1 - \frac{1}{5040} = \frac{5039}{5040}$.

e. The probability that any particular ingredient is third is $\frac{1}{7}$, so the probability that beans come third is $\frac{1}{7}$.

11. a. The number of sets of six different numbers is $_{50}C_6 = 15,890,700$.

b. The probability that one particular number is a winner is $\frac{1}{15,890,700} \approx 0.00000006$.

c. Let W represent a win and L represent a loss.
$P(W) = \frac{100}{15,890,700} = \frac{1}{158,907} \approx 0.000006;$
$P(L) = 1 - \frac{1}{158,907} = \frac{158,906}{158,907} \approx 0.999994.$

d. *(See figure at bottom of page.)*

$$P(\text{L for four weeks}) = \left(\frac{158{,}906}{158{,}907}\right)^4 \approx 0.999975$$

e. $P(\text{L for 52 weeks}) = \left(\frac{158{,}906}{158{,}907}\right)^{52} \approx 0.999673$

f. \$5,200

12. a. Possible answers: Pupil diameter decreases as a person gets older. Pupils are larger in the dark. The diameter of pupils in daylight decreases more slowly with age than the diameter of pupils in darkness. As people age, the diameters for their pupils in daylight and darkness get closer together.

b.

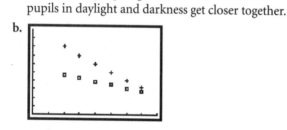

[0, 80, 10, 0, 10, 1]

c. Let a = age in years and d = pupil diameter in millimeters.

Daylight:

For the a-values: Q1 = 30, Q3 = 60

For the d-values: Q1 = 3.1, Q3 = 4.3

A scatter plot will show that the Q-points are (30, 4.3) and (60, 3.1). The slope of the line between these points is $\frac{3.1 - 4.3}{60 - 30} = \frac{-1.2}{30} = -0.04$. Using the point (30, 4.3), the point-slope form of the line through these points is $d = 4.3 - 0.04(a - 30)$.

Darkness

For the a-values: Q1 = 30, Q3 = 60

For the d-values: Q1 = 4.1, Q3 = 7.0

A scatter plot will show that the Q-points are (30, 7.0) and (60, 4.1). The slope of the line between these points is $\frac{4.1 - 7.0}{60 - 30} = \frac{-2.9}{30} \approx -0.097$. Using the point (30, 7.0), the point-slope form of the line through these points is $d = 7.0 - 0.097(a - 30)$.

d. To solve the system $\begin{cases} d = 4.3 - 0.04(a - 30) \\ d = 7.0 - 0.097(a - 30) \end{cases}$ by substitution, substitute $d = 7.0 - 0.097(a - 30)$ for d in the first equation.

$$7.0 - 0.097(a - 30) = 4.3 - 0.04(a - 30)$$
$$7.0 - 0.097a + 2.91 = 4.3 - 0.04a + 1.2$$
$$9.91 - 0.097a = 5.5 - 0.04a$$
$$4.41 = 0.057a$$
$$a \approx 77.37$$

Substitute 77.37 for a in the first original equation and solve for d.

$$d = 4.3 - 0.04(77.37 - 30)$$
$$d \approx 2.41$$

The point of intersection is approximately (77.37, 2.41). At about age 77, a person's pupil has the same diameter, about 2.41 mm, in both daylight and darkness.

13. Answers will vary. About 90% of the population is right-handed. The probability of getting a single head when a coin is flipped four times is $\frac{4}{16} = \frac{1}{4}$.

14. She can give A's to 7 students.

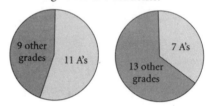

LESSON 10.6

EXERCISES

1.

Outcome	$2	$5	$10	
Probability	$\frac{1}{3}$	$\frac{1}{2}$	$\frac{1}{6}$	Sum
Product	$0.\bar{6}$	2.5	$1.\bar{6}$	$4.8\bar{3}$

The expected value is \$4.83.

Lesson 10.5, Exercise 11. d.

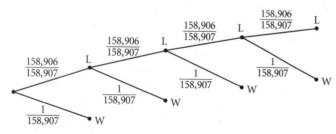

2. a.   1st draw   2nd draw

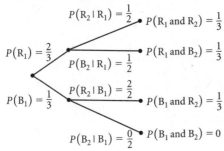

$P(R_1) = \frac{2}{3}$

$P(B_1) = \frac{1}{3}$

$P(R_2 \mid R_1) = \frac{1}{2}$ $P(R_1 \text{ and } R_2) = \frac{1}{3}$

$P(B_2 \mid R_1) = \frac{1}{2}$ $P(R_1 \text{ and } B_2) = \frac{1}{3}$

$P(R_2 \mid B_1) = \frac{2}{2}$ $P(B_1 \text{ and } R_2) = \frac{1}{3}$

$P(B_2 \mid B_1) = \frac{0}{2}$ $P(B_1 \text{ and } B_2) = 0$

b. The outcomes are the number of red marbles drawn.

Outcome	0	1	2	
Probability	0	$\frac{2}{3}$	$\frac{1}{3}$	Sum
Product	0	$\frac{2}{3}$	$\frac{2}{3}$	$\frac{4}{3}$

The expected number of red marbles drawn is $\frac{4}{3}$, or about 1.3.

3.

Outcome	$200,000	−$30,000	
Probability	0.75	0.25	Sum
Product	150,000	−7,500	142,500

The expected value for concert income is $142,500.

4. a. Add the heights of the bins: $2 + 4 + 7 + 8 + 5 + 3 = 29$, so there are 29 students in the class.

b. Two of the 29 students are in the first bin, so the probability is $\frac{2}{29}$, or about 0.07.

c.

Outcome	125	135	145	155	165	175	
Probability	$\frac{2}{29}$	$\frac{4}{29}$	$\frac{7}{29}$	$\frac{8}{29}$	$\frac{5}{29}$	$\frac{3}{29}$	Sum
Product	$\frac{250}{29}$	$\frac{450}{29}$	$\frac{1015}{29}$	$\frac{1240}{29}$	$\frac{825}{29}$	$\frac{525}{29}$	$\frac{4395}{29}$

The expected value is $\frac{4395}{29} \approx 151.6$, so the average (expected) height of a randomly selected student is 151.6 cm.

5. a. The expected value of the game is $\frac{1}{4}(\$4) + \frac{1}{4}(\$7) + \frac{1}{4}(\$3) + \frac{1}{4}(\$8) = \$1.00 + \$1.75 + \$0.75 + \$2.00 = \$5.50$.

b. Yes, it is a good deal, because over the long run you'll come out $0.50 ahead per spin.

6. a.

	Second die					
	1	2	3	4	5	6
First die 1	2	3	4	5	6	7
2	3	4	5	6	7	8
3	4	5	6	7	8	9
4	5	6	7	8	9	10
5	6	7	8	9	10	11
6	7	8	9	10	11	12

b.

Outcome	2	3	4	5	6	7
Probability	$\frac{1}{36}$	$\frac{2}{36}$	$\frac{3}{36}$	$\frac{4}{36}$	$\frac{5}{36}$	$\frac{6}{36}$
Product	$\frac{2}{36}$	$\frac{6}{36}$	$\frac{12}{36}$	$\frac{20}{36}$	$\frac{30}{36}$	$\frac{42}{36}$

Outcome	8	9	10	11	12	
Probability	$\frac{5}{36}$	$\frac{4}{36}$	$\frac{3}{36}$	$\frac{2}{36}$	$\frac{1}{36}$	Sum
Product	$\frac{40}{36}$	$\frac{36}{36}$	$\frac{30}{36}$	$\frac{22}{36}$	$\frac{12}{36}$	$\frac{252}{36} = 7$

The expected sum for rolling two dice is 7.

7. a. Let G represent a good throw and M represent a miss.

1st throw   2nd throw

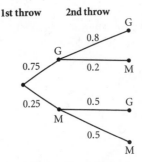

Using the tree diagram and the multiplication rule, $P(G_1 \text{ and } G_2) = (0.75)(0.8) = 0.6$.

b.

Outcome	0	1	2	
Probability	0.125	0.275	0.6	Sum
Product	0	0.275	1.2	1.475

Cheryl's expected number of points in a two-shot free throw attempt is 1.475.

c. Because the expected number of points she will make in one chance to make two free throws is 1.475, in five chances, she can expect to make $5(1.475) = 7.375$ points.

8. a. $9

b. $\frac{1}{6}$

c.

Outcome	1	4	9	16	25	36	
Probability	$\frac{1}{6}$	$\frac{1}{6}$	$\frac{1}{6}$	$\frac{1}{6}$	$\frac{1}{6}$	$\frac{1}{6}$	Sum
Product	$\frac{1}{6}$	$\frac{4}{6}$	$\frac{9}{6}$	$\frac{16}{6}$	$\frac{25}{6}$	$\frac{36}{6}$	$\frac{91}{6} \approx 15.17$

The expected payment is $15.17.

d. The store will receive an average payment of $15.17 for each DVD player sold.

9. a. $\frac{1}{4}(\$16,000) + \frac{3}{4}(\$1,000) = \$4,750$

b. $\frac{1}{3}(\$16,000) + \frac{2}{3}(\$1,000) = \$6,000$

10. a.

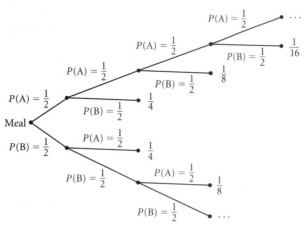

b. Make an expected value table using the probabilities from the tree diagram. The outcomes are the number of meals that need to be purchased to get both CDs.

Outcome	2	3	4	5	6	7
Probability	$\frac{1}{2}$	$\frac{1}{4}$	$\frac{1}{8}$	$\frac{1}{16}$	$\frac{1}{32}$	$\frac{1}{64}$
Product	1	$\frac{3}{4}$	$\frac{1}{2}$	$\frac{5}{16}$	$\frac{3}{16}$	$\frac{7}{64}$

Outcome	8	9	10	
Probability	$\frac{1}{128}$	$\frac{1}{256}$	$\frac{1}{512}$	Sum
Product	$\frac{1}{16}$	$\frac{9}{256}$	$\frac{5}{256}$	$\frac{381}{128} \approx 2.977$

As more and more terms are added, the sum appears to be approaching 3, so the expected number of meals you will need to purchase to receive both CDs is 3.

11. a. $16 + 10 + 12 + 10 = 48$ **b.** $\frac{10}{48} \approx 0.208$

c. $\frac{10}{48} \approx 0.208$ **d.** $\frac{16}{26} \approx 0.615$

12. a. Solutions may vary. Possible solution: Let x represent the number of consecutive free throws needed to increase Jackson's rate to 80%. That gives the equation $\frac{35 + x}{50 + x} = \frac{80}{100}$.
Solve this proportion.

$$\frac{35 + x}{50 + x} = \frac{80}{100}$$
$$35 + x = \frac{80}{100} \cdot (50 + x)$$
$$35 + x = 0.8 \cdot (50 + x)$$
$$35 + x = 0.8(50) + 0.8(x)$$
$$35 + x = 40 + 0.8x$$
$$0.2x = 5$$
$$x = 25$$

Jackson must make 25 consecutive free throws to improve his success rate to 80%.

b. $(0.7)^{25} \approx 0.00013$

CHAPTER 10 Review

EXERCISES

1. a. $\frac{49}{99}$

b. $\frac{33}{99}$, or $\frac{1}{3}$

c. $\frac{19}{99}$

d. $\frac{9}{99}$, or $\frac{1}{11}$

2. To find the number of students with each eye color, read the percentage from the graph and then find that percentage of 350. For example, the graph indicates that 30% of the 350 students have blue eyes. You can find the number of students with blue eyes by solving this proportion $\frac{x}{350} = \frac{30}{100}$. 105 students have blue eyes, approximately 52 or 53 have gray eyes, 70 have green eyes, and approximately 122 or 123 have brown eyes.

3. Approximate degrees: China 75°, India 60°, United States 16°, Indonesia 13°, Brazil 10°, Other 185°. Degrees sum to less than 360° because of rounding.

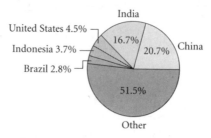

4. a. $25

b. 6%, or 0.06

c. One person is $500 ahead, 5 people are $100 ahead, 10 people are even, and 84 people are $25 behind. This is a net loss of $1,100, or $11 per person.

5. a. 12.5 cm²; $\frac{12.5}{40} = 0.3125$

b. 32.5 cm²; $\frac{32.5}{45} = 0.7\overline{2}$

6. Use the counting principle. The number of possible license plates of this type is $9 \cdot 26^3 \cdot 10^3 = 158{,}184{,}000$.

7. a. The number of possible arrangements is $4 \cdot 3 \cdot 2 \cdot 1 = 24$.

b. This is a permutation because the order is important and no person can have more than one role.

c. Because not every person is available for every role, use the counting principle rather than the permutation formula. Any of the three people other than Jesse can be assigned as recorder, any of the remaining three (including Jesse) can be assigned as director, any of the remaining two can be assigned as timekeeper, and the remaining person must be the reporter. Therefore, the number of possible arrangements is $3 \cdot 3 \cdot 2 \cdot 1 = 18$.

8. a. Each possible arrangement is a combination. There are 31 students other than Jenny, so the number of possible groups that include Jenny and 3 other students is $_{31}C_3 = 4495$.

b. There are 30 students other than Jenny and Yoana, so the number of groups containing Jenny, Yoana, and 2 other students is $_{30}C_2 = 435$. Because 435 of the 4495 groups that contain Jenny also contain Yoana, the probability that both girls will be in the same group is $\frac{435}{4495} \approx 0.097$.

9. a.

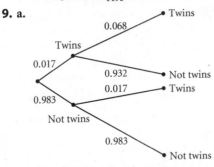

b. $P(T_1 \text{ and } T_2) = (0.017)(0.068) = 0.001156$

10. For this exercise, refer to the table of outcomes for rolling a pair of dice in the solution for Lesson 10.6, Exercise 6a.

a. The sum is greater than 5 in 26 of the 36 possible outcomes, so the probability that Nozomi earns points in each round is $\frac{26}{36} = 0.7\overline{2}$.

b. The sum is less than or equal to 5 in 10 of the 36 possible outcomes, so the probability that Chase earns points in each round is $\frac{10}{36} = 0.2\overline{7}$. (The events in 10a and 10b are complementary, so this probability can also be found as $1 - \frac{26}{36} = \frac{10}{36}$, or $1 - 0.7\overline{2} = 0.2\overline{7}$.)

c. Nozomi's expected point total for one round is $\frac{26}{36}(3) + \frac{10}{36}(0) = 2.1\overline{6}$.

d. Nozomi's expected point total for ten rounds is $10(2.1\overline{6}) = 21.\overline{6}$.

e. Chase's expected point total for ten rounds is $10\left[\frac{10}{36}(6)\right] = 16.\overline{6}$. Using the answer from d, $21.\overline{6} - 16.\overline{6} = 5$. So Nozomi is expected to win by 5 points.

TAKE ANOTHER LOOK

Permutations

$_nP_r$ represents the number of arrangements of r items from a group of n items, where order matters and repeats are not allowed. Apply the counting principle: There are n choices for the first item, $(n - 1)$ choices for the second item, $(n - 2)$ choices for the third, and so on. Following this pattern, for the final item chosen, which is the rth choice, the number of items left from which to choose is $n - r + 1$. Therefore, $_nP_r = n(n - 1)(n - 2) \cdots (n - r + 1)$.

To write $_nP_r$ using factorials, remember that $n!$ has factors all the way down to 1: $n! = n(n - 1)(n - 2) \cdots 3 \cdot 2 \cdot 1$. The factors $(n - r) \cdot (n - r - 1) \cdots 3 \cdot 2 \cdot 1$, or $(n - r)!$, must be divided out. This can be expressed in factorial notation as follows:

$$_nP_r = n(n - 1)(n - 2) \cdots (n - r + 1) =$$
$$\frac{n(n - 1)(n - 2) \cdots (n - r + 1)(n - r)(n - r - 1) \cdots 3 \cdot 2 \cdot 1}{(n - r)(n - r - 1) \cdots 3 \cdot 2 \cdot 1}$$
$$= \frac{n!}{(n - r)!}$$

Combinations

Because order doesn't matter in combinations, all the permutations of the same set of items count as the same combination. For example, if three distinct letters are chosen from the alphabet, then ABC, ACB, BAC, BCA, CAB, and CBA are six permutations, but {ABC} is only one combination. This means that to obtain the factorial expression for $_nC_r$, the expression for $_nP_r$ should be divided by the number of different orders in which r items can be arranged, which is $_rP_r = r!$. Thus, $_nC_r = \frac{_nP_r}{r!} = \frac{n!}{r!(n - r)!}$.

Tests of formulas

$$_6P_3 = \frac{6!}{(6 - 3)!} = \frac{6!}{3!} = \frac{720}{6} = 120$$

$$_6C_3 = \frac{6!}{3!(6 - 3)!} = \frac{6!}{3!3!} = \frac{720}{6 \cdot 6} = \frac{720}{36} = 20$$

$$_9P_4 = \frac{9!}{(9 - 4)!} = \frac{9!}{5!} = \frac{9 \cdot 8 \cdot 7 \cdot 6}{1} = 3024$$

$$_9C_4 = \frac{9!}{4!(9 - 4)!} = \frac{9!}{4!5!} = \frac{9 \cdot 8 \cdot 7 \cdot 6}{4 \cdot 3 \cdot 2 \cdot 1} = \frac{3024}{24} = 126$$

CHAPTER 11

LESSON 11.1

EXERCISES

1. a. If you write the equation in point-slope form, $y = 7 + 0.8(x - 4)$, you can see that the slope is 0.8.

b. The equation is in intercept form. The slope is -2.

c. If you write the equation in point-slope form, $y = 1 - 1.25(x - 3)$, you can see that the slope is -1.25.

d. The equation is in intercept form. The slope is 2.

e. If you write the equation in intercept form, $y = -\frac{11}{4} + \frac{3}{2}x$, you can see that the slope is $\frac{3}{2}$.

f. If you write the equation in intercept form, $y = 6 - \frac{3}{2}x$, you can see that the slope is $-\frac{3}{2}$.

g. If you write the equation in intercept form, $y = -\frac{2}{3} + \frac{3}{2}x$, you can see that the slope is $\frac{3}{2}$.

h. If you write the equation in intercept form, $y = -\frac{7}{15} + \frac{2}{3}x$, you can see that the slope is $\frac{2}{3}$.

2. a. The slopes of the lines are 0.8 and -1.25. Because -1.25 is the negative reciprocal of 0.8 $\left(\text{that is,} -1.25 = -\frac{1}{0.8}\right)$, the lines are perpendicular.

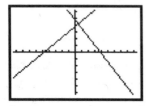

$[-9.4, 9.4, 1, -6.2, 6.2, 1]$

b. The slopes of the lines are -2 and 2. Because the slopes are not the same and they are not negative reciprocals, the lines are neither parallel nor perpendicular.

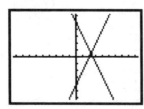

$[-9.4, 9.4, 1, -6.2, 6.2, 1]$

c. Rewriting the equations in intercept form gives the equations $y = -\frac{11}{4} + \frac{3}{2}x$ and $y = -\frac{2}{3} + \frac{3}{2}x$. Because both lines have the same slope, $\frac{3}{2}$, they are parallel.

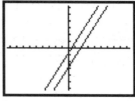

$[-9.4, 9.4, 1, -6.2, 6.2, 1]$

d. Rewriting the equations in intercept form gives the equations $y = 6 - \frac{3}{2}x$ and $y = -\frac{7}{15} + \frac{2}{3}x$. Because the slopes, $-\frac{3}{2}$ and $\frac{2}{3}$, are negative reciprocals, the lines are perpendicular.

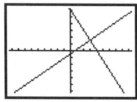

$[-9.4, 9.4, 1, -6.2, 6.2, 1]$

3. 1.2

4. a. Because line m is perpendicular to line ℓ, its slope must be the negative reciprocal of the slope of ℓ. So, the slope of m is $\frac{-1}{1.2} = -\frac{5}{6} = -0.8\overline{3}$.

b. -1

5. The slope of the given line is 3, so the slope of any line perpendicular to it will be the opposite reciprocal of 3, which is $-\frac{1}{3}$. The point-slope form of the line with slope $-\frac{1}{3}$ that passes through the point $(8, -2)$ is $y = -2 - \frac{1}{3}(x - 8)$.

6. A: right trapezoid; B: square; C: rectangle; D: trapezoid; E: parallelogram

7. The polygon is a right trapezoid. The slopes of the sides are $\frac{2}{3}, -\frac{1}{5}, \frac{2}{3}$, and $-\frac{3}{2}$. The sides with slope $\frac{2}{3}$ are parallel, and the side with slope $-\frac{3}{2}$ is perpendicular to both of these sides.

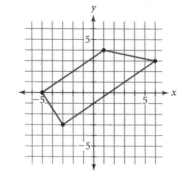

8. The polygon is a rectangle. The slopes of the sides are $\frac{1}{2}, -2, \frac{1}{2}$, and -2. The opposite sides have the same slope, so they are parallel. The adjacent sides have slopes that are opposite reciprocals, so they are perpendicular.

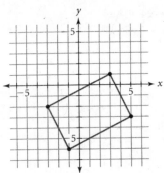

9. The polygon is a trapezoid. The slopes of the sides are $0, -\frac{4}{3}$, undefined, and $-\frac{4}{3}$. Two sides have the same slope, so the figure has one pair of parallel sides.

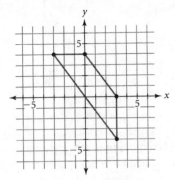

10. The polygon is a parallelogram. The slopes of the sides are $1, -3, 1$, and -3. The opposite sides have the same slope, so they are parallel.

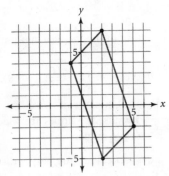

11. The polygon is a quadrilateral. The slopes of the sides are $4, -\frac{1}{4}, -3$, and $\frac{4}{7}$. Because none of the sides have

the same slope, the figure is not a parallelogram, rectangle, or trapezoid.

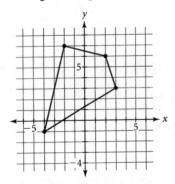

12. The polygon is a trapezoid. The slopes of the sides are $2, -\frac{5}{2}, -\frac{1}{4}$, and $-\frac{5}{2}$. Two sides have the same slope, so the figure has one pair of parallel sides.

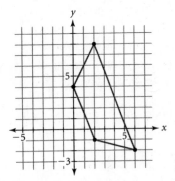

13. The polygon is a rectangle. The slopes of the sides are $\frac{3}{2}, -\frac{2}{3}, \frac{3}{2}$, and $-\frac{2}{3}$. The opposite sides have the same slope, so they are parallel. The adjacent sides have slopes that are opposite reciprocals, so they are perpendicular.

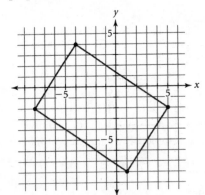

14. The polygon is a quadrilateral. The slopes of the sides are $1, -1, \frac{5}{3}$, and $-\frac{5}{3}$. Because none of the sides have the same slope, the figure is not a parallelogram, rectangle, or trapezoid.

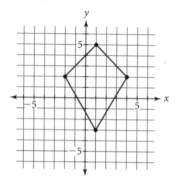

15. Possible answer: $(-2, 5), (0, 6), (2, 5), (0, 1)$

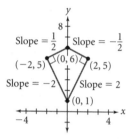

16. a. Deductive; hypothesis: *Tyrannosaurus rex* had sharp teeth; conclusion: *Tyrannosaurus rex* was a carnivore.

   b. Inductive; hypothesis: two consecutive numbers are added; conclusion: the result is an odd number.

   c. Deductive; hypothesis: $2(x - 3) = 10$; conclusion: $x = 8$.

17. a. To find the product $x(x + 2)(2x - 1)$, first use a rectangle diagram to find the product $(x + 2)(2x - 1)$.

	x	2
$2x$	$2x^2$	$4x$
-1	$-x$	-2

From the diagram, $(x + 2)(2x - 1) = 2x^2 + 4x - x - 2 = 2x^2 + 3x - 2$. Use the distributive property to complete the required multiplication:
$x(x + 2)(2x - 1) = x(2x^2 + 3x - 2) = 2x^3 + 3x^2 - 2x$

   b. To find the product $(0.1x - 2.1)(0.1x + 2.1)$, use a rectangle diagram.

	$0.1x$	-2.1
$0.1x$	$0.01x^2$	$-0.21x$
2.1	$0.21x$	-4.41

$(0.1x - 2.1)(0.1x + 2.1) = 0.01x^2 - 4.41$

18. a. $\dfrac{3 + 11}{2} = \dfrac{14}{2} = 7$

   b. $\dfrac{-4 + 7}{2} = \dfrac{3}{2} = 1.5$

   c. $\dfrac{-12 + (-1)}{2} = \dfrac{-13}{2} = -6.5$

   d. $\dfrac{2 + 47}{2} = \dfrac{49}{2} = 24.5$

LESSON 11.2

EXERCISES

1. a. $\left(\dfrac{4 + -3}{2}, \dfrac{5 + -2}{2}\right) = (0.5, 1.5)$

   b. $\left(\dfrac{7 + 5}{2}, \dfrac{-1 + -8}{2}\right) = (6, -4.5)$

2. $\left(\dfrac{a + c}{2}, \dfrac{b + d}{2}\right)$

3. a. Midpoint of $\overline{AB}$: $\left(\dfrac{4 + 28}{2}, \dfrac{7 + 11}{2}\right) = (16, 9)$

   b. Midpoint of $\overline{BC}$: $\left(\dfrac{28 + -3}{2}, \dfrac{11 + -1}{2}\right) = (12.5, 5)$

   c. Midpoint of $\overline{AC}$: $\left(\dfrac{4 + -3}{2}, \dfrac{7 + -1}{2}\right) = (0.5, 3)$

4. a. The perpendicular bisector goes through the midpoint of $\overline{AB}$ and is perpendicular to $\overline{AB}$. From 3a, the midpoint of $\overline{AB}$ is $(16, 9)$. The slope of $\overline{AB}$ is $\dfrac{11 - 7}{28 - 4} = \dfrac{4}{24} = \dfrac{1}{6}$. The slope of the perpendicular bisector is the opposite reciprocal of $\dfrac{1}{6}$, which is -6. Therefore, an equation for the perpendicular bisector in point-slope form is $y = 9 - 6(x - 16)$.

   b. The median connects the midpoint of $\overline{AC}$ to point B. From 3c, the midpoint of $\overline{AC}$ is $(0.5, 3)$. Now, use the coordinates of B and the midpoint of $\overline{AC}$ to find the slope of the median.

$$\text{Slope} = \dfrac{11 - 3}{28 - 0.5} = \dfrac{8}{27.5} = \dfrac{16}{55}$$

Therefore, the equation of the median in point-slope form is
$$y = 3 + \dfrac{16}{55}(x - 0.5) \text{ or } y = 11 + \dfrac{16}{55}(x - 28).$$

5. Yes. Possible explanation: The slope of $\overline{AB}$ is 5 and the slope of $\overline{BC}$ is $-\dfrac{1}{5}$. Because the slopes are opposite reciprocals, angle B is a right angle.

6. A horizontal line and a vertical line are perpendicular, but the product of their slopes is not -1. A horizontal line has a slope of 0, and a vertical line has an undefined slope, so the product of their slopes is undefined.

7. a. $\left(\dfrac{2 + 4}{2}, \dfrac{1 + 6}{2}\right) = (3, 3.5)$

   b. The slope of $\overline{AB}$ is $\dfrac{5}{2}$, so the slope of the perpendicular bisector is $-\dfrac{2}{5}$. The perpendicular bisector passes through $(3, 3.5)$. So the equation in point-slope form is $y = 3.5 - \dfrac{2}{5}(x - 3)$.

Discovering Algebra Solutions Manual
©2007 Key Curriculum Press

8. a. Midpoint of $\overline{AB}$: $\left(\dfrac{3+17}{2}, \dfrac{2+4}{2}\right) = (10, 3)$

Midpoint of $\overline{BC}$: $\left(\dfrac{17+13}{2}, \dfrac{4+12}{2}\right) = (15, 8)$

Midpoint of $\overline{CD}$: $\left(\dfrac{13+5}{2}, \dfrac{12+8}{2}\right) = (9, 10)$

Midpoint of $\overline{DA}$: $\left(\dfrac{5+3}{2}, \dfrac{8+2}{2}\right) = (4, 5)$

b. The polygon is a parallelogram. The sides of the polygon have slopes 1, $-\frac{1}{3}$, 1, and $-\frac{1}{3}$. Because the opposite sides have the same slope, they are parallel.

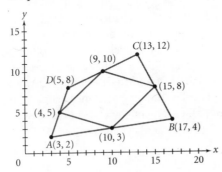

c. The slopes of the diagonals are $\frac{3}{11}$ and -7. Because the slopes are not opposite reciprocals, the diagonals are not perpendicular.

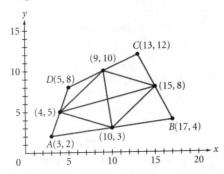

9. a. $D(7.5, -1)$, $E(-1, -1)$, $F(2.5, 6)$

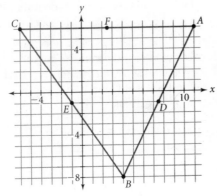

b. Slope of median $\overline{AE} = \dfrac{6-(-1)}{11-(-1)} = \dfrac{7}{12}$; slope of median $\overline{BF} = \dfrac{-8-6}{4-2.5} = \dfrac{-14}{1.5} = -\dfrac{28}{3}$; slope of median $\overline{CD} = \dfrac{6-(-1)}{-6-7.5} = \dfrac{7}{-13.5} = -\dfrac{14}{27}$.

c. Possible answers: median $\overline{AE}$: $y = 6 + \frac{7}{12}(x-11)$; median $\overline{BF}$: $y = 6 - \frac{28}{3}\left(x - \frac{5}{2}\right)$; median $\overline{CD}$: $y = 6 - \frac{14}{27}(x+6)$.

d. $\begin{cases} y = 6 + \dfrac{7}{12}(x-11) \\ y = 6 - \dfrac{28}{3}\left(x - \dfrac{5}{2}\right) \end{cases}$

To solve this system by the substitution method, substitute $6 + \frac{7}{12}(x-11)$ for y in the second equation and solve for x.

$6 + \dfrac{7}{12}(x-11) = 6 - \dfrac{28}{3}\left(x - \dfrac{5}{2}\right)$

$\dfrac{7}{12}(x-11) = -\dfrac{28}{3}\left(x - \dfrac{5}{2}\right)$ Subtract 6 from each side.

$12\left[\dfrac{7}{12}(x-11)\right] = 12\left[-\dfrac{28}{3}\left(x - \dfrac{5}{2}\right)\right]$ Multiply each side by the least common denominator, 12.

$7(x-11) = -112\left(x - \dfrac{5}{2}\right)$

$7x - 77 = -112x + 280$ Use the distributive property.

$119x - 77 = 280$ Add $112x$ to each side.

$119x = 357$ Add 77 to each side.

$x = 3$ Divide each side by 119.

Substitute 3 for x in the first equation of the system and solve for y.

$y = 6 + \dfrac{7}{12}(3 - 11)$

$y = 6 + \dfrac{7}{12}(-8)$

$y = 6 + \left(-\dfrac{14}{3}\right)$

$y = \dfrac{4}{3}$

Thus, the intersection of median $\overline{AE}$ and median $\overline{BF}$ is $\left(3, \frac{4}{3}\right)$.

e. $\begin{cases} y = 6 + \dfrac{7}{12}(x-11) \\ y = 6 - \dfrac{14}{27}(x+6) \end{cases}$

To solve this system by the substitution method, substitute $6 + \frac{7}{12}(x-11)$ for y in the second equation and solve for x.

$6 + \dfrac{7}{12}(x-11) = 6 - \dfrac{14}{27}(x+6)$

$\dfrac{7}{12}(x-11) = -\dfrac{14}{27}(x+6)$

$$108\left[\frac{7}{12}(x-11)\right] = -108\left[\frac{14}{27}(x+6)\right]$$
$$63(x-11) = -56(x+6)$$
$$63x - 693 = -56x - 336$$
$$119x - 693 = -336$$
$$119x = 357$$
$$x = 3$$

The first equation is the same in the systems in 9d and 9e, so when $x = 3$, $y = \frac{4}{3}$.

Therefore, the intersection of median $\overline{AE}$ and median $\overline{CD}$ is also $\left(3, \frac{4}{3}\right)$.

f. Possible answer: The medians of a triangle meet at a single point.

g. The conjecture is based on an example, so inductive reasoning was used.

10. a. Let (x, y) represent the other endpoint. Then, $\frac{x+2}{2} = 7$ and $\frac{y+4}{2} = 4$. Solving these equations gives $x = 12$ and $y = 4$, so the endpoint is $(12, 4)$.

b. Let (x, y) represent the other endpoint. Then, $\frac{x+15}{2} = 9$ and $\frac{y+9}{2} = 7$. Solving these equations gives $x = 3$ and $y = 5$, so the endpoint is $(3, 5)$.

c. Let (x, y) represent the other endpoint. Then, $\frac{x+3}{2} = -1$ and $\frac{y+-7.5}{2} = -2$. Solving these equations gives $x = -5$ and $y = 3.5$, so the endpoint is $(-5, 3.5)$.

11. a. Rewrite the equation in intercept form:
$$Ax + By = C$$
$$By = C - Ax$$
$$y = \frac{C}{B} - \frac{A}{B}x$$

The slope of line ℓ is $-\frac{A}{B}$. The slope of a line perpendicular to ℓ is the opposite reciprocal of $-\frac{A}{B}$, which is $\frac{B}{A}$.

b. A line parallel to line ℓ has slope $-\frac{A}{B}$, the same slope as line ℓ.

12. a. Solve the system $\begin{cases} 2x - 3y + 12 = 1 \\ x = 2y - 7 \end{cases}$ by substituting $2y - 7$ for x in the first equation. The solution to the system, $(-1, 3)$, is the point of intersection.

b. Answers will vary. Possible answer: The graph of any equation with point-slope form $y = 3 + m(x + 1)$, where m is any number, will pass through $(-1, 3)$. So, any two lines with equations in this form will intersect at $(-1, 3)$. An equation in this form and the vertical line $x = -1$ will also intersect at $(-1, 3)$.

c. Answers will vary. Possible answer: $y = (x + 1)^2 + 3$. (The graph of any equation in the form $y = a(x + 1)^2 + 3$ will have its vertex at $(-1, 3)$.)

13. a. Possible answers:

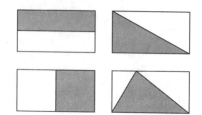

b. Answers will vary. Any method that uses only one line segment will form congruent polygons. Some other methods may also produce congruent polygons.

c. Yes. If you imagine a vertical segment through the upper vertex of the shaded triangle, the pair of triangles to the left of the segment are congruent and the pair of triangles to the right of the segment are congruent. Because the shaded section includes one triangle from each side of the segment and the unshaded section includes one triangle from each side of the segment, the areas of the shaded and unshaded sections are equal.

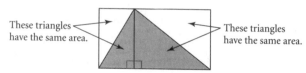

These triangles have the same area.   These triangles have the same area.

So the area of the rectangle is divided in half.

IMPROVING YOUR GEOMETRY SKILLS

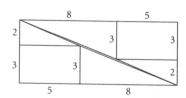

The slope of each small triangle's hypotenuse is $-\frac{2}{5}$, or -0.4. The slope of each large triangle's hypotenuse is $-\frac{3}{8}$, or -0.375. The slopes of these segments are close enough to fool the eye, but the segments do not lie on the same line. Instead, they create a parallelogram whose area is 1.

This and 59 other puzzles and paradoxes are collected in *One Equals Zero and Other Mathematical Surprises* by Nitsa Movshovitz-Hadar and John Webb, © Key Curriculum Press, 1998.

LESSON 11.3

EXERCISES

1. a. $x^2 = 47$
$$x = \pm\sqrt{47}$$

b. $(x - 4)^2 = 28$
$$x - 4 = \pm\sqrt{28}$$
$$x = 4 \pm \sqrt{28}$$

c. $(x + 2)^2 - 3 = 11$

$(x + 2)^2 = 14$

$x + 2 = \pm\sqrt{14}$

$x = -2 \pm \sqrt{14}$

d. $2(x - 1)^2 + 4 = 18$

$2(x - 1)^2 = 14$

$(x - 1)^2 = 7$

$x - 1 = \pm\sqrt{7}$

$x = 1 \pm \sqrt{7}$

2. a. ± 6.856 **b.** $-1.292, 9.292$

c. $-5.742, 1.742$ **d.** $-1.646, 3.646$

3. a. You can draw a square with horizontal and vertical sides around the rectangle. The area of the rectangle is the area of the square minus the sum of the areas of the four triangles.

$$\text{Area} = 9 - \left(2 + 2 + \frac{1}{2} + \frac{1}{2}\right)$$

$$= 9 - 5$$

$$= 4 \text{ square units}$$

b. You can draw a square with horizontal and vertical sides around the rectangle. The area of the rectangle is the area of the square minus the sum of the areas of the four triangles.

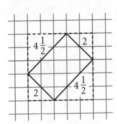

$$\text{Area} = 25 - \left(2 + 2 + 4\frac{1}{2} + 4\frac{1}{2}\right)$$

$$= 25 - 13$$

$$= 12 \text{ square units}$$

c. You can draw a rectangle with horizontal and vertical sides around the triangle. The area of the triangle is the area of the rectangle minus the sum of the areas of the three surrounding triangles.

$$\text{Area} = 6 - \left(2 + 1\frac{1}{2} + \frac{1}{2}\right)$$

$$= 6 - 4$$

$$= 2 \text{ square units}$$

d. 6 square units   **e.** 20 square units

f. 18 square units

4. The square has an area of 18 square units, so the side length is $\sqrt{18}$ units.

5. To find the length of each side, draw a square on the side and then find the area of the square. The side length is the square root of this area.

For the rectangle in 3a, a square on the short side has an area of 2 square units, so the length of the short side is $\sqrt{2}$ units. A square on the long side has an area of 8 square units, so the length of the long side is $\sqrt{8}$ units.

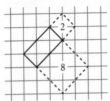

Polygon 3b: $\sqrt{8}$ units and $\sqrt{18}$ units

Polygon 3e: $\sqrt{50}$ units, $\sqrt{50}$ units, and $\sqrt{40}$ units

6. a–e. If you consider the horizontal side of each triangle to be the base, then each triangle has a base of length 9 units and a height of 4 units. So, the area of each triangle is $\frac{1}{2}(9)(4)$, or 18 square units.

7. a. 36 square units, 18 square units, and 18 square units

b. The length of each side is the square root of the area of the square constructed on it. So, the length of $\overline{AB}$ is 6 units, the length of $\overline{BC}$ is $\sqrt{18}$ units, and the length of $\overline{AC}$ is $\sqrt{18}$ units.

8. $(6, 11)$ and $(12, 7)$ or $(-2, -1)$ and $(4, -5)$.

9. a. $\overline{AC}$ is the hypotenuse. $\overline{AB}$ and $\overline{BC}$ are the legs.

b.

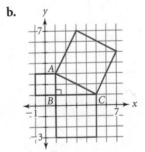

c. Area of square on $\overline{AB}$: 4 square units; area of square on $\overline{BC}$: 16 square units; area of square on $\overline{AC}$: 20 square units

d. Length of $\overline{AB}$: 2 units; length of $\overline{BC}$: 4 units; length of $\overline{AC}$: $\sqrt{20}$ units

e. The area of the largest square is equal to the sum of the areas of the two smaller squares.

10. a. City A: $47{,}000(1 + 0.045)^5 \approx 58{,}571$; the population will be 58,571 in five years.

City B: $56{,}000(1 - 0.012)^5 \approx 52{,}720$; the population will be 52,720 in five years.

b. $47{,}000(1 + 0.045)^{26} \approx 147{,}612$ and
$47{,}000(1 + 0.045)^{27} \approx 154{,}254$, so the population
will first exceed 150,000 in 27 years.

c. $56{,}000(1 - 0.012)^{-10} \approx 63{,}186$; the population
was 63,186 ten years ago.

11. From the first clue, the equation must be in the form
$y = a(x - b)(x - c)$. Using the second clue, the
equation must be in the form $y = a(x + 7)(x - c)$.
Look at the last clue. If the axis of symmetry passes
through $(-4, -2)$, its equation must be $x = -4$. This
line of symmetry is halfway between the x-intercepts,
which are -7 and c. So, c must be -1. Now you
know the equation must be in the form
$y = a(x + 7)(x + 1)$. The third clue indicates that the
point $(0, 14)$ is on the graph. Substituting these values
into the equation gives $14 = 7a$, so $a = 2$. The
equation is $y = 2(x + 7)(x + 1)$.

IMPROVING YOUR VISUAL THINKING SKILLS

Weaving over one, under four is the only way to get a
$(1, -2)$-solution. (It might be called a $(1, 3)$-solution as
well.) Over one, under three either creates diagonal stripes
or creates rhombuses, not squares, which leave alternating
white strands without any brown strands over them, so
the mat would fall apart. Over one, under two creates
diagonal stripes, not squares. Over one, under five creates
stripes or parallelograms that fall apart.

Over one, under nine is the $(1, -3)$-solution.

Some students may conjecture that the $(1, -k)$-solution
must go over one, under k^2. This is indeed true. The
$(1, -4)$-solution goes over one, under sixteen. The
$(1, -1)$-solution goes over one, under one. In general,
imagine one square A in which a brown strand appears.
In the next column to the right, the brown strand to which
the first one is connected in a tilted square is k white
strands lower. So, the appearance of the next brown strand
below A must be connected to a point right k units and up
1 unit. This will be an appearance of a brown strand only
if each brown strand passes under k^2 white strands.

LESSON 11.4

EXERCISES

1. The area of the square on side c is equal to the sum of
the areas of the squares on sides a and b. So, the area
of the square on side a is $2601 - 2025$, or 576 cm².

2. Length of side $a = \sqrt{576}$ cm $= 24$ cm; length of side
$b = \sqrt{2025}$ cm $= 45$ cm; length of side
$c = \sqrt{2601}$ cm $= 51$ cm.

3. $a^2 + b^2 = c^2$
$10^2 + b^2 = 20^2$
$b^2 = 20^2 - 10^2$
$b^2 = 400 - 100$
$b^2 = 300$
$b = \sqrt{300}$ cm

4. a. The two legs are equal in length. The hypotenuse
must be longer than either of them.

b. If c is the hypotenuse, then $c^2 = 8^2 + 8^2 = 128$, so
$c = \sqrt{128}$ cm.

5. a. Each half is similar to a right triangle with side
lengths 3, 4, and 5. The length of the longer leg is
18 ft (half of 36 ft). Let x represent the length of
the shorter leg, which is the distance from the
attic floor to the roof peak. To find x, solve the
proportion $\frac{x}{18} = \frac{3}{4}$ to get $x = 13.5$. The distance
from the attic floor to the roof peak is 13.5 ft.

b. The distance from the roof peak to the roof edge is
the length of the hypotenuse of one of the two
right triangles. If c represents this length, then
$c^2 = 18^2 + 13.5^2 = 506.25$, so $c = \sqrt{506.25}$. This
distance is $\sqrt{506.25}$ ft, or 22.5 ft. This could also
be found by solving the proportion $\frac{x}{18} = \frac{5}{4}$.

c. Each half of the roof is a rectangle with length 48 ft
and width 22.5 ft (the length of the hypotenuse).
The area of each half is 48 ft $\cdot$ 22.5 ft, or 1080 ft²,
so the area of the entire roof is 2(1080 ft²), or
2160 ft².

6. Al is right. Explanations will vary. As an example,
$\sqrt{9 + 4} \neq \sqrt{9} + \sqrt{4}$.

7. a. Approximately 21.6 cm by 27.6 cm

b. If the diagonal length is c, then
$c^2 = 21.6^2 + 27.6^2 = 1228.32$. So, the diagonal
length is $\sqrt{1228.32}$ cm, or about 35.0 cm.

c. Answers will vary but should be close to 35 cm.

d. Answers will vary. The two results should be
approximately the same.

8. Answers will vary. If $x = 1$, then Miya is claiming that
$1^2 + 4^2 = 5^2$, but $17 \neq 25$. You have to isolate x before
you take the square root: $x^2 + 16 = 25$, $x^2 = 9$,
$x = \pm 3$.

9. First, convert miles to feet: 1.2 mi $\cdot \frac{5280 \text{ ft}}{1 \text{ mi}} = 6336$ ft.
Then, let c represent the distance and use the
Pythagorean Theorem:
$c^2 = 6336^2 + 3000^2 = 49{,}144{,}896$
$c = \sqrt{49{,}144{,}896} \approx 7010$. The balloon is
approximately 7010 ft away.

10. a.   i. Right triangle   ii. Right triangle
      iii. Not a right triangle   iv. Right triangle

b. Yes, the theorem works in reverse for these triangles.

11. a. $L_1 = \{1, 2, 3, \ldots, 26\}$

b. Length² $= 27^2 - 1^2 = \sqrt{728}$, so
length $= \sqrt{728}$ in., or about 26.98 in.

c. $L_1^2 + L_2^2 = 27^2$, so $L_2 = \sqrt{\left(27^2 - L_1^2\right)}$.

d. Using the calculator table, the length of the screen
is about 26.926 inches, so the area is about
2 in. $\cdot$ 26.926 in., or 53.85 in².

e. $L_3 = L_1 \cdot L_2$, or $L_3 = L_1 \cdot \sqrt{(27^2 - L_1^2)}$

f. A model that works is $y = x\sqrt{27^2 - x^2}$, where x is the width and y is the area.

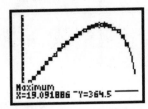

$[0, 27, 5, -50, 450, 50]$

g. Trace the graph or use a table to find that a 19-by-19 in. square gives the maximum area.

12. a. Answers will vary. Possible answer: The ratios $\frac{10}{5}$, $\frac{24}{12}$, and $\frac{26}{13}$ are all equal to 2, so the sides are proportional and the triangles are similar.

b. Yes. Possible explanations: Similar polygons have congruent angles. Or, the side lengths 10, 24, and 26 satisfy the Pythagorean Theorem, so the triangle is a right triangle.

13. a.

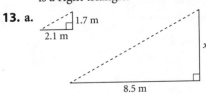

b. $\frac{1.7}{2.1} = \frac{x}{8.5}$; $x \approx 6.88$, or 6.9 m

c. You could measure the length of the tree's shadow and write a proportion using a person's height and the length of his or her shadow.

14. Let x represent the side length of the original deck. Then, $(x + 3)(x + 2) = 210$. Solve this equation for x.

$(x + 3)(x + 2) = 210$ — Original equation.

$x^2 + 5x + 6 = 210$ — Expand the left side.

$x^2 + 5x - 204 = 0$ — Subtract 210 from both sides.

$x = -17$ or $x = 12$ — Solve using the quadratic formula.

Only the positive solution makes sense in this situation. The original deck measured 12 ft by 12 ft.

LESSON 11.5

EXERCISES

1. a. $2\sqrt{3} + \sqrt{3} = 3\sqrt{3}$

b. $\sqrt{5} \cdot \sqrt{2} \cdot \sqrt{5} = \sqrt{5} \cdot \sqrt{5} \cdot \sqrt{2} = \sqrt{25} \cdot \sqrt{2}$
$= 5\sqrt{2}$

c. $\sqrt{2}(\sqrt{2} + \sqrt{3}) = \sqrt{2}\sqrt{2} + \sqrt{2}\sqrt{3}$
$= \sqrt{4} + \sqrt{6} = 2 + \sqrt{6}$

d. $\sqrt{5} - \sqrt{2} + 3\sqrt{5} + 6\sqrt{2}$
$= \sqrt{5} + 3\sqrt{5} - \sqrt{2} + 6\sqrt{2} = 4\sqrt{5} + 5\sqrt{2}$

e. $\sqrt{3}(\sqrt{2}) + 5\sqrt{6} = \sqrt{6} + 5\sqrt{6} = 6\sqrt{6}$

f. $\sqrt{2}(\sqrt{21}) + \sqrt{3}(\sqrt{14}) = \sqrt{42} + \sqrt{42} = 2\sqrt{42}$

g. $\frac{\sqrt{35}}{\sqrt{7}} = \sqrt{\frac{35}{7}} = \sqrt{5}$

h. $\sqrt{5}(4\sqrt{5}) = 4\sqrt{25} = 4 \cdot 5 = 20$

2. a. $a = \sqrt{91}$ **b.** $b = \sqrt{10}$

c. $c = 4$ **d.** $d = \sqrt{13}$

3. For each part, you can use a rectangle diagram or the distributive property to expand the right side of the equation.

a. The general form is $y = x^2 - 3$.

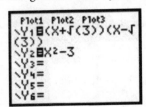

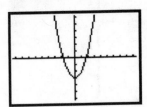

$[-9.4, 9.4, 1, -6.2, 6.2, 1]$

b. $y = x^2 + 2x\sqrt{5} + 5$

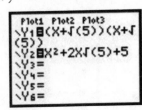

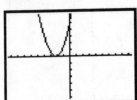

$[-9.4, 9.4, 1, -6.2, 6.2, 1]$

4. a. $x = \pm\sqrt{3} \approx \pm 1.732$ **b.** $x = -\sqrt{5} \approx -2.236$ **c.** $y = x^2 + 6x + 7$

5. a. The x-coordinate of the vertex is 0 (the value halfway between the x-intercepts $-\sqrt{3}$ and $\sqrt{3}$). To find the y-coordinate of the vertex, substitute 0 for x in the equation:
$y = (0 + \sqrt{3})(0 - \sqrt{3}) = -3$. So the vertex is $(0, -3)$.

b. The vertex of this graph is the x-intercept, so it is $(-\sqrt{5}, 0) \approx (-2.236, 0)$.

6. For each part, you can use the distributive property or a rectangle diagram to expand the right side of the equation.

a. $y = x^2 - 112$

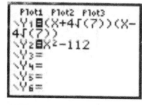

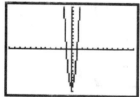

$[-120, 120, 10, -120, 120, 10]$

X	Y1	Y2
-3	-103	-103
-2	-108	-108
-1	-111	-111
0	-112	-112
1	-111	-111
2	-108	-108
3	-103	-103
X=-3		

b. $y = 2x^2 + 2x\sqrt{6} - 72$

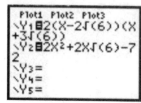

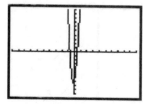

$[-100, 100, 10, -100, 100, 10]$

X	Y1	Y2
-3	-68.7	-68.7
-2	-73.8	-73.8
-1	-74.9	-74.9
0	-72	-72
1	-65.1	-65.1
2	-54.2	-54.2
3	-39.3	-39.3
X=-3		

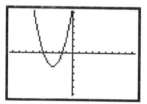

$[-9.4, 9.4, 1, -6.2, 6.2, 1]$

X	Y1	Y2
-3	-2	-2
-2	-1	-1
-1	2	2
0	7	7
1	14	14
2	23	23
3	34	34
X=-3		

7. a. $x = \pm 4\sqrt{7} \approx \pm 10.583$

b. $x = 2\sqrt{6} \approx 4.899$ and $x = -3\sqrt{6} \approx -7.348$

c. $x = -3 - \sqrt{2} \approx -4.414$ and $x = -3 + \sqrt{2} \approx -1.586$

8. a. The x-coordinate of the vertex is 0 (the x-value halfway between the x-intercepts). To find the y-coordinate of the vertex, substitute 0 for x in the equation:
$y = (0 + 4\sqrt{7})(0 - 4\sqrt{7}) = -16\sqrt{49} = -112$. So, the vertex is $(0, -112)$.

b. To find the x-coordinate of the vertex, average the x-intercepts: $\dfrac{2\sqrt{6} + (-3\sqrt{6})}{2} = \dfrac{-\sqrt{6}}{2}$. To find the y-coordinate of the vertex, substitute $\dfrac{-\sqrt{6}}{2}$ for x in the equation:

$$y = 2\left(-\frac{\sqrt{6}}{2} - 2\sqrt{6}\right)\left(-\frac{\sqrt{6}}{2} + 3\sqrt{6}\right)$$
$$= 2(-2.5\sqrt{6})(2.5\sqrt{6}) = -12.5\sqrt{36}$$
$$= -12.5 \cdot 6 = -75$$

So, the vertex is $\left(\dfrac{-\sqrt{6}}{2}, -75\right) \approx (-1.225, -75)$.

c. To find the x-coordinate of the vertex, average the x-intercepts: $\dfrac{-3 - \sqrt{2} - 3 + \sqrt{2}}{2} = \dfrac{-6}{2} = -3$. To find the y-coordinate of the vertex, substitute -3 for x in the equation:
$y = (-3 + 3 + \sqrt{2})(-3 + 3 - \sqrt{2})$
$= \sqrt{2}(-\sqrt{2}) = -\sqrt{4} = -2$. So, the vertex is $(-3, -2)$.

9. a. $4\sqrt{7} = \sqrt{16} \cdot \sqrt{7} = \sqrt{112}$

b. $5\sqrt{22} = \sqrt{25} \cdot \sqrt{22} = \sqrt{550}$

c. $18\sqrt{3} = \sqrt{324} \cdot \sqrt{3} = \sqrt{972}$

d. $30\sqrt{5} = \sqrt{900} \cdot \sqrt{5} = \sqrt{4500}$

10. a. $\sqrt{72} = \sqrt{36 \cdot 2} = \sqrt{36} \cdot \sqrt{2} = 6\sqrt{2}$

b. $\sqrt{27} = \sqrt{9 \cdot 3} = \sqrt{9} \cdot \sqrt{3} = 3\sqrt{3}$

c. $\sqrt{1800} = \sqrt{900 \cdot 2} = \sqrt{900} \cdot \sqrt{2} = 30\sqrt{2}$

d. $\sqrt{147} = \sqrt{49 \cdot 3} = \sqrt{49} \cdot \sqrt{3} = 7\sqrt{3}$

11. a. $\dfrac{25 \pm \sqrt{75}}{15} = \dfrac{25 \pm \sqrt{25} \cdot \sqrt{3}}{15} = \dfrac{25 \pm 5\sqrt{3}}{15} =$

$\dfrac{5(5 \pm \sqrt{3})}{5 \cdot 3} = \dfrac{5 \pm \sqrt{3}}{3}$

b. $\dfrac{21 \pm \sqrt{98}}{7} = \dfrac{21 \pm \sqrt{49} \cdot \sqrt{2}}{7} = \dfrac{21 \pm 7\sqrt{2}}{7} =$

$\dfrac{7(3 \pm \sqrt{2})}{7} = 3 \pm \sqrt{2}$

c. $\dfrac{-2\sqrt{5} \pm \sqrt{180}}{4\sqrt{5}} = \dfrac{-2\sqrt{5} \pm \sqrt{36} \cdot \sqrt{5}}{4\sqrt{5}} =$

$\dfrac{-2\sqrt{5} \pm 6\sqrt{5}}{4\sqrt{5}} = \dfrac{4\sqrt{5}}{4\sqrt{5}} = 1$

$\dfrac{-2\sqrt{5} - 6\sqrt{5}}{4\sqrt{5}} = \dfrac{-8\sqrt{5}}{4\sqrt{5}} = -2$

12. a. The red line creates two right triangles, each with a leg length of $\frac{1}{2}(8)$ cm, or 4 cm, and a hypotenuse length of 8 cm. By the Pythagorean Theorem, the length of the other leg is $4\sqrt{3}$ cm.

b. The height forms a right triangle with the answer from 12a as the hypotenuse length and a leg length of 4 cm (shown in black). By the Pythagorean Theorem, the height (the length of the other leg) is $4\sqrt{2}$.

c. Approximately 566 ft

13.

$0 = 0.5x^2 - 6x + 8$	Original equation.
$0 = 0.5(6 + \sqrt{20})^2 - 6(6 + \sqrt{20}) + 8$	Substitute $6 + \sqrt{20}$ for x.
$0 = 0.5(6 + \sqrt{20})^2 - 36 - 6\sqrt{20} + 8$	Distribute the -6 over $6 + \sqrt{20}$.
$0 = 0.5(36 + 6\sqrt{20} + 6\sqrt{20} + 20) - 36 - 6\sqrt{20} + 8$	Use a rectangle diagram to square the expression $6 + \sqrt{20}$.

	6	$\sqrt{20}$
6	36	$6\sqrt{20}$
$\sqrt{20}$	$6\sqrt{20}$	20

$0 = 18 + 3\sqrt{20} + 3\sqrt{20} + 10 - 36 - 6\sqrt{20} + 8$	Distribute the 0.5 over the expression in parentheses.
$0 = 18 + 10 - 36 + 8$	Combine the radical expressions.
$0 = 0$	Add and subtract.

14.

$0 = 0.5x^2 - 6x + 8$	Original equation.
$0 \stackrel{?}{=} 0.5(6 - \sqrt{20})^2 - 6(6 - \sqrt{20}) + 8$	Substitute $6 - \sqrt{20}$ for x.
$0 \stackrel{?}{=} 0.5(6 - \sqrt{20})^2 - 36 + 6\sqrt{20} + 8$	Distribute the -6 over $6 - \sqrt{20}$.
$0 \stackrel{?}{=} 0.5(36 - 6\sqrt{20} - 6\sqrt{20} + 20) - 36 + 6\sqrt{20} + 8$	Square the expression $6 - \sqrt{20}$.
$0 \stackrel{?}{=} 18 - 3\sqrt{20} - 3\sqrt{20} + 10 - 36 + 6\sqrt{20} + 8$	Distribute the 0.5 over the expression in parentheses.
$0 \stackrel{?}{=} 18 + 10 - 36 + 8$	Combine the radical expressions.
$0 = 0$	Add and subtract.

15. a. In a rectangular box, all the surfaces, or faces, are rectangles. Diagonal $\overline{BD}$ of rectangle $ABCD$ is the hypotenuse of two right triangles. Consider $\triangle ABD$ on the bottom of the box. Because $ABCD$ is a rectangle and opposite sides of a rectangle are congruent, the length of $\overline{AD}$ is 3 cm. Let c represent the length of $\overline{BD}$, and apply the Pythagorean Theorem: $c^2 = 4^2 + 3^2 = 25$, so $c = \sqrt{25} = 5$, and the length of $\overline{BD}$ is 5 cm.

b. Now look at $\triangle BDH$ inside the box, with hypotenuse $\overline{BH}$. From 15a, the length of $\overline{BD}$ is 5 cm. Because $CDHG$ is a rectangle and the length of $\overline{GC}$ is 12 cm, the length of $\overline{HD}$ is also 12 cm. Let d represent the length of $\overline{BH}$. Again, use the Pythagorean Theorem to find the length of the hypotenuse: $d^2 = 5^2 + 12^2 = 169$, so $d = \sqrt{169} = 13$, and the length of $\overline{BH}$ is 13 cm.

16. a. $9^{1/2} \cdot 8^{1/3} \cdot 2^{-1} = \sqrt{9} \cdot \sqrt[3]{8} \cdot \dfrac{1}{2} = 3 \cdot 2 \cdot \dfrac{1}{2} = 3$

b. $(2^{1/3})^3 + (3^4)^{1/4} = 2^{(1/3)(3)} + 3^{4(1/4)} = 2^1 + 3^1 = 5$

c. $2^{1/2} \cdot 8^{1/2} = 2^{1/2} \cdot 2^{3(1/2)} = 2^{(1/2+3/2)} = 2^2 = 4$

d. $(m^2)^{1/4} \cdot \sqrt{m} = m^{1/2} \cdot m^{1/2} = m^{(1/2+1/2)} = m$

e. $(x^4 y^{1/2})^6 \sqrt{x^2 y^2} = x^{4(6)} y^{(1/2)(6)} x^{2(1/2)} y^{2(1/2)} = x^{24} y^3 x^1 y^1 = x^{25} y^4$

17. Use the Pythagorean Theorem to find each length, starting with a:

$a = \sqrt{2^2 + 2^2} = \sqrt{8} = 2\sqrt{2}$ cm

$b = \sqrt{2^2 + (\sqrt{8})^2} = \sqrt{4 + 8} = \sqrt{12} = 2\sqrt{3}$ cm

$c = \sqrt{(2 + \sqrt{12})^2 - (2)^2} = \sqrt{4 + 4\sqrt{12} + 12 - 4}$

$\quad = \sqrt{4\sqrt{12} + 12} = \sqrt{8\sqrt{3} + 12}$ cm

18. a. The area of a square is the square of its side length. $\left(\sqrt{93}\right)^2 = 93$, so the area of the top face is 93 mm^2.

b. $(9.6)^2 = 92.16$, so this value gives an area of 92.16 mm^2. This is almost 1 mm^2 too low.

c. Each tile is a rectangular prism. To find the volume, multiply the area of a square face by the thickness, or height, of the tile.

Using $\sqrt{93}$ mm as the side length: $93 \cdot 8 = 744$, so the volume is 744 mm^3.

Using 9.6 mm as the side length: $92.16 \cdot 8 = 737.28$, so the volume is 737.28 mm^3.

The first volume calculation is accurate; the second is almost 7 mm^3 too low.

d. Using $\sqrt{93}$ mm as the side length, the volume of 1000 tiles is $1000 \cdot 744$ mm$^3 = 744{,}000$ mm^3.

Using 9.6 mm as the side length, the volume of 1000 tiles is $1000 \cdot 737.28$ mm$^3 = 737{,}280$ mm^3.

The first volume calculation is accurate; the second is 6720 mm^3 too low.

e. Using 9.64 as the side length, the volume of 1000 tiles is $1000 \cdot 9.64^2 \cdot 8 = 743{,}436.8$ mm^3.

f. When you use an estimated square root value to make calculations, if you estimate with more precision, the errors in the calculated values are smaller.

19. a. $y = (x - 2)^2 + 3$ **b.** $y = -x^2 + 4$

c. $y = 3(x - 1)^2$

20. a. No x-intercepts   **b.** Two x-intercepts

c. One x-intercept

LESSON 11.6

EXERCISES

1. No, because $9^2 + 16^2 \ne 25^2$.

2. a. Possible answer:

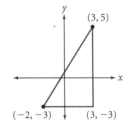

b. Horizontal length: $3 - (-2) = 5$ units; vertical length: $5 - (-3) = 8$ units

c. Using the Pythagorean Theorem, the square of the distance is $5^2 + 8^2 = 89$, so the distance is $\sqrt{89}$ units.

3. a. $\sqrt{(3 - 0)^2 + (4 - 0)^2} = \sqrt{3^2 + 4^2} = \sqrt{25} = 5$

b. $\sqrt{(-3 - 1)^2 + (-5 - 2)^2} =$
$\sqrt{(-4)^2 + (-7)^2} = \sqrt{16 + 49} = \sqrt{65} \approx 8.06$

c. $\sqrt{(s - 2)^2 + (t - 0)^2} = \sqrt{(s - 2)^2 + t^2}$, or
$\sqrt{(2 - s)^2 + t^2}$, or $\sqrt{s^2 - 4s + 4 + t^2}$

4. Possible answer: $(6, 3)$ and $(1, 7)$

5. a. Slope of $\overline{AB}$ and $\overline{DC}$: $\frac{4}{5}$; slope of $\overline{AD}$ and $\overline{BC}$: $-\frac{2}{3}$

b. Parallelogram

c. Length of $\overline{AB} = \sqrt{(10 - 5)^2 + (6 - 2)^2}$
$\quad = \sqrt{25 + 16} = \sqrt{41}$ units

Length of $\overline{DC} = \sqrt{(7 - 2)^2 + (8 - 4)^2}$
$\quad = \sqrt{25 + 16} = \sqrt{41}$ units

Length of $\overline{AD} = \sqrt{(2 - 5)^2 + (4 - 2)^2}$
$\quad = \sqrt{9 + 4} = \sqrt{13}$ units

Length of $\overline{BC} = \sqrt{(7 - 10)^2 + (8 - 6)^2}$
$\quad = \sqrt{9 + 4} = \sqrt{13}$ units

6. a. The coordinates of the Refreshment Stand are $(-5, 2)$. The coordinates of the Bumper Cars are $(-4, -3)$. Use the distance formula:

$d = \sqrt{[-4 - (-5)]^2 + (-3 - 2)^2}$
$\quad = \sqrt{1^2 + (-5)^2} = \sqrt{26}$

The attractions are $\sqrt{26}$ units, or about 0.5 mile apart.

b. The coordinates of the Acrobats are $(-1, 4)$. The coordinates of the Hall of Mirrors are $(3, 1)$. Use the distance formula:

$d = \sqrt{[3 - (-1)]^2 + (1 - 4)^2}$
$\quad = \sqrt{4^2 + (-3)^2} = \sqrt{25} = 5$

The attractions are 5 units, or 0.5 mile apart.

7. a. The coordinates of the Sledge Hammer are $(2, -3)$, and the coordinates of the Roller Coaster are $(-4, 5)$, so the slope of the line connecting these two points is $\frac{5 - (-3)}{-4 - 2} = \frac{8}{-6} = -\frac{4}{3}$. Using the point-slope form with the point $(2, -3)$ gives the equation $y = -3 - \frac{4}{3}(x - 2)$. If the point $(-4, 5)$ is used, the point-slope equation will be $y = 5 - \frac{4}{3}(x + 4)$.

b. $d = \sqrt{(x - 2)^2 + (y + 3)^2}$

c. $d = \sqrt{(x - 2)^2 + \left[-3 - \frac{4}{3}(x - 2) + 3\right]^2} =$
$\sqrt{(x - 2)^2 + \left[-\frac{4}{3}(x - 2)\right]^2}$

d. $6 = \sqrt{(x-2)^2 + \left[-\frac{4}{3}(x-2)\right]^2}$

Graph $y = \sqrt{(x-2)^2 + \left[-\frac{4}{3}(x-2)\right]^2}$ and $y = 6$ and trace to find the intersection points.

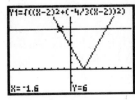 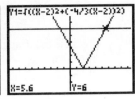

$[-9.4, 9.4, 1, -3.2, 9.2, 1]$

The two graphs intersect at $x = -1.6$ and $x = 5.6$, so the equation has two solutions, -1.6 and 5.6.

e. There is no point with x-coordinate 5.6 on the segment connecting $(2, -3)$ and $(-4, 5)$, so only the solution -1.6 is relevant to this situation. Find the y-coordinate of the point on this segment with x-coordinate -1.6 by using the equation from 7a.

$y = 5 - \frac{4}{3}(-1.6 + 4)$

$y = 5 - \frac{4}{3}(2.4)$

$y = 5 - 3.2$

$y = 1.8$

The coordinates of the breakdown point are $(-1.6, 1.8)$.

8. The pole is the hypotenuse of a right triangle in which one leg is the height of the box and the other is a diagonal of the base. The height of the box is 20 cm. To find the length of the diagonal of the base, use the Pythagorean Theorem: $d^2 = 50^2 + 30^2 = 3400$, so $d = \sqrt{3400}$ cm. Now, use the Pythagorean Theorem again to find the length of the pole: $p^2 = 20^2 + (\sqrt{3400})^2 = 3800$, so $p = \sqrt{3800}$ cm, or $10\sqrt{38}$ cm.

9. a. $\sqrt{20 - x} = x$

$20 - x = x^2$

$0 = x^2 + x - 20$

$0 = (x + 5)(x - 4)$

$x = -5$ or $x = 4$

b. Answers will vary. Possible answer: The graphs of $Y_1 = \sqrt{20 - x}$ and $Y_2 = x$ intersect once at $x = 4$.

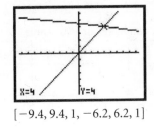

$[-9.4, 9.4, 1, -6.2, 6.2, 1]$

c. Squaring both sides to solve the equation symbolically introduces an extra solution. $x = 4$ is a solution, because $\sqrt{16} = 4$. But though -5 is a square root of 25, $x = -5$ is not a realistic solution, because the square root symbol in the original equation indicates only the positive root.

10. a. $a = 63$

b.

$\frac{1}{\sqrt{2}} = \frac{b}{7\sqrt{2}}$		Original equation.
$7\sqrt{2} \cdot \frac{1}{\sqrt{2}} = \frac{b}{7\sqrt{2}} \cdot 7\sqrt{2}$		Multiply both sides by $7\sqrt{2}$.
$7 = b$		Multiply and divide.

c.

$\frac{\sqrt{3}}{2} = \frac{c}{\sqrt{12}}$		Original equation.
$\sqrt{12} \cdot \frac{\sqrt{3}}{2} = \frac{c}{\sqrt{12}} \cdot \sqrt{12}$		Multiply both sides by $\sqrt{12}$.
$\frac{\sqrt{36}}{2} = c$		Multiply and divide.
$\frac{6}{2} = c$		Evaluate the square root.
$3 = c$		Divide.

11. a. If the slope is to be $\frac{5}{12}$, then the small right triangle in the sketch will be similar to a right triangle with side lengths 5, 12, and 13. The awning is the hypotenuse of this triangle. If a represents the length of the awning, then $\frac{13}{12} = \frac{a}{8}$, so $a = \frac{104}{12} = \frac{26}{3} = 8.\overline{6}$. So, the length of the awning will be $8.\overline{6}$ ft, or 8 ft 8 in.

b. Let s represent the short leg of the right triangle. Using the fact that the right triangle in the sketch is similar to a right triangle with side lengths 5, 12, and 13, $\frac{5}{12} = \frac{s}{8}$, so $s = 3\frac{1}{3}$ ft. The length of the support post is then 14 ft $-3\frac{1}{3}$ ft, which is $10\frac{2}{3}$ ft, or 10 ft 8 in.

12. a. $\sqrt{200} = \sqrt{100 \cdot 2} = \sqrt{100} \cdot \sqrt{2} = 10\sqrt{2}$

b. $\sqrt{612} = \sqrt{36 \cdot 17} = \sqrt{36} \cdot \sqrt{17} = 6\sqrt{17}$

c. $\sqrt{45} = \sqrt{9 \cdot 5} = \sqrt{9} \cdot \sqrt{5} = 3\sqrt{5}$

d. $\sqrt{243} = \sqrt{81 \cdot 3} = \sqrt{81} \cdot \sqrt{3} = 9\sqrt{3}$

LESSON 11.7

EXERCISES

1. a. $x = 27$ **b.** $x = 35$

c.

$\frac{1}{4} = \frac{\sqrt{10}}{\sqrt{x}}$	Original equation.
$4 = \frac{\sqrt{x}}{\sqrt{10}}$	Invert both sides.
$16 = \frac{x}{10}$	Square both sides.
$160 = x$	Multiply both sides by 10.

d. $\dfrac{2}{x} = \dfrac{x}{8}$ Original equation.

$\dfrac{16}{x} = x$ Multiply both sides by 8.

$16 = x^2$ Multiply both sides by x.

$\pm 4 = x$ Take the square root of both sides.

2. Solve $\dfrac{1}{50} = \dfrac{3.6}{x}$. The cities are 180 miles apart.

3. a. For angle D, $o = 7$ and $h = 25$, so $\sin D = \dfrac{o}{h} = \dfrac{7}{25}$.

  b. For angle E, $a = 7$ and $h = 25$, so $\cos E = \dfrac{a}{h} = \dfrac{7}{25}$.

  c. For angle D, $o = 7$ and $a = 24$, so $\tan D = \dfrac{o}{a} = \dfrac{7}{24}$.

4. a. Yes. Possible explanation: Angle A is common to both triangles and angles B and D are both right angles, so angles C and E must also be congruent. Because all three angles are congruent, the triangles are similar.

  b. $\dfrac{8}{4} = 2$ **c.** 6 cm and 10 cm

  d. 24 cm^2 and 6 cm^2 **e.** $\dfrac{24}{6} = \dfrac{4}{1}$

5. a. Solve $\dfrac{x}{6} = \dfrac{x + 2}{7}$; $x = 12$

  b. Solve $\dfrac{x + 1}{5} = \dfrac{x - 2}{4}$; $x = 14$

  c. Solve $\dfrac{9}{0.25} = \dfrac{10 + x}{1.25}$; $x = 35$

6. a. $\sqrt{60}$ m, or approximately 7.75 m

  b. $\sqrt{28}$ m, or approximately 5.29 m

7. a. $\dfrac{d}{w} = \dfrac{\text{length of adjacent leg}}{\text{length of hypotenuse}}$, so $\dfrac{d}{w}$ is the cosine of 65°.

  b. $\dfrac{h}{w} = \dfrac{\text{length of opposite leg}}{\text{length of hypotenuse}}$, so $\dfrac{h}{w}$ is the sine of 65°.

  c. $\dfrac{h}{d} = \dfrac{\text{length of opposite leg}}{\text{length of adjacent leg}}$, so $\dfrac{h}{d}$ is the tangent of 65°.

  d. $\cos 65° \approx 0.4226$; $\sin 65° \approx 0.9063$; $\tan 65° \approx 2.1445$

  e. $\tan 65° = \dfrac{h}{2.6}$, so $h = 2.6 \cdot \tan 65° \approx 5.58$. The pole is about 5.6 m high.

8. a. $\tan 28° = \dfrac{y}{x}$ or $y = x \cdot \tan 28°$

  b. Sample description: The graph is a direct variation.

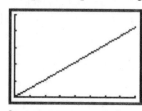

[0, 200, 25, 0, 125, 25]

  c. $y = 100 \cdot \tan 28° \approx 53.2$

  d. $x = \dfrac{80}{\tan 28°} \approx 151$

---

9. a.

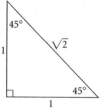

Because the triangle is isosceles, the length of the second leg is also 1 unit. Then, by the Pythagorean Theorem, the length of the hypotenuse is $\sqrt{1^2 + 1^2} = \sqrt{2}$ units.

b.

Trigonometric Functions for a 45° Angle

	Sine	Cosine	Tangent
Exact value of ratio	$\dfrac{1}{\sqrt{2}}$	$\dfrac{1}{\sqrt{2}}$	$\dfrac{1}{1}$
Decimal approximation of exact value	0.7071	0.7071	1.0000
Value by trigonometric function keys	0.7071	0.7071	1.0000

10. a–b.

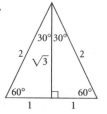

Because the segment drawn from the top vertex goes to the midpoint of the opposite side, the length of the shorter leg of either 30°-60°-90° triangle (the side opposite the 30° angle) is 1 unit. Then, by the Pythagorean Theorem, the length of the longer leg of each 30°-60°-90° triangle is $\sqrt{2^2 - 1^2} = \sqrt{3}$ units.

c.

Trigonometric Functions for a 30° Angle

	Sine	Cosine	Tangent
Exact value of ratio	$\dfrac{1}{2}$	$\dfrac{\sqrt{3}}{2}$	$\dfrac{1}{\sqrt{3}}$
Decimal approximation of exact value	0.5000	0.8660	0.5774
Value by trigonometric function keys	0.5000	0.8660	0.5774

Trigonometric Functions for a 60° Angle

	Sine	Cosine	Tangent
Exact value of ratio	$\dfrac{\sqrt{3}}{2}$	$\dfrac{1}{2}$	$\dfrac{\sqrt{3}}{1}$
Decimal approximation of exact value	0.8660	0.5000	1.7321
Value by trigonometric function keys	0.8660	0.5000	1.7321

Discovering Algebra Solutions Manual
©2007 Key Curriculum Press

11. a. A rectangle

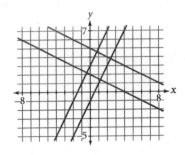

b. Students might solve each system by substitution, by tracing in a friendly window, or using tables. $(1.2, 1.4)$, $(2.4, 3.8)$, $(0.8, 4.6)$, $(-0.4, 2.2)$

c. $y = 11 - 8x$, $y = \frac{17}{7} + \frac{4}{7}x$

d. The diagonals of a rectangle intersect at their midpoints. So, you can find the midpoint of the diagonal from $(1.2, 1.4)$ and $(0.8, 4.6)$. The diagonals intersect at $(1, 3)$.

12. $a = 26$

$b = 13\sqrt{2} \approx 18.38$

$c = 13\sqrt{3} - 13 \approx 9.52$

LESSON 11.8

EXERCISES

1. a. d **b.** A **c.** A **d.** $\frac{d}{c}$

  e. A **f.** A

2. a.

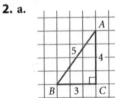

b. Trigonometric ratios and inverse functions may vary. Possible answer: $\sin A = \frac{3}{5}$, so $A = \sin^{-1}\left(\frac{3}{5}\right) \approx 37°$; $\sin B = \frac{4}{5}$, so $B = \sin^{-1}\left(\frac{4}{5}\right) \approx 53°$.

c. The angles should measure approximately 37° and 53°.

3. $\tan 42° = \frac{x}{49.5}$, so $x = 49.5 \cdot \tan 42° \approx 44.6$ m.

4. $\tan 25° = \frac{6.8}{b}$, so $b = \frac{6.8}{\tan 25°} \approx 14.6$ cm.

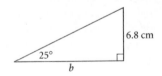

5. $\sin 28° = \frac{a}{20}$, so $a = 20 \cdot \sin 28° \approx 9.4$ cm.

$\cos 28° = \frac{b}{20}$, so $b = 20 \cdot \cos 28° \approx 17.7$ cm.

$\tan 64° = \frac{c}{2}$, so $c = 2 \cdot \tan 64° \approx 4.1$ cm.

$\cos 64° = \frac{2}{d}$, so $d = \frac{2}{\cos 64°} \approx 4.6$ cm.

$e^2 = 17^2 - 12^2 = 145$, so $e = \sqrt{145} \approx 12.0$ cm.

$\sin F = \frac{12}{17}$, so $F = \sin^{-1}\left(\frac{12}{17}\right) \approx 44.9°$.

$g^2 = 5^2 + 18^2 = 349$, so $g \approx \sqrt{349} \approx 18.7$ cm.

$\tan H = \frac{5}{18}$, so $H = \tan^{-1}\left(\frac{5}{18}\right) \approx 15.5°$.

6. a. 17 cm   **b.** $\frac{1}{2}(8)(15) = 60$ cm^2

  c. $P \approx 28°$ **d.** $Q \approx 62°$

  e. $P + Q + R = 180°$

7. $\tan 31° = \frac{height}{135}$, so height $= 135 \cdot \tan 31° \approx 81.1$ m.

8. Answers will vary. An average rise-to-run ratio for stairs is $\frac{7}{12}$. The answers provided are based on this ratio.

  a. Approximately 30°   **b.** Rise: 7; run: 12

  c. $\frac{7}{12}$ **d.** $\tan^{-1}\left(\frac{7}{12}\right) \approx 30.26°$

  e. $0.58\overline{3}$, or $\frac{7}{12}$

9. a. The tangent of the angle of elevation is 5%, or 0.05, so the angle of elevation is $\tan^{-1}(0.05)$, or about 2.86°.

  b. The angle of elevation is $\tan^{-1}(0.15) \approx 8.5308$. $\sin(8.5308) \approx 0.14834$. The change in elevation is $0.14834(1000)$, or about 148 ft.

10. a. If ℓ represents the length of the rectangle, then $\tan 20° = \frac{5}{\ell}$. Solving this equation gives $\ell \approx 13.74$ cm. The area is then about 13.74 cm $\cdot$ 5 cm, or 68.7 cm^2.

  b. Draw the height to the 8 cm side. This forms a right triangle with a 15° angle. The side opposite the 15° angle has a length of 4 cm. You can use the tangent function to find the height: $\tan 15° = \frac{4}{h}$, $h = \frac{4}{\tan 15°} \approx 14.93$ cm. The area of the original triangle is about $\frac{1}{2}(8$ cm$)(14.93$ cm$)$, or 59.7 cm^2.

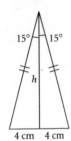

11. a. Let a represent the length of the part of the trunk that is still standing.

$$\tan 22° = \frac{a}{47}$$

$$47 \tan 22° = a$$

$$19.0 \approx a$$

The part of the trunk that is still standing is approximately 19 ft high.

b. Let b represent the length of the portion of the tree that is bent over.

$$\cos 22° = \frac{47}{b}$$

$$b \cos 22° = 47$$

$$b = \frac{47}{\cos 22°} \approx 50.7$$

(This value can also be found by using the Pythagorean Theorem to find the length of the hypotenuse of a right triangle with legs of lengths 47 ft and 19 ft.)

The portion of the tree that is bent over is approximately 51 ft long.

c. The height of the original tree is the sum of the lengths found in 11a and 11b. Because 19 ft + 51 ft = 70 ft, the tree was originally about 70 ft tall.

12. $\begin{cases} y < 2 \\ x \geq -3 \\ y > -\frac{8}{3} - \frac{1}{3}x \\ y \geq -2 + x \end{cases}$

13. From the given x-intercepts, the factored form of the equation of the parabola is of the form $y = a(x + 1)(x - 3)$. Because the point $(1, -6)$ is on the parabola, substitute -6 for y and 1 for x to find a.

$$-6 = a(1 + 1)(1 - 3)$$

$$-6 = a(2)(-2)$$

$$-6 = -4a$$

$$a = \frac{-6}{-4} = 1.5$$

Therefore, the equation of the parabola in factored form is $y = 1.5(x + 1)(x - 3)$. To rewrite this equation in general form, first use a rectangle diagram to find the product $(x + 1)(x - 3)$; then, apply the distributive property.

	x	1
x	x^2	$1x$
-3	$-3x$	-3

From the diagram, $(x + 1)(x - 3) = x^2 + 1x - 3x - 3 = x^2 - 2x - 3$, so $1.5(x + 1)(x - 3) = 1.5(x^2 - 2x - 3) = 1.5x^2 - 3x - 4.5$. Thus, the equation of the parabola in general form is $y = 1.5x^2 - 3x - 4.5$.

CHAPTER 11 Review

EXERCISES

1. a. $8\sqrt{5}$ **b.** $4\sqrt{17}$ **c.** $123\sqrt{3}$ **d.** $\sqrt{15}$

     e. $4\sqrt{5} \cdot 4\sqrt{5} = 16\sqrt{25} = 16 \cdot 5 = 80$

     f. $\left(10\sqrt{17}\right)^2 = 10^2\left(\sqrt{17}\right)^2 = 100 \cdot 17 = 1700$

     g. $\sqrt{6} \cdot \sqrt{15} = \sqrt{90} = \sqrt{9 \cdot 10} = \sqrt{9}\sqrt{10} = 3\sqrt{10}$

     h. $4\sqrt{25} \cdot 4\sqrt{5} = 4 \cdot 5 \cdot 4\sqrt{5} = 80\sqrt{5}$

     i. $\sqrt{2} + \sqrt{3}$

     j. $\sqrt{2} + \sqrt{8} = \sqrt{2} + \sqrt{4 \cdot 2} = \sqrt{2} + \sqrt{4}\sqrt{2}$
        $= \sqrt{2} + 2\sqrt{2} = 3\sqrt{2}$

     k. $\dfrac{\sqrt{18}}{\sqrt{3}} = \sqrt{\dfrac{18}{3}} = \sqrt{6}$

     l. $\sqrt{3} + \sqrt{27} = \sqrt{3} + \sqrt{9 \cdot 3} = \sqrt{3} + \sqrt{9}\sqrt{3}$
        $= \sqrt{3} + 3\sqrt{3} = 4\sqrt{3}$

2. The area is 5 square units. Here are two possible strategies:

   i. Draw a square around the tilted square using the grid lines. Subtract the areas of the outer triangles from the area of the larger square: $9 - 4(1) = 5$.

   ii. Use the distance formula to find the length of the side between $(1, 0)$ and $(3, 1)$:
$\sqrt{(3 - 1)^2 + (1 - 0)^2} = \sqrt{5}$. Square the side length to find the area: $(\sqrt{5})^2 = 5$.

3. The slopes of the sides are $\frac{1}{2}, -2, \frac{1}{2}$, and -2. The slopes of each pair of adjacent sides are opposite reciprocals, so the adjacent sides are perpendicular. Possible hypothesis: The given figure is a square. Conclusion: Its sides are perpendicular.

4. Answers will vary. Possible answer: Draw a 7-by-7 square on graph paper and remove triangles with areas of 5 square units (legs 2 units and 5 units) from each corner. The area of the remaining square is $49 - 4 \cdot 5 = 29$ square units.

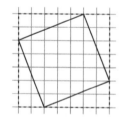

5. Answers will vary. Possible answer: Sides of 5 ft, 12 ft, and 13 ft satisfy the Pythagorean Theorem and therefore a similar triangle with sides twice as long will form a right triangle. If the corner is a right angle, then the construction worker should be able to form a right triangle with the first 10 ft of the rope along one side of the corner, the next 24 ft of rope along the other side of the corner, and the remaining 26 ft as the hypotenuse.

6. a. $A(-4, 2)$, $B(0, 5)$, $C(6, -3)$, $D(2, -6)$

b. Slope of $\overline{AB}$: $\frac{3}{4}$; slope of $\overline{BC}$: $-\frac{4}{3}$; slope of $\overline{CD}$: $\frac{3}{4}$; slope of $\overline{AD}$: $-\frac{4}{3}$.

c. It is a rectangle. The slopes of opposite sides are the same, so they are parallel. The slopes of adjacent sides are opposite reciprocals, so they are perpendicular.

d.

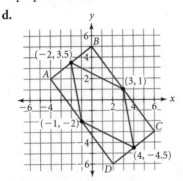

e. Each side measures $\sqrt{31.25}$ units, or about 5.59 units.

f. The slopes are -0.5, -5.5, -0.5, and -5.5.

g. It is a rhombus. The sides are all the same length, and opposite sides have the same slope, so they are parallel.

7. $\sin 25° = \frac{a}{8}$

$8 \sin 25° = a$

$3.38 \approx a$

$\cos 25° = \frac{b}{8}$

$8 \cos 25° = b$

$7.25 \approx b$

Thus, the lengths of the legs of the right triangle are approximately 3.38 m and 7.25 m.

8. a. Sample answer:

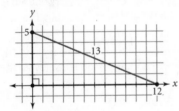

b. Approximately 23°

c. Find $\sin^{-1}\left(\frac{5}{13}\right) \approx 23°$, $\cos^{-1}\left(\frac{12}{13}\right) \approx 23°$, and $\tan^{-1}\left(\frac{5}{12}\right) \approx 23°$.

d. Answers will vary. Possible answer: Because the angle measures must add to 180°, the angle opposite the 12-unit side has measure $180° - (90° + 23°)$, or 67°.

9. a. Draw diagonal $\overline{AC}$, which divides rectangle $ABCD$ into two right triangles, each with hypotenuse $\overline{AC}$.

Look at $\triangle ABC$ on the bottom of the box. Because $ABCD$ is a rectangle, the length of $\overline{DC}$ is 10 cm. Let b represent the length of $\overline{AC}$, and use the Pythagorean Theorem to find the length of the hypotenuse: $b^2 = 10^2 + 4^2 = 116$, so $b = \sqrt{116}$, and the length of $\overline{AC}$ is $\sqrt{116}$ cm, or about 10.77 cm.

b. Now, draw diagonal $\overline{AG}$ and look at $\triangle ACG$ inside the box. From 9b, the length of $\overline{AC}$ is $\sqrt{116}$ cm. Because $BCGF$ is a rectangle and the length of $\overline{FB}$ is 5 cm, the length of $\overline{GC}$ is also 5 cm. Let c represent the length of $\overline{AG}$. Again, use the Pythagorean Theorem to find the length of the hypotenuse: $c^2 = \left(\sqrt{116}\right)^2 + 5^2 = 116 + 25 = 141$, so $d = \sqrt{141}$, and the length of $\overline{AG}$ is $\sqrt{141}$ cm, or about 11.87 cm.

10. Answers will vary. Possible answer: If a triangle has base 8 cm and height 4 cm, its area is 16 sq. cm. If the triangle is enlarged by a factor of 3, its base will be 24 cm, its height will be 12 cm, and its area will be 144 sq. cm, which equals $3^2 \times 16$ sq. cm. For a triangle with base b and height h, the area is $A = \frac{1}{2}bh$. If the sides are enlarged by a factor of k, the base and height become kb and kh, and the area becomes $A = \frac{1}{2}(kb)(kh)$, or $A = \frac{1}{2}bh \cdot k^2$. So, the area is enlarged by a factor of k^2.

11. a. For the x-values: Q1 $= 15$, Q3 $= 40$

For the y-values: Q1 $= 34$, Q3 $= 61$

A scatter plot will show that the Q-points are $(15, 34)$ and $(40, 61)$. The slope of the line between these points is $\frac{61 - 34}{40 - 15} = \frac{27}{25} = 1.08$.

Either the point $(40, 61)$ or the point $(15, 34)$ can be used in the point-slope form, so the equation of the line can be written in point-slope form as $y = 61 + 1.08(x - 40)$ or $y = 34 + 1.08(x - 15)$.

b. The two equations obtained in 11a are equivalent, so they will give the same results for 10b and 10c.

Substitute 31 for x in the first equation from 11a, and solve for y.

$y = 61 + 1.08(31 - 40)$

$y = 51.28$

The equation predicts that the normal maximum January temperature for Memphis is approximately 51°F.

c. Substitute 59 for y in the first equation from 11a, and solve for x.

$59 = 61 + 1.08(x - 40)$

$59 = 61 + 1.08x - 43.2$

$59 = 17.8 + 1.08x$

$41.2 = 1.08x$

$38 \approx x$

The equation predicts that the normal minimum January temperature for Charleston is approximately 38°F.

12. a. $\begin{cases} 3a + 1.5p = 13.74 \\ 2a + 3p = 16.32 \end{cases}$, where a is the price per pound for dried apricots and p is the price per pound for dried papaya.

b. The elimination method is a good way to solve this system. To eliminate p, multiply the first equation by -2 to obtain $-6a - 3p = -27.48$, and add this equation to the second equation of the original system to obtain $-4a = -11.16$. Solving this equation gives $a = 2.79$. Now substitute 2.79 for a in the second equation of the original system and solve for p.

$$2a + 3p = 16.32$$
$$2(2.79) + 3p = 16.32$$
$$5.58 + 3p = 16.32$$
$$3p = 10.74$$
$$p = 3.58$$

A pound of dried apricots costs $2.79, and a pound of dried papaya costs $3.58.

13. a. There are 20 cards, so $P(0) = \frac{1}{20}$, or 0.05.

b. There are three cards with integers less than zero, so $P(\text{less than zero}) = \frac{3}{20}$, or 0.15.

c. $\frac{1}{2} \cdot \frac{1}{2} \cdot \frac{1}{2} = \frac{1}{8}$, or 0.125

d. $\frac{10}{20} \cdot \frac{9}{19} \cdot \frac{8}{18} = \frac{2}{19}$, or about 0.105

14. a. Inverse variation. Possible explanation: The product of x and y is constant; $xy = 2$, or $y = \frac{2}{x}$.

b. Neither. Possible explanation: The product is not constant, so it is not an inverse variation. The y-value for $x = 0$ is not 0, so it is not a direct variation.

c. Direct variation. Possible explanation: The ratio of y to x is constant; $y = 0.25x$.

d. Neither. Possible explanation: The graph is not a curve, so the relationship is not an inverse variation. The line does not pass through the origin, so it is not a direct variation.

e. Inverse variation. Possible explanation: The product of the x- and y-coordinates for any point on the curve is 8; $xy = 8$, or $y = \frac{8}{x}$.

f. Direct variation. Possible explanation: The graph is a straight line through the origin; $y = 1.5x$.

15. a. Answers will vary. Possible answer: For $0 < x < 3$, f is nonlinear and increasing at a slower and slower rate. For $3 < x < 5$, f is linear and decreasing. For $5 < x < 7$, f is linear and increasing. For $7 < x < 9$, f is linear and constant (neither increasing nor decreasing). For $9 < x < 12$, f is nonlinear and decreasing at a slower and slower rate.

b. $0 \le y \le 5$ **c.** 3

d. 1, 5, 12 **e.** $7 \le x \le 9$

16. a. $(3x^2y)^3 = 3^3(x^2)^3(y)^3 = 3^3x^{2 \cdot 3}y^3 = 27x^6y^3$

b. $\frac{5^2p^7q^3}{5p^3q} = 5^{2-1}p^{7-3}q^{3-1} = 5^1p^4q^2 = 5p^4q^2$

c. $x^{-4}y^{-2}x^5 = x^{-4+5}y^{-2} = x^1y^{-2} = \frac{x}{y^2}$

d. $m^2(n^{-4} + m^{-6}) = m^2 \, n^{-4} + m^2 \, m^{-6} = m^2 \, n^{-4} + m^{2+(-6)} = m^2 \, n^{-4} + m^{-4} = \frac{m^2}{n^4} + \frac{1}{m^4}$

17. a. Mean: 108.4; median: 105; mode: 105

b. Five-number summary: 82, 99, 105, 112, 179

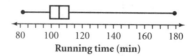
Running time (min)

c. Bin widths may vary.

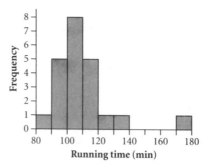
Running time (min)

d. Sample answers:

(1) About 75% of the new releases have running times of 112 min or less. (2) None of the new releases have running times between 140 and 169 min. (3) Most (18) of the running times are between 90 and 119 min.

18. a. $y = (x + 3)(x - 1)$ **b.** $y = (x + 1)^2 - 4$

c. $y = x^2 + 2x - 3$

19. Because the value of the collection increases by a constant percent, this is an example of exponential growth, so this situation can be modeled by the exponential growth equation $y = A(1 + r)^x$.

a. Substitute 1900 for y, 0.08 for r, and 6 for x in the exponential growth equation and solve for A, the starting value.

$$y = A(1 + r)^x$$
$$1900 = A(1 + 0.08)^6$$
$$1900 = A(1.08)^6$$
$$\frac{1900}{(1.08)^6} = A$$

$A \approx 1{,}197$, so when Maya first received it, the collection was worth approximately $1,197.

b. Substitute 1900 for A, 0.08 for r, and 10 for x in the exponential growth equation, and solve for y, the value 10 years from now.

Discovering Algebra Solutions Manual
©2007 Key Curriculum Press

$$y = A(1 + r)^x$$

$$y = 1900(1 + 0.08)^{10}$$

$$y = 1900(1.08)^{10}$$

$y \approx 4{,}102$, so 10 years from now, the collection will be worth approximately \$4,102.

20. a. $f(-5) = (-5)^2 + |-5| - 4 = 25 + 5 - 4 = 26$

b. $f(2) = (2)^2 + |2| - 4 = 4 + 2 - 4 = 2$

c. $f(-7) - f(4) = (49 + 7 - 4) - (16 + 4 - 4) = 52 - 16 = 36$

d. $f(-7 - 4) = f(-11) = 121 + 11 - 4 = 128$

e. $-3 \cdot f(3) = -3 \cdot (9 + 3 - 4) = -3 \cdot 8 = -24$

21. a. The discounted price is $79.99(1 - 0.22) = \$79.99(0.78) = \$62.39$.

b. The total price, including sales tax, is $\$62.39(1 + 0.05) = \$62.39(1.05) = \$65.51$.

22. Answers will vary. Possible answers:

a. A reflection across the y-axis and a vertical shrink by a factor of 0.5

b. $(-x, 0.5y)$

23. a.

$0 = (x + 5)(x - 2)$	Original equation.
$x + 5 = 0$ or $x - 2 = 0$	Use the zero product property.
$x = -5$ or $x = 2$	Solve.

b.

$0 = x^2 + 8x + 16$	Original equation.
$0 = (x + 4)^2$	Factor.
$x + 4 = 0$	Use the zero product property or take the square root of each side.
$x = -4$	Solve.

c.

$x^2 - 5x = 2x + 30$	Original equation.
$x^2 - 7x - 30 = 0$	Rewrite the equation in general form.
$(x + 3)(x - 10) = 0$	Factor.
$x + 3 = 0$ or $x - 10 = 0$	Use the zero product property.
$x = -3$ or $x = 10$	Solve.

d.

$x^2 = 5$	Original equation.
$x = \pm\sqrt{5}$	Take the square root of each side.

24. a. This graph can be obtained by translating the graph of the parent function $y = x^2$ left 2 units and down 4 units, so the equation is $y = (x + 2)^2 - 4$.

b. This graph can be obtained from the graph of the parent function $y = |x|$ by a vertical shrink by a factor of 0.5, reflection across the x-axis, and translation left 3 units. So, the equation is $y = -0.5\,|x + 3|$.

25. a. \$35   **b.** \$225

c. $\{0, 225\}$ ENTER ; $\{\text{Ans}(1) + 1, \text{Ans}(2) + 35\}$ ENTER , ENTER , . . .

d. $y = 225 + 35x$ **e.** \$645

f. 8

26. a.

Segment	Length	Slope
$\overline{AB}$	10	$\dfrac{3}{4}$
$\overline{BC}$	10	$-\dfrac{3}{4}$
$\overline{AC}$	16	0

b. Isosceles triangle. Two sides have equal length.

c. $D(2, 1)$

d. Right triangles. Possible explanation: $\overline{BD}$ has an undefined slope, so it is vertical; $\overline{AC}$ has slope 0, so it is horizontal.

e. A drawing should confirm 26a–d.

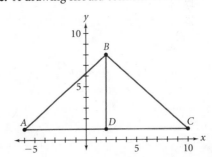

TAKE ANOTHER LOOK

For acute triangles, $a^2 + b^2 > c^2$. For obtuse triangles, $a^2 + b^2 < c^2$. Possible summary: If the angle opposite the longest side is *less than* 90°, then the square of the length of the longest side is *less than* the sum of the squares of the lengths of the other two sides. If the angle opposite the longest side is *equal to* 90°, then the square of the length of the longest side is *equal to* the sum of the squares of the lengths of the other two sides. If the angle opposite the longest side is *greater than* 90°, then the square of the length of the longest side is *greater than* the sum of the squares of the lengths of the other two sides.

Key Curriculum Press

Innovators in Mathematics Education

Comment Form

Please take a moment to provide us with feedback about this book. We are eager to read any comments or suggestions you may have. Once you've filled out this form, simply fold it along the dotted lines and drop it in the mail. We'll pay the postage. Thank you!

Your Name _____

School _____

School Address _____

City/State/Zip _____

Phone _____ Email _____

Book Title _____

Please list any comments you have about this book.

_____

_____

_____

_____

_____

_____

_____

_____

_____

_____

_____

Do you have any suggestions for improving the student or teacher material?

_____

_____

_____

_____

_____

_____

_____

To request a catalog, or place an order, call us toll free at 800-995-MATH, or send a fax to 800-541-2242. For more information, visit Key's website at www.keypress.com.

Fold carefully along this line.

BUSINESS REPLY MAIL
FIRST CLASS   PERMIT NO. 338   EMERYVILLE, CA

POSTAGE WILL BE PAID BY ADDRESSEE

Key Curriculum Press
Innovators in Mathematics Education

Attn: Editorial Department
1150 65th Street
Emeryville, CA 94608-9740

Fold carefully along this line.